Photo, Ridge Studio; Courtesy Ogden Chamber of Commerce

A great ledge in Ogden Canyon near Ogden, Utah. The rock, still retaining its stratification, was deposited layer upon layer horizontally mostly as sand upon the floor of a sea which covered the region fully 500,000,000 years ago. That the sea was of very early Paleozoic (i. e., Cambrian) age has been proved by fossils in associated strata. Long after their deep burial and consolidation within the earth, the strata were subjected to tremendous mountain-making pressure, notably altered to a rock called "Quartzite," raised high above sea level, and tilted almost vertically. Then through long ages (millions of years) overlying rocks of great thickness have been cut away (eroded) by weathering and stream action, laying bare the ledge as we see it to-day.

POPULAR SCIENCE LIBRARY

EDITOR-IN-CHIEF
GARRETT P. SERVISS

AUTHORS

DAVID TODD	*WILLIAM J. MILLER*
D. W. HERING	*A. RUSSELL BOND*
ROBIN BEACH	*HIPPOLYTE GRUENER*
ERNEST J. STREUBEL	*ADAM WARD*
ALBERT A. HOPKINS	*A. P. PECK*
H. H. SHELDON	*JOHN E. MERRILL*

Six Volumes · *Illustrated*

GEOLOGY

P. F. COLLIER & SON CORPORATION
Publishers - - - - - - - New York

The Story of Our Earth

THE SCIENCE OF GEOLOGY
THE HISTORY OF THE WORLD
CAN BE READ FROM ROCKS AND
MINERAL DEPOSITS

by

WILLIAM J. MILLER
PROFESSOR OF GEOLOGY
UNIVERSITY OF CALIFORNIA AT LOS ANGELES

P. F. COLLIER & SON CORPORATION
Publishers, New York

PREFACE

IN the preparation of this book the author has attempted to present, in popular form, the salient points of a general survey of the whole great science of geology, the science which deals with the history of the earth and its inhabitants as revealed in the rocks.

The use of technical and unusual terms has been reduced to a minimum compatible with a reasonable understanding of the subject by the layman. Each of the relatively few scientific terms is explained where first used in the text, and a glossary of common geological terms has been appended.

The matter of illustrations has received very careful attention, and only pictures, maps, and diagrams are used which actually illustrate important features of the text. A special point has been made to introduce only cuts of simple construction comparatively free from technicalities. Nearly every illustration is accompanied by a really explanatory title.

A number of the pictures are from the author's collection of photographs, and many of the line-cuts have either been made or considerably modified by the author. Among the numerous sources of illustrations, special mention should be made of the United States Geological Survey, the New York State Museum, the American Museum of Natural History, the University of Chicago Press, and various individuals, full credit being given wherever due.

WILLIAM J. MILLER.

NORTHAMPTON, MASS.

PREFACE TO THE 1938 EDITION

In this edition the text has been carefully revised, involving various changes and corrections as well as addition of some new material. Various new halftone illustrations have been added, and estimates of geologic time have been brought into agreement with the more recent determinations in regard to the age of the earth.

WILLIAM J. MILLER.

UNIVERSITY OF CALIFORNIA AT LOS ANGELES.

CONTENTS

5

LIST OF ILLUSTRATIONS

CHAPTER I

INTRODUCTION

EARTH features are not fixed. The person of ordinary intelligence, surrounded as he is by a great variety of physical features, is, unless he has devoted some study to the subject, very likely to regard those features as practically unchangeable, and to think that they are now essentially as they were in the beginning of the earth's history. Some of the most fundamental ideas taught in this book are that the physical features of the earth, as we behold them to-day, represent but a single phase of a very long-continued history; that significant changes are now going on all around us; and that we are able to interpret present-day earth features only by an understanding of earth changes in the past.

Geology, meaning literally "earth science," deals with the history of the earth and its inhabitants as revealed in the rocks. The science is very broad in its scope. It treats of the processes by which the earth has been, and is now being, changed; the structure of the earth; the stages through which it has passed; and the evolution of the organisms which have lived upon it.

Geography deals with the distribution of the earth's physical features, in their relation to one another, to the life of sea and land, and human life and culture. It is the present and outward expression of geological effects.

As a result of the work of many able students of geology during the past century and a quarter, it is now well established that our planet has a definitely recorded history of many millions of years, and that during the lapse of those eons, revolutionary changes in earth features have occurred, and also that there has been a vast succession of living things which, from very early times, have gradually passed from simple into more and more complex forms. The physical changes and the organisms of past ages have left abundant evidence of their character, and the study of the rock formations has shown that within them we have a fairly complete record of the earth's history. Although very much yet remains to be learned about this old earth, it is a remarkable fact that man, through the exercise of his highest faculty, has come to know so much concerning it.

The following words, by the late Professor Barrell, admirably summarize the significance of geological history. "The great lesson taught by the study of the outer crust is that the earth mother, like her children, has attained her present form through ceaseless change, which marks the pulse of life and which shall cease only when her internal forces slumber and the cloudy air and surf-bound ocean no more are moving garments. The flowing landscapes of geologic time may be likened to a kinetoscopic panorama. The scenes transform from age to age, as from act to act; seas and plains and mountains of different types follow and replace each other through time, as the traveler sees them succeed each other in space. At times the drama hastens, and unusual rapidity of geologic action has, in fact, marked those epochs since man has been a spectator upon the earth. Science demonstrates that mountains are transitory forms, but the eye of man through all his lifetime sees no change, and his reason is appalled at the conception of a duration so vast that the milleniums of written history have not accomplished the shifting of even one of the fleeting views which blend into the moving picture."*

Or in the words of Tennyson:

> There rolls the deep where grew the tree.
> O, earth, what changes hast thou seen!
> There where the long street roars, hath been
> The stillness of the central sea.
> The hills are shadows, and they flow
> From form to form, and nothing stands;
> They melt like mist, the solid lands,
> Like clouds they shape themselves and go.

The following statement of some of the more definite important conclusions regarding earth changes may serve to make still clearer the general scope of the science of geology. The evidences upon which these conclusions are based are discussed in various parts of this book. For untold millions of years the rocks at and near the earth's surface have been crumbling; streams have been incessantly sawing into the lands; the sea has been eating into continental masses; the winds have been sculpturing desert lands; and, more intermittently and locally, glaciers have plowed through mountain valleys, and even great sheets of ice have spread over considerable portions of continents. Throughout geologic time, the crust of the earth has shown marked instability. Slow upward and downward

* Central Connecticut in the Geologic Past, pp. 1-2.

movements of the lands relative to sea level have
been very common, in many cases amounting to
even thousands of feet. Various parts of the earth
have been notably affected by sudden movements
(resulting in earthquakes) along fractures in the
outer crust. During millions of years molten materials have, at various times, been forced into the
earth's crust, and in many cases to its surface.
Mountain ranges have been brought forth and cut
down. The site of the Appalachian Mountains
was, millions of years ago, the bottom of a shallow sea. Lakes have come and gone. The Great
Lakes have come into existence very recently
(geologically), that is to say, since the great Ice
Age. A study of stratified rocks of marine origin
shows that all, or nearly all, of the earth's surface
has at some time, or times, been covered by sea
water. Over certain districts the sea has transgressed and retrogressed repeatedly. Organisms
have inhabited the earth for many millions of years.
In earlier known geologic time, the plants and animals were comparatively simple and low in the scale
of organization, and through the succeeding ages
higher and more complex types were gradually
evolved until the highly organized forms of the
present time, including the human race, were
produced.

The rocks of the earth constitute the special field
of study for the geologist because they contain the
records of events through which the earth and its
inhabitants have passed during the millions of
years of time until their present conditions have
been reached. All the rocks of the earth's crust
may be divided into three great classes: *igneous,*
sedimentary, and *metamorphic.*

Igneous rocks comprise all those which have ever been in a molten condition, and of these we have the *volcanic* rocks (for example, lavas), which have cooled at or near the surface; *plutonic* rocks (for example, granites), which have cooled in great masses at considerable depths below the surface; and the *dike* rocks which, when molten, have been forced into fissures in the earth's crust and there cooled.

Sedimentary rocks comprise all those which have been deposited under water, except some wind-blown deposits, and they are nearly always arranged in layers (stratified). Such rocks are called strata. They may be of mechanical origin such as clay or mud which hardens to *shale;* sand, which consolidates into *sandstone;* and gravel, which when cemented becomes *conglomerate*. They may be of organic origin such as limestone, most of which is formed by the accumulation of calcareous shells; *flint* and *chert,* which are accumulations of siliceous *shells;* or *coal,* which is formed by the accumulation of partly decayed organic matter. Or, finally, they may be formed by chemical precipitation, as beds of *salt, gypsum, bog iron ore,* etc.

Metamorphic rocks include both sedimentary and igneous rocks which have been notably changed from their original condition.

Traces or remains of organisms preserved in the rocks are *fossils*. The term originally meant anything dug out of the earth, organic or inorganic; it is now strictly applied to organic remains. Many thousands of species of fossils are known from rocks of all ages except the oldest, and more are constantly being brought to light, but these represent only a small part of the life of past ages because relatively few organic remains were deposited under conditions favorable for preservation in fossil form. The fossils in the rocks are, however, a fair average of the groups of organisms to which they belong. It is really remarkable that such a vast number of fossils are imbedded in the rocks, and from a study of these many fundamental conclusions regarding the history of life on our planet may be drawn.

As early as the fifth century B. C., Xenophanes is said to have observed fossil shells and plants in the rocks of Paros, and to have attributed their presence to incursions of the sea over the land. Herodotus, about a century later, came to a similar conclusion regarding fossil shells in the mountains of Egypt. None of the ancients, however, seemed to have the slightest conception of the significance of fossils as time markers in the history of the earth. (See discussion below.)

In the Middle Ages, distinguished writers held curious views regarding fossils. Thus Avicenna (979-1037) believed that fossils represented unsuccessful attempts on the part of nature to change inorganic materials into organisms within the earth by a peculiar creative force (*vis plastica*). About two centuries later, Albertus Magnus held a somewhat similar view. Leonardo da Vinci (1452-1519), the famous artist, architect, and engineer, while engaged in canal building in northern Italy, saw fossils imbedded in the rocks, and concluded that these were the remains of organisms which actually lived in sea water which spread over the region. During the seventeenth and eighteenth centuries, many correctly held that fossils were really of organic origin, but it was commonly taught that all fossils represented remains of organisms of an earlier creation which were buried in the rocks during the great Deluge (Noah's Flood). William Smith (1769-1839), of England, was, however, the first to recognize the fundamental significance of fossils for determining the relative ages of sedimentary rocks. This discovery laid the foundation for the determination of earth chronology which is of great importance in the study of the history of the earth. (See discussions below.)

Organic remains, dating as far back as tens of millions of years, have been preserved in the rocks of the earth in various ways. A very common kind of fossilization is the preservation of only the hard parts of organisms. Thus the soft parts have disappeared by decomposition, while the hard parts, such as bones, shells, etc., remain. In many cases practically complete skeletons of large and small animals which lived millions of years ago have been found intact in the rocks. Fossils which show none of the original material, but only the shape or form, are also very abundant. When sediment hardens around an imbedded organism, and the organism then decomposes or dissolves away, a cavity or fossil mold only is left. Casts of organisms or parts of them are formed by filling shells or molds with sediment or with mineral matter carried in solution by underground water. Only rarely have casts of wholly soft animals been found in ancient rocks. In other cases both original form and structure are preserved, but none of the original material. This is known as petrifaction which takes place when a plant or hard part of an animal has been replaced, particle by particle, by mineral matter from solution in underground water. Not uncommonly organic matter, such as wood, or inorganic matter,

such as carbonate of lime shells, has been so perfectly replaced that the original structures are preserved almost as in life. The popular idea that
petrified wood is wood which has been changed
into stone is, of course, incorrect. It is doubtful if
flesh has ever been truly petrified. In many cases
mainly the carbon only of organisms has been preserved. This is also true of plants where, under
conditions of slow chemical change or decomposition, the hydrogen and oxygen mostly disappear,
leaving much of the carbon with original structures
often remarkably preserved. Fine examples are
fossils plants in the great coal-bearing strata. Much
more rarely entire organisms have been preserved
either by freezing or by natural embalmment. Most
remarkable are the species of mammoths and rhinoceroses, extinct for thousands of years, bodies of
which, with flesh, hide, and hair still intact, have
been held in cold storage in the frozen soils of Si-
beria, or other cases. Insects have been perfectly
preserved in amber, as, for example, in the Baltic
region. This amber is a hardened resin in which
the insects were caught while it was still soft and
exuding from the trees. Finally, we should mention
the preservation of tracks and trails of land and
water animals. Thousands of tracks of long-extinct
great reptiles occur in the sandstones and shales of
the Connecticut Valley of Massachusetts. The foot-
prints were made in soft sandy mud which hardened
and then became covered with more sediment.

Few fossils occur in other than the sedimentary
rocks. Most numerous, by far, are fossils in rocks
of marine origin, because on relatively shallow sea
bottoms, where sediments of the geologic ages have
largely accumulated, the conditions for fossilization

have been most favorable. Among the many conditions which have produced great diversity in numbers and distribution of marine organisms during geologic time are temperature, depth of water, clearness of water, nature of sea bottom, degree of salinity, and food supply. River and lake deposits also not uncommonly contain remains of organisms which inhabited the waters, but also others which were carried in. "Surrounding trees drop their leaves, flowers, and fruit upon the mud flats, insects fall into the quiet waters, while quadrupeds are mired in mud or quicksand and soon buried out of sight. Flooded streams bring in quantities of vegetable debris, together with carcasses of land animals drowned by the sudden rise of the flood" (W. B. Scott).

In the study of the many changes which have taken place in the history of the earth, a fundamental consideration is the determination of the relative ages of the rocks, especially the strata. How can the geologist assign a rock formation of any part of the earth to a particular age in the history of the earth? How can it be proved that certain rock formations in various parts of the earth originated practically at the same time? There are two important criteria. First, in any region where the strata have not been disturbed from their normal order, the older strata underlie the younger because the underlying sediments must have been deposited first. Now, the total thickness of the stratified series of the earth has been estimated to be no less than 200,000 feet and only a small part of this is actually present in any given locality or region. It is, therefore, evident that the order of superposition of strata is in itself not sufficient for the determination of the relative ages of all the strata in even a considerable portion of a single continent, not to mention its utter inadequacy in building up the geological column of the whole earth. When, however, the second criterion, namely, the fossil content of the strata, is used in direct connection with the order of superposition, we have the real basis for determining the relative ages of strata for all parts of the earth. The discovery of this method was very largely due to the painstaking field work in England by William Smith about the beginning of the nineteenth century.

It is a well-established fact that organisms have inhabited the earth for many millions of years and that, through the geologic ages, they have continuously changed, with gradual development of higher and higher types. Tens of thousands of species have come and gone. Accepting this fact, it is then clear that strata which were formed at notably different times must contain notably different fossils, while strata which accumulated at practically the same time contain similar fossils, allowing, of course, for reasonable differences in geographical distribution of organisms as at the present time. Each epoch of earth history or series of strata has its characteristic assemblage of organisms. In short, "a geological chronology is constructed by carefully determining, first of all, the order of superposition of the stratified rocks, and next by learning the fossils characteristic of each group of strata. . . . The order of succession among the fossils is determined from the order of superposition of the strata in which they occur. When that succession has been thus established, it may be employed as a general standard" (W. B. Scott). It should, however, be borne in mind that precise contemporaneity of strata in widely separated districts can rarely, if ever, be determined because of the very great length of geologic time and the general slowness of the evolution of organisms. Rocks carrying remarkably similar fossils may really be several thousand years different in age; but this is, indeed, a very small limit of error when one considers the vast antiquity of the earth. Much very accurate and satisfactory work has been done, especially in Europe and North America, in correlating strata and assigning them to their places in the geological time table (see below), but a vast amount of work yet remains to be done before the task is complete.

Certain types or species of organisms are much more useful than others in the determination of earth chronology. Best of all for world-wide correlations are species which were widely distributed and which persisted for relatively short times. Thus any species which lived in the surface waters of the ocean and was easily distributed over wide areas, while, at the same time, it existed as such only a short time, is the best type of chronologic indicator.

The known history of the earth has been more or less definitely divided into great eras and lesser periods and epochs, constituting what may be called the geologic time scale. In the accompanying table the era and period names, except those representing earlier time, are mostly world-wide in their usage. Epoch names, being more or less locally applied, are omitted from the table. Very conservative estimates of the length of time represented by the eras and the most characteristic general features of the life of the main divisions are also given.

PRINCIPAL DIVISIONS OF GEOLOGIC TIME

(Modified after U. S. Geological Survey.)

Era.	Period.	Characteristic life.	Millions of years duration.
Cenozoic	Quaternary.	"Age of man." Animals and plants of modern types.	50
	Tertiary.	"Age of mammals." Rise of highest animals except man. Rise and development of highest orders of plants.	
Mesozoic	Cretaceous.	"Age of reptiles." Rise and culmination of huge land reptiles (dinosaurs), of cephalopods with complexly partitioned coiled shells (ammonites), and of great flying reptiles. First appearance (in Jurassic) of birds and (in Triassic) of mammals. Rise of cycads, an order of palm-like plants (in Triassic); and of angiospermous plants, among which are palms and hardwood trees (in Cretaceous).	150
	Jurassic.		
	Triassic.		
Paleozoic.	Permian	"Age of amphibians." Dominance of club mosses (lycopods) and plants of horsetail and fern types. Primitive gymnospermous plants and earliest cone-bearing trees. Beginnings of backboned land animals (land vertebrates), and insects. Cephalopods with coiled shells (ammonoids) and sharks abundant.	300
	Pennsylvanian.		
	Mississippian.		
	Devonian.	"Age of fishes." Shellfish (mollusks) also abundant. Rise of amphibians and land plants.	
	Silurian.	Shell-forming sea animals dominant, especially those related to the nautilus (cephalopods). Rise and culmination of the marine animals sometimes known as sea lilies (crinoids) and of giant scorpion-like crustaceans (eurypterids). Rise of fishes and of reef-building corals.	
	Ordovician.	Shell-forming sea animals, especially cephalopods and mollusklike brachiopods, abundant. Culmination of the buglike marine crustaceans known as trilobites.	
	Cambrian.	Trilobites and brachiopods most characteristic animals. Seaweeds (algæ) abundant. No trace of land animals found.	
Proterozoic.	Algonkian.	First life that has left distinct record. One-celled plants (algæ) and traces of invertebrates.	1,000
Archeozoic.	Archean.	Organic matter in form of graphite (black lead). Indistinct traces of simple one-celled plants.	

(The Silurian, Ordovician, and Cambrian periods are bracketed under the heading "Age of invertebrates.")

The length of time represented by human history is very short compared to the vast time of known geological history. The one is measured by thousands of years, while the other must be measured by tens of millions of years. Indeed, according to recent methods, based upon radioactive changes in certain minerals of rocks, the age of the earth is now considered to be possibly two billion years. Just as we may roughly divide human history into certain ages according to some notable person, nation, principle, or force as, for example, the "Age of Pericles," the "Roman Period," the "Age of the French Revolution," or the "Age of Electricity," so geologic history may be subdivided according to great predominant physical or organic phenomena, such as "the Appalachian Mountain Revolution" (toward the end of the Paleozoic era), the "Age of Fishes" (Devonian period), or the "Age of Reptiles" (Mesozoic era).

In the study of earth history, as in the study of human history, it is important to distinguish between events and records of events. Historical events are continuous, but they are by no means all recorded. Records of events are often interrupted and seemingly sharply separated from each other.

CHAPTER II

WEATHERING AND EROSION

ALL rocks at and near the surface of the earth crumble or decay. The term "weathering" includes all the processes whereby rocks are broken up, decomposed, or dissolved. A mass of very hard and seemingly indestructible granite, taken from a quarry, will, in a very short time, geologically considered, crumble (Plate 1). During the short span of the ordinary human life weathering effects are generally of very little consequence, but during the long ages of geologic time the various processes of weathering have been slowly and ceaselessly at work upon the outer crust of the earth, and such tremendous quantities of rock material have been broken up that the lands of the earth have everywhere been profoundly affected.

Most of us have noticed buildings and monuments in which the stones show marked effects of weathering. A good case in point is Westminster Abbey, London, in which many of the stones are badly weathered, some of the more ornamental parts having crumbled beyond recognition since the building was erected in the thirteenth century. In many countries, tombstones and monuments only one or two centuries old are so badly weathered that the inscriptions are scarcely if at all legible.

What are some of the processes of nature whereby rocks are weathered? In cold countries, and often in mountains of generally mild climate regions, the alternate freezing and thawing of water is a potent agency in breaking up rocks where the soils are thin or absent. On freezing, water expands about one-tenth of its volume and exerts the enormous pressure of thousands of pounds per square inch. Nearly all relatively hard rock formations are separated into more or less distinct blocks by natural cracks called "joints" (Plate 10). Very commonly the rocks also contain minute crevices, fissures, and pores. Repeated freezing and thawing of water which finds its way into such openings finally causes even the most resistant rocks to break up into smaller and smaller fragments. A very striking example of difference in climatic effect upon a given rock mass is the obelisk in Central Park, New York. For many centuries this famous monument stood practically without change in the dry, frostless climate of Egypt, but very soon after its removal to the moist, frosty climate of New York, it began to crumble so rapidly that it was necessary to cover it with a coating of glaze to protect it from the atmosphere.

Temperature change, especially in dry regions, is also an important agency for mechanical breaking up of rocks. On high mountains and on deserts, a daily range of temperature of from 70 degrees to 80 degrees is frequent. Due to heat absorption, rocks in desert regions, during the day, not uncommonly reach temperatures of fully 120 degrees, while during the night, due to heat radiation, their temperature falls greatly. During the heating of the outer portion of the rock, the various minerals each expand differently, thus setting up a series of stresses and strains tending to cause the minerals to pull apart. The outer portions of the rocks which are subjected to unstable and relatively rapid temperature changes, often crack or peel off in slabs or flakes, this process being called exfoliation. Stone Mountain in Georgia, and some of the mountains of the southern Sierra Nevada range in California, are excellent examples of mountains which are being rounded off by exfoliation. The principle is the same as that which causes the "spalling" of stones in buildings during fires.

Masses of débris consisting of more or less angular rock fragments of all sizes commonly occur at the bases of cliffs and mountains. They represent materials which have weathered off the ledges mainly by frost action and temperature changes.

Where electrical storms are frequent, lightning often shatters portions of rock ledges. Many such cases have come under the writer's observation in the Adirondack Mountains of New York. The total effect of lightning as a weathering agency is, however, relatively small.

Another minor weathering effect is the mechanical action of plants. The principle is well illustrated by the breaking or tilting of sidewalks by the wedging action of the growing roots of trees. In many places the roots of plants growing in cracks in rocks, exert powerful pressure causing the rocks or blocks of rocks to wedge apart.

Let us now briefly consider some of the chemical processes of weathering. The solvent effect of perfectly pure water upon rocks is very slight and slow. But such water is not found in nature because certain atmospheric gases, especially oxygen and carbonic acid gas, are always present in it, and they notably increase the solvent power of the water. Such water has the power to slowly but completely dissolve the common rock called limestone which consists of carbonate of lime. This material is then carried away by the streams. Rocks, like certain sandstones which contain carbonate of lime cementing material, are caused to crumble due to removal of the cement in solution. Carbonic acid gas in water also has the power to chemically alter various minerals in many common rocks and thus the rocks fall apart and the carbonates which result from the action usually are carried away in solution. One of the most important changes of this kind takes place when the very common mineral feldspar is attacked by water containing carbonic acid gas and the mineral alters to a soluble carbonate, kaolin (or clay) and silica.

The oxygen, both of the air and that which is contained in water, is a very important chemical agent of decomposition of many rocks. Water at the surface and the upper part of the crust of the earth as well as moisture in the air are also important chemical agents which bring about rock decay. We are all familiar with the rusting of iron which is due to the chemical union of the iron with oxygen, thus forming an iron oxide which in turn commonly unites with water from air or earth. Now, many rocks contain iron, not as such, but held in combination with other substances in the form of various minerals, and this iron of the rocks, where subjected to the oxygen and moisture of air or water, slowly unites with the oxygen and water to form a hydrated iron oxide which is essentially iron-rust. The minerals containing considerable iron are, therefore, decomposed and the rocks crumble. There are various iron oxides, usually more or less hydrated, ranging in color from red through brown to yellow, and

these constitute probably the most common and
striking colors of the rocks of the earth. The gor-
geously colored Grand Canyon of the Yellowstone
River is a very fine example of large scale coloring
due to development of much hydrated oxide of iron
during the weathering of lava rock, the process having been aided by the action of heated underground
waters.

Most of the soils of the earth are the direct result of weathering. Important exceptions are soils
which have been transported by the action of water,
ice, or wind. Although the process of weathering
is very slow and relatively superficial, it is, nevertheless, true that in many places, the products of
weathering form faster than they can be carried
away. Such weathered materials accumulate in
their place of origin to form soils. The upper few
hundred feet of the earth's crust is everywhere more
or less fractured and porous and the rocks are there
affected in varying degrees by most of the ordinary
agents of weathering. In such cases, outside the
areas which were recently covered by ice during
the great Ice Age, it is common to find the loose soil
grading downward into rotten rock, and this in turn
into the fresh practically unaltered bedrock. Soils
of this kind are generally not more than ten or
twenty feet deep, though under exceptional conditions, as in parts of Brazil, they attain depths of
several hundred feet.

In order to make still clearer some of the above
principles of weathering and also to give the reader
some understanding of the most common types of
residual soils, we shall consider what happens to a
few rather definite types of ordinary rocks when
they are subjected to weathering. A very simple

case is that of a sandstone, the mineral grains (mostly quartz) of which are held together by carbonate of lime. The lime simply dissolves and is carried away, while many of the mineral grains may remain to form a soil of nearly pure sand. Where oxide of iron forms the cementing material, the rock yields less readily to weathering, and the sandy soil will be yellowish brown or red according to the climate. Another simple case is that of limestone which when perfectly pure yields no soil because it is all soluble. Pure limestone is, however, rare, and the various mineral impurities in it, being to a considerable degree insoluble, tend to remain to form a residual soil which may vary from sandy to clayey, and usually brown or red due to the setting free of oxides of iron. According to one estimate a thickness of about 100 feet of a certain fairly impure limestone formation in Virginia must weather to yield a layer of soil one foot thick. Soils of this kind, which are usually rich, are common in many limestone valleys of the Appalachian Mountains. In the case of shale rock, which is hardened mud, the cementing materials are removed, some chemical changes in the minerals may take place, and the rock crumbles to a claylike soil. What happens to a very hard, resistant igneous rock like granite when attacked by the weather? Such a rock always consists mainly of the two very common minerals feldspar and quartz, usually with smaller amounts of other minerals such as mica, hornblende, augite, or magnetite. The feldspar, which when fresh is harder than steel, slowly yields when attacked by water containing carbonic acid gas and crumbles or decays to a mixture of kaolin (clay), carbonate of potash, and silica (quartz). Clay is an important constituent of most good soils, while the carbonate of potash is essential as a food for most plants. Due to yielding of the grains or crystals of feldspar, the granite falls apart (see Plate 1). The grains of quartz remain chemically unchanged, though they may be more or less broken by changes of temperature, and the other minerals, which are mostly iron-bearing, yield more or less to weathering, resulting in a variety of products, among which are oxides of iron. A typical granite, therefore, gives rise to a good heavy soil which is yellow, brown or red according to climate. Such granite soils are common in many parts of the Piedmont Plateau from Maryland to Georgia. Most of the dark-colored igneous rocks, like ordinary basaltic lava, contain much feldspar, various iron bearing minerals, and little or no quartz. Such rocks yield to the weather like granite but, because of lack of quartz, the soils are more clayey. Rich soils of this kind occur in the great lava fields of the northwestern United States and in the Hawaiian Islands.

The importance of the breaking down of feldspar under the influence of the weather, as above described, not only from the standpoint of soil development, but also as regards the wearing down of the lands of the earth, is difficult to overemphasize because that mineral is by far the most abundant constituent of the earth's crust.

The term "erosion" is one of the most important in geologic science. It comprises all the processes whereby the lands of the earth are worn down. It involves the breaking up of earth material, and its transportation through the agency of water, ice, or wind. Weathering, including the various subprocesses as above described, is a very important process of erosion. By this process much rock material is got into condition for transportation. Another process of erosion, called "corrasion," consists in the rubbing or bumping of rocks fragments of all sizes carried by water, ice, or wind against the general country rock, thus causing the latter to be gradually worn away. A fine illustration of exceedingly rapid corrasion of very hard rock was that of the Sill tunnel in Austria, which was paved with granite blocks several feet thick. Water carrying large quantities of rock fragments over the pavement at high velocity caused the granite blocks to be worn through in only one year. Ordinarily in nature, however, the rate of wear is much slower than this. Pressure exerted upon the country rock by any agency of transportation may cause relatively loose joint blocks, into which most rock formations are separated, to be pushed away. This process, called "plucking," is especially effective in the case of flowing ice.

CHAPTER III

STREAM WORK

MOST streams are incessantly at work cutting or eroding their way into the earth's crust and carrying off the products of weathering. By this means the general level of lands is gradually being reduced to nearer and nearer sea level. Base level of erosion is reached when any stream has eroded to its greatest possible depth, and a whole region is said to be base-leveled when, by the action of streams, it has been reduced to a practically flat condition. A region of this kind is known as a "peneplain."

To one who has not seriously considered the matter, the power of even moderately swift water to transport rock débris seems incredible. A well-established law of transportation by running water is that the transporting power of a current varies as the sixth power of its velocity. For example, a current which is just able to move a rock fragment of a given size will, when its velocity is merely doubled, be able to move along a piece of similar rock sixty-four times as large! That this must be the case may be readily proved as follows: A current of given velocity is just able to move a block of rock, say, of one cubic inch in the form of a cube. A cubic block sixty-four times as large has a face of sixteen square inches. By doubling the velocity of the current, therefore, twice as much water must strike each of the sixteen square inches of the face of the larger block with twice the force, thus exerting sixty-four times the power against the face of the larger block, or enough to move it along. This surprising law accounts for the fact that in certain floods, like the one which rushed over Johnstown, Pennsylvania, in 1889, locomotives, massive iron bridges, and great boulders were swept along with great velocity. It is obvious, then, that ordinarily swift rivers in time of flood accomplish far more work of erosion (especially transportation) than during many days or even some months of low water.

Few people have the slightest idea as to the enormous amount of earth material which the rivers are carrying into the sea each year. The burden carried by the Mississippi River has been carefully studied for many years. Each year this river discharges about 400,000,000 tons of material in suspension; 120,000,000 tons in solution; and 40,-000,000 tons rolled along the bottom. This all represents earth material eroded from the drainage basin of the river. It is sufficient to cover a square mile 325 feet deep, or if placed in ordinary freight cars it would require a train reaching around the earth several times to contain it. Since the drainage basin of the Mississippi covers about 1,250,-000 square miles, it is, therefore, evident that this drainage area is being worn down at the average rate of about one foot in 5,000 years, and this is perhaps, a fair average for the rivers of the earth. The Ganges River, being unusually favorably situated for rapid erosion, wears down its drainage basin about one foot in 1,750 years. It has been estimated that nearly 800,000,000 tons of material are annually carried into the sea by the rivers of the United States. According to this the country, as a whole, is being cut down at the rate of about one foot in 9,000 years. In arriving at this figure it should, of course, be borne in mind that the average level of hundreds of thousands of square miles of the western United States, particularly the so-called Great Basin, is practically not being reduced at all because none of the streams there reach the sea.

Deposition of sediment is an important natural consequence of erosion. The destination of most streams is the sea, and where tides are relatively slight the sediments discharged mostly accumulate relatively near the mouths of the rivers in the form of flat, fan-shaped delta deposits. Some rivers, like the Ganges, which carry such unusual quantities of sediment, are able to construct deltas in spite of considerable tides. Deltas also form in lakes. In most cases, however, rivers enter the sea where there are considerable tides and their loads are more widely spread over the marginal sea bottom. But in many cases some of the sediment does not reach the mouth of the stream. It is, instead, deposited along its course either where the velocity is sufficiently checked, as is the case over many floodplain areas of rivers, or where a heavily loaded, relatively swift stream has its general velocity notably diminished. An excellent example of the latter type of stream is the Platte River, which is swift and loaded with sediment in its descent from the Rocky Mountains, but, on reaching the relatively more nearly level Nebraska country, it has its current sufficiently checked to force it to deposit sediment and build up its channel along many miles of its course, and this in spite of the fact that it

PLATE 1.—(a) GRANITE WEATHERING TO SOIL NEAR NORTHAMPTON, MASS.
Under the action of weathering all of the once hard, fresh, mass of
granite has crumbled to soil except the fairly fresh rounded masses
which are residual cores of "joint blocks." (*Photo by the author.*)

PLATE 1.—(b) GRANITE WEATHERING BY EXFOLIATION. North face
of Long's Peak, Colorado. (*Photo by the author.*)

PLATE 2.—GRAND CANYON OF THE YELLOWSTONE RIVER IN YELLOWSTONE NATIONAL PARK. The great waterfall 308 feet high is shown. The large swift river has here sunk its channel (by erosion) to a maximum depth of 1,200 feet during very recent geological time, and the process is still going on. The wonderful coloring is due to iron oxides set free during weathering of the lava rock. (*Photo by Hillers, U. S. Geological Survey.*)

still maintains a considerable current. In a mountainous arid region a more or less intermittent stream at times of flood becomes heavily loaded with rock débris and rushes down the mountain side. On reaching the valley floor the velocity is greatly checked and most of the load is deposited at the base of the mountain, successive accumulations of such materials, called alluvial cones or fans, having not uncommonly built up to depths of hundreds, or even several thousand feet.

Any newly formed land surface, like a recently drained lake bed or part of the marginal sea bottom which has been raised into land, has a drainage system developed upon it. In the early or youthful stage of such a new land area lying well above sea level, under ordinary climatic conditions, a few streams only form and these tend to follow the natural or initial slope of the land. These streams carve out narrow, steep-sided valleys, and all of them are actively engaged in cutting down their channels, or, in other words, none of them have reached base level, and flood plains and meandering curves are therefore lacking. During this youthful stage there are no sharp drainage divides; gorges and waterfalls are not uncommonly present; and the relief of the land in general is not rugged. A good example of youthful topography is the region around Fargo, North Dakota, which is part of the bed of a great recently drained lake. The Grand Canyon of the Yellowstone River is an excellent illustration of a youthful valley cut in a high plateau of geologically recent origin. (Plate 2.)

As time goes on, a region in youth gradually gives way to region in maturity, during which stage the maximum number (usually a network) of streams in broader V-shaped valleys have developed; divisions of drainage are sharp; the maximum ruggedness of relief has developed; the larger streams only have cut down so near base level that winding (meandering) courses and flood plains are well developed along them; and waterfalls and gorges are rarely present. An almost perfect example of a region in maturity is that around Charleston, West Virginia.

The old-age stage develops next in the history of the region, during which only a moderate number of streams remain, most of these being at or close to base level so that sweeping curves or meanders (Plate 4) and cut-off meanders or "ox bows" and wide flood plains are characteristic and common. The relief is greatly subdued and the term "rolling country" might be applied to the moderately hilly region. Divisions of drainage are, of course, not at all sharp and the valleys are wide and shallow. Oxbow lakes are common, but gorges and waterfalls are absent. A region typical of old-age topography is that around Caldwell, Kansas.

Finally, after the remaining low hills have been cut down, the region is in the condition of a broad monotonous plain, practically devoid of relief, over which the sluggish streams pursue very winding, more or less shifting or indefinite courses. For the attainment of this final stage (called a "peneplain") in the normal cycle of erosion a proportionately very long time is necessary, because the rate of erosion becomes slower and slower as the region is being cut down. Then, too, some change of level between the land and the sea is very likely to take place before the peneplain stage is reached. It is doubtful if any extensive region was ever brought

to the condition of a perfect peneplain. Some masses of more resistant or more favorably situated
rocks are almost sure to maintain at least moderate
heights above the general plain level. Geologically
recently upraised, fairly well developed peneplains
are southern New England and the great region of
eastern Canada. The remarkably even sky lines of
these regions mark the peneplain level before the
uplift took place, and occasionally masses, called
"monadnocks" from Mount Monadnock in southern
New Hampshire, rise above the general level. The
valleys in such an uplifted peneplain region have
been carved out by streams since the uplift began.
We have positive evidence that more or less well-
developed peneplains of considerable extent existed
in various parts of the earth at various times during the many millions of years of known earth
history.

The normal cycle of erosion which, as outlined
above, tends toward the peneplain condition may be
interrupted at any stage by other processes. An
excellent case in point is the upper Mississippi
Valley, which had reached the old-age stage, even
approximating a peneplain, just before the great
Ice Age. Then, during the withdrawal of the vast
sheet of ice from the region toward the close of
the Ice Age, extensive deposits (moraines, etc.) of
glacial débris were left irregularly strewn over the
country, giving rise to many low hills, lake basins,
and altered drainage lines, in some cases with re-
sultant gorge development. Some distinct features
of a youthful topography are, therefore, developed
over what was otherwise a region well along in old
age. The general district around the Dells of Wisconsin River well illustrates this principle.

Changes in level between land and sea which take place during the erosion of a region may also disturb the normal cycle of erosion. For example, a region in old age may be considerably upraised so that the streams have their velocities notably increased. Such a region is said to be "rejuvenated" and the streams, which are revived in activity, begin to cut youthful valleys in the bottom of the old ones and, after a time, the general surface of the region is subjected to vigorous erosion and a new cycle of erosion will be carried out unless interfered with in some way, as by relative change of level between the land and the sea. In this connection the history of the topography in the general vicinity of Harrisburg, Pennsylvania, may be of interest by way of illustration of the principle just described. The long, narrow, parallel Appalachian Mountain ridges there rise to about the same level, causing a remarkably even sky line as viewed from one of the summits. This even sky line marks approximately the surface of what was a peneplain early in the Cenozoic era. Then in succeeding Cenozoic time, the broad peneplain was notably upraised to nearly the present altitudes of the ridge tops. The revived Susquehanna River kept the old course which it had on the peneplain surface, and began to carve out its present valley, while tributaries (subsequent streams) to it developed along belts of weaker rock and thus they formed the present parallel valleys separated by belts of more resistant rocks which stand out as ridges. In this way, the mature stage of topography was reached. Very recently, geologically, the region has been rejuvenated enough to cause the larger streams to appreciably sink their channels below the general valley floors. The reader will find a general discussion of movements of the earth's crust in a succeeding chapter.

If, for example, a region along the seaboard has reached the mature stage of erosion, and the land notably subsides relative to sea level, the tidewater

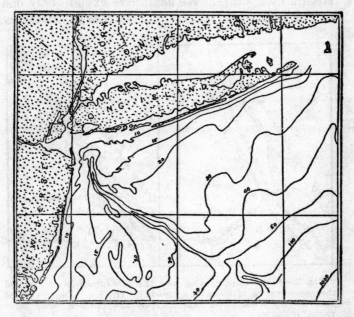

Fig. 1.—The submerged Hudson River channel is clearly shown by the contour lines on the sea floor. Figures indicate depth of water in fathoms. Geologically recent sinking of the land has caused the "drowning" of the river valley. (Coast and Geodetic Survey).

will enter the lower valleys to form estuaries and the valleys are said to be "drowned." The large streams, or at least their lower courses, are thus obliterated and also the general erosion of the region is distinctly diminished. The recently sunken coast of Maine well illustrates the idea of "drowned valleys." The drowned valley of the lower Hudson River is another fine example.

What is termed stream "piracy" is of special interest in connection with stream work. By this is meant the stealing of one stream or part of a stream by another. We shall here explain only one of the various ways by which stream capture may

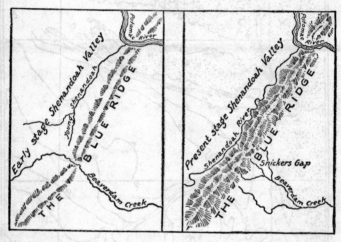

FIG. 2.—Sketch maps showing how the Shenandoah River captured the upper waters of Beaverdam Creek in Virginia. The abandoned valley of the creek across Blue Ridge is now called a "wind gap." (After B. Willis.)

be effected. One of two fairly active streams, flowing roughly parallel to each other, is more favorably situated and has cut its channel deeper. Its tributaries are, therefore, more favorable to extension of headwaters and, in time, one of its tributaries eats back far enough to tap a branch of the less favorably situated stream so that the waters of this branch are diverted into the more favorably situated stream. The Shenandoah River of Virginia has been such a pirate. This river developed as a tributary of the Potomac. By headward extension toward the south, the Shenandoah finally tapped and diverted the upper waters of the smaller, less favorably situated Beaverdam Creek. The notch or so-called "wind gap" through which the upper waters of Beaverdam Creek formerly flowed across the Blue Ridge is still plainly visible. Such abandoned water gaps, known as "wind gaps," are common in the central Appalachian Mountain region.

A remarkable type of river is one which has been able to maintain its course through a barrier, even a mountain range, which has been built across it. Thus, the Columbia River, after flowing many miles across the great lava plateau, has maintained its course right across the growing Cascade Range by cutting a deep canyon while the mountain uplift has been in progress. In a similar manner the Ogden River of Utah has kept its westward course by cutting a deep canyon into the Wasatch Range which has geologically recently, though slowly, risen across its path. In no other way can we possibly explain the fact that such a river, rising on one side of a high mountain range, cuts right across it.

A feature of minor though considerable popular interest is the development of "potholes" by stream action. Where eddies occur, in rather active streams, rock fragments of varying sizes may be whirled around in such manner as to corrade or grind the bedrock, resulting in the development of cylinder-shaped "potholes." Such holes vary in diameter up to fifty feet or more in very exceptional cases. In the production of large "potholes" many rock fragments are worn away and new ones supplied to continue the work. Locally, some stream beds are honeycombed with "potholes."

Strikingly narrow and deep valleys, called gorges and canyons, are rather exceptional features of stream action. Most wonderful of all features of this kind is the Grand Canyon of the Colorado River in Arizona. In fact, this canyon takes high rank among the most remarkable works of nature. The canyon is over 200 miles long, from 4,000 to 6,000 feet deep, and from 8 to 15 miles wide. Contrary to popular opinion, this mighty canyon is not a result of some violent process, such as volcanic action, or the sudden sinking of part of the earth's crust. Nor is it the result of the scouring action of a great glacier. It is simply a result of the operation of the ordinary processes of erosion where the conditions have been exceptionally favorable. Some of the favorable conditions have been, and are, a large volume of very swift water (Colorado River) continually charged with an abundance of rock fragments for the work of corrasion, and a great thickness of rock which the river must cut through before reaching base-level. Aridity of climate also tends to preserve the canyon form. The whole work has been accomplished in very late geological time, and the tremendous volume of rock which has been weathered and eroded to produce the canyon has all been carried away by the Colorado River and accumulated in the great delta deposit near where the river empties into the Gulf of California. Even now the canyon is growing deeper and wider because the very active Colorado River is still from 2,000 to 3,000 feet above sea level. Standing on the southern rim near Grand Canyon station at an alti-

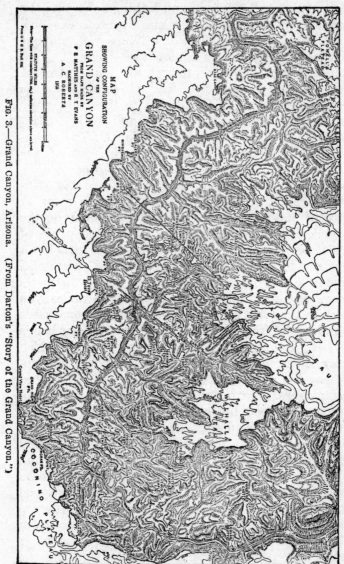

FIG. 3.—Grand Canyon, Arizona. (From Darton's "Story of the Grand Canyon.")

tude of nearly 7,000 feet, and looking down into the canyon, one beholds a vast maze of side canyons, high, vertical rock walls which follow very sinuous courses, giving rise to a steplike topography, and countless rock pinnacles, towers, and mesas often of mountainlike proportions. The side canyons are the result of erosion by tributaries to the main river which have gradually developed and worked headward as the main river has cut down. The mountainlike sculptured forms which rise out of the canyon are erosion remnants, or, in other words, masses of rock which were more favorably situated against erosion by either the main river or any of its tributaries. All of the rocks of the broader, main portions of the canyon are strata of Paleozoic age, arranged as a vast pile of almost horizontal layers, including sandstone, limestone, and shale. Some of these layers, being distinctly more resistant than others, stand out in the canyon wall in the form of conspicuous cliffs, in some cases hundreds of feet high. The very striking color bands (mostly light gray, red, and greenish gray), which may be traced in and out along the canyon sides, represent the outcropping edges of variously colored rock layers. Far down in the canyon lies the steep-sided, V-shaped inner gorge, or canyon which is fully 1,000 feet deep. The rocks are there not ordinary strata, but rather metamorphic and igneous rocks, mostly dark gray, not in layers, and about uniformly resistant to erosion. There is reason to believe that this inner gorge has developed mainly since a distinct renewed uplift (rejuvenation) of the Colorado Plateau after the river began its canyon cutting. The narrow, steep-sided inner gorge may thus be readily accounted for and the

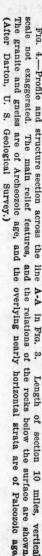

Kaibab limestone
Coconino sandstone
Supai formation
Redwall limestone
Tonto group (Shale
Tonto group (Sandstone
Granite and gneiss

8,000 feet
above sea level

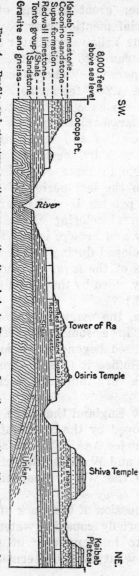

SW.

Cocopa Pt.

River

Red sandstone (Supai)
Redwall limestone
Shale

Tower of Ra

Osiris Temple

Red shale

Unkar

Shiva Temple

Kaibab
Plateau

NE.

FIG. 4.—Profile and structure section across the line A-A in Fig. 3. Length of section 10 miles, vertical scale not exaggerated. The main relief features, and the relations of the rocks below the surface are shown. The granite and gneiss are of Archeozoic age, and the overlying nearly horizontal strata are of Paleozoic age. (After Darton, U. S. Geological Survey.)

general lack of step-like forms on its sides is due to essential uniformity of the rock material as regards resistance to erosion.

The wonderful King's River Canyon of the southern Sierra in California is remarkable for its combined narrowness and depth. It is a steep V-shaped canyon whose maximum depth is 6,900 feet, c a r v e d out in mostly solid granite by the action of weathering and running water. Some idea of the vast antiquity of the earth may be gleaned f r o m t h e f a c t that this tremendously deep canyon has been produced by erosion in one of the most resistant of all known rocks in very late geologic time! Conditions favorable for cutting this canyon have been volume and swiftness of water and a liberal supply of grinding tools.

Among the many other great canyons of the western United States brief mention may be made of the Grand Canyon of the Yellowstone River in the National Park. The plateau into which the river has cut its steep-sided, narrow, V-shaped canyon, with maximum depth of 1,200 feet, was formed in a geologically recent time by outpourings of vast sheets of lava. The large volume of very swift water, aided by decomposition and weakening of the ordinarily very hard rock by the action of the hot springs, has been able to carve out this deep canyon practically within the last period of earth history. The deepening process is still vigorously in progress. The wonderful coloring of the rock, mostly in tones of yellow and brown, is due to the hydrated iron oxides developed during the decay of the iron-bearing minerals of the lava, the chemical action having been greatly aided by the action of the hot waters. (See Plate 2.)

In regard to its origin, the marvelous Yosemite Valley, or canyon, falls in a somewhat different category, and it is discussed beyond in connection with the work of ice. Suffice it to say here that running water has been a very important factor in its origin.

In New York and New England there are many gorges which have developed by the action of running water since the Great Ice Age. Famous among these are Ausable Chasm and Watkins Glen of New York, and the Flume in the White Mountains of New Hampshire.

Before leaving our discussion of the work of running water, we should briefly consider waterfalls. True waterfalls originate in a number of ways. Most common of all is what may be termed the

"Niagara type" of waterfall. Niagara Falls merit
more than passing mention not only because of their
scenic grandeur, but also because of the unusual
number of geologic principles which their origin
and history so clearly illustrate. Niagara Falls are
divided into two main portions, the Canadian, or
so-called "Horseshoe Fall," and the "American
Fall," separated by a large island. The crest of the
American Fall is about 1,000 feet long and nearly
straight, while the crest of the Canadian Fall is
notably curved inward upstream, and it is about
3,000 feet long. The height of the Falls is 167 feet.
Downstream from the Falls there is a very steep-
sided gorge about 200 feet deep and seven miles long.
The exposed rocks of the region are nearly horizontal layers of limestone underlain with shales. Relatively more resistant limestone forms the crest of
the falls, and directly underneath are the much
weaker shales. Herein lies the principle of this
type of waterfall because, due to weathering and
the swirling action of the water, the weaker underlying rocks erode faster, thus causing the overlying
rock to overhang so that from time to time blocks
of it already more or less separated by cracks
(joints), fall down and are mostly carried away in
the swift current. Thus the waterfall maintains
itself while it steadily retreats upstream. Careful
estimates based upon observations made between
1827 and 1905 show that the Canadian Fall retreated at the rate of from three to five feet per year,
while the American Fall retreated during the same
time at the rate of only several inches per year. It
has been well established that Niagara Falls came
into existence soon after the ice of the great Ice
Age had retreated from the district. The falls

started by plunging over a limestone escarpment, situated at what is now the mouth of the gorge seven miles downstream from the present falls. If we consider the rate of recession of the falls to have

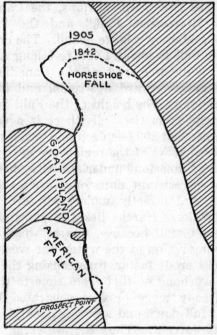

FIG. 5.—Sketch map showing the retreat of the crest of Niagara Falls from 1842 to 1905, based upon actual surveys. The retreat of the inner part of the Horseshoe Fall was more than 300 feet. (Modified by the author after Gilbert, U. S. Geological Survey.)

been always five feet per year, the length of time required to cut the gorge would be something over 7,000 years. But the problem is not so simple, because we know that, at the time of, or shortly after, the beginning of the falls, the upper Great Lakes drained farther north and not over the falls;

and that this continued for a considerable, though unknown, length of time. During this interval the volume of water in Niagara River was notably diminished, and hence the recession of the falls must have been slower. On the other hand, judging by the width of the gorge, the length of the crest of the falls has generally been considerably less than at present, which in turn means greater concentration of water over the crest and more rapid wear. Various factors considered, the best estimates for the age of the falls vary from 10,000 to 50,000 years, an average being about 20,000 years. Although this figure is not precise, it is, nevertheless, of considerable geologic interest because it shows that the age of Niagara Falls (and gorge) is to be reckoned in some tens of thousands of years, rather than hundreds of thousands or millions of years. Although waterfalls of the Niagara type are the most common of all, it is by no means necessary that the particular rocks should be limestone and shale.

Another common kind of waterfall may be termed the "Yosemite type," so named from the high falls in the Yosemite Valley of California. At the great falls of the Yosemite, the rock is a homogeneous granite and the undermining process does not operate. Yosemite Creek first plunges vertically over a granite cliff for 1,430 feet to form the Upper Falls, which must rank among the very highest of all true water falls. The water then descends about 800 feet by cascading through a narrow gorge, after which it makes a final vertical plunge of over 300 feet. A brief history of the falls is about as follows. A great steep-sided V-shaped canyon several thousand feet deep had been carved out by the action of the Merced River which now flows through the valley. Then, during the Ice Age, a mighty glacier plowed through the canyon, filling it to overflowing. The granite of this district having been unusually highly fractured by great vertical joint cracks was relatively easy prey for ice erosion. Due to its great weight, the erosive power of the ice was most potent toward the bottom, successive joint blocks were removed, and the valley was thus widened and the sides steepened or even commonly made practically vertical. (See Plate 7.) After the melting of the ice, certain of the streams, like Yosemite Creek and Bridal Veil Creek, were forced to enter the valley by plunging over great perpendicular, granite cliffs which are in reality joint faces. This type of waterfall does not retreat, but it constantly diminishes in height by cutting into the crest. A number of other high falls of this kind occur in the Yosemite region, and also in other mountain valleys which formerly contained glaciers, as in the Canadian Rockies, the Alps, and Norway, the rocks in these regions being of various kinds.

In the case of the "Yellowstone type" of waterfall a different principle is involved, namely, a distinctly harder or more resistant mass of rock which extends vertically across the channel of the stream. At the Great Falls of the Yellowstone a mass of relatively fresh, hard lava lies athwart the course of the river, while just below it the lava has been much weakened by decomposition. The harder rock therefore acts as a barrier, while, in the course of time, the weak rock on the downstream side has been worn away until a waterfall 308 feet high has developed. This waterfall does not retreat very appreciably, but it is probably increasing in height, due both to the scouring action of the water at the base

PLATE 3.—THE GORGE OF NIAGARA RIVER BELOW THE GREAT FALLS. The strata (containing fossils) were accumulated on the bottom of the Silurian sea which overspread the region fully 350,000,000 years ago. Since the Ice Age, or within a period of some 20,000 years, the river has carved out the gorge. (*Courtesy of the Haines Photo Company, Conneaut, Ohio.*)

PLATE 4.—(*a*) A WINDING STREAM IN THE ST. LAWRENCE VALLEY OF NEW YORK. Due to its low velocity the stream cuts its channel down very little, but it swings or "meanders" slowly from one side of its valley to the other, developing a wide flood plain. The stream once flowed against the valley wall shown at the middle left. (*Photo by the author.*)

PLATE 4.—(*b*) NUMEROUS PINNACLES AND TOWERS CARVED OUT OF SOFT, HORIZONTAL, HIGHLY JOINTED STRATA. BRYCE CANYON, UTAH. (*Photo by the author.*)

of the fall and the unusual clearness of the river
water here, thus causing little wear at the crest. It
should be noted, in this connection, that the channel just on the upstream side of the barrier cannot
be cut down faster than the top of the barrier itself.

The famous Victoria Falls of the Zambezi River
in South Africa, represents a relatively uncommon
type of waterfall. Considering height of the fall,
length of crest, and volume of water, this is perhaps
the greatest waterfall in the world. The Zambezi
River, a mile wide, plunges over 400 feet vertically
into a chasm only a few hundred feet wide and at
right angles to the main course of the stream. The
general country rock is hard lava, but locally a narrow belt of the rock has been highly fractured vertically, due to earth movements or faulting (see explanation beyond) and therefore weakened and more
subject to weathering than the general body of the
lava rock. This belt of weakened rock has been
easy prey for erosion by the Zambezi River and the
chasm has there developed. In fact the chasm is
still being increased in depth. Leaving the chasm toward one end, the river flows through a narrow zig-
zag gorge whose position has been determined by big
joint cracks. The mile-wide crest of the falls is interrupted by a good many ledges and even small islands. The thundering noise of this great waterfall
is most impressive, but a good complete view is impossible because most of the chasm is constantly
filled with dense spray.

Still another type of waterfall develops by the removal of joint blocks by the action of running water.
Falls of this type are fairly common though they
seldom attain really great heights. Where the rock
in the bed of a stream is traversed by well-developed

vertical joint cracks, slabs of rock cleaved by the
joints may fall away due to weathering or they may
be pushed away by pressure of the water. Such a fall
retreats upstream by removal of joint blocks even in
comparatively homogeneous rocks. Taughannock
Falls, 215 feet high, in southern central New York,
has developed by this manner in a shaly sandstone.
The several falls (one 50 feet high) in the famous
gorge at Trenton Falls, in central New York, have
developed in this way in limestone.

CHAPTER IV

THE SEA AND ITS WORK

IT is well known that the waters of the sea cover nearly three-fourths of the surface of the earth. We think of the United States as being a large piece of land of over three million square miles—but the sea is about forty-five times as large, that is, it covers approximately 140,000,000 square miles. It is a remarkable fact that the average depth of the great oceans of the earth is nearly two and one-half miles. If the sea were universally present everywhere with the same depth, it would be almost two miles deep. Yet this vast body of water is an extremely thin layer when compared with the earth's diameter of 8,000 miles. The Pacific is the deepest of the oceans with an average depth of about two and three-fourths miles. The deepest ocean water ever sounded is the Mindanao Deep, approximately 35,400 feet, near the Philippines. The second is southeast of Tokyo, Japan, 34,626 feet. The third is 32,212 feet. A fourth, near the Philippines, is the Planet Deep, 32,113 feet. Each of these four has a depth of more than six miles. Two more in the North Pacific and one in the South Pacific are each more than 30,000 feet. The deepest sounding ever made in the Atlantic is 27,972 feet, not far from Puerto Rico.

Many substances are known to be in solution in sea water, but in spite of this the composition is remarkably uniform. The most abundant substance

51

by far in solution is common salt. In every 100 pounds of sea water, there are 3.5 pounds of mineral matter of various kinds dissolved. Nearly 78 per cent of the dissolved matter is common salt. The principal other constituents in solution are chloride and sulphate of magnesia, and the sulphates of lime and potash. All other dissolved mineral substances together make up less than one per cent of the total. It has been estimated that if all the dissolved mineral matter should be brought together, it would form a layer 175 feet thick over the whole sea bottom. The salts of the sea have been mostly supplied by the rivers, which in turn have derived them from the disintegration and chemical decay of the rocks.

If we make a general comparison with the surface of the land, the floor of the ocean is a vast monotonous plain. None of the sea bottom compares with the ruggedness of mountains, and even the more level portions of land surface show many sharp minor irregularities such as stream trenches. But the sea bottom is characterized by its smoothness of surface. There are under the sea, however, mountainlike ridges, plateaus, submarine volcanoes and valleys known as "deeps." But these rarely show ruggedness of relief like similar features on land.

One of the most remarkable relief features of the ocean bottom is the so-called "continental shelf." This is a relatively narrow platform covered by shallow water bordering nearly all the lands of the earth. Seaward, the depth of water is greatest, and it is seldom over 600 or 800 feet. The continental shelves of the world cover about 10,000,000 square miles or about one-fourteenth of the area of the sea.

Viewed in a broad way, there are two great classes of marine deposits; first, those laid down comparatively near the borders of the land, that is, on the continental shelf and continental slope, and second, the abysmal deposits laid down on the bottom of the deep ocean. Those found along and near the continental borders are largely land-derived materials, that is to say, they are mostly sediments carried from the land into the sea by rivers, and to a lesser extent rock material broken up by waves along many shores. Practically all such land-derived material is deposited within 100 to 300 miles of the shores. The continental border deposits are extremely variable. Near shore they are chiefly gravel and sands, while farther out they become gradually finer, and on the continental slope only very fine muds are deposited. These deposits usually contain more or less organic materials and shells or skeletons of organisms. In some cases the shells or skeletons of organisms predominate or even exist to the exclusion of nearly all other material, as is true of the coral deposits or reefs which form only in shallow water. Deposits like those just described as accumulating on the bottom of the shallow sea, comparatively near the lands, are of great significance to the geologist because just such marine deposits now consolidated into sandstone, conglomerate, shale, and limestone, are so widely exposed over the various continents. A knowledge of the conditions under which shallow sea deposits are now forming, is, therefore, of great value in interpreting events of earth history as they are recorded in similar rocks which have been accumulating through millions of years of time. One specific instance will make this matter clearer. Using the method outlined in Chapter I for the determination of earth chronology, and our knowledge of present conditions under which shallow sea deposits are formed, it has been well established that a shallow sea spread over fully four-fifths of the area of North America during the middle Ordovician period of the early Paleozoic era. Beyond this main conclusion, a careful study of these rocks has revealed many important facts regarding the physical geography, life, and climate of that time. The importance of this whole matter is still further emphasized by the statement that five-sixths of the exposed rocks of the earth are strata—mostly of shallow sea origin.

The deposits on the deep sea bottom are very largely either organic or the shells and skeletons of organisms which have fallen to the bottom from near the surface as already explained. Most common of these are the deep sea "oozes" which are made up of the remains and shells of tiny organisms called "foraminifers." These "oozes" cover about 50 million square miles of the sea bottom down to depths of from two to three miles.

At depths greater than from two to three miles, a peculiar red clay is the prevailing deposit. This is most extensive of all, covering an area of 55 million square miles, or nearly the total area of lands of the earth. Some remains of organisms are mixed with this clay, but since most of the shells are of carbonate of lime and very thin, they are dissolved without reaching the bottom in the deep sea water which is under great pressure and rich in carbonic acid gas.

The deep sea deposits, both "oozes" and red clay, do, however, contain some land-derived and other materials. Thus off the west coast of Africa some dust carried by the prevailing winds from the Sahara Desert, is known to fall in the deep sea several hundred miles from shore. Volcanic dust is carried for many miles and deposited in the deep sea—particularly in the South Pacific Ocean. Bits of porous volcanic rock called "pumice" sometimes float long distances out over the deep sea, before becoming water soaked. Icebergs often drift far out from the polar regions over the deep sea, and on melting the rock débris which they carry is dropped to the sea bottom. Also, particles of iron and dust from meteorites ("shooting stars") have been dredged from the deep sea.

One important geological significance of the deep sea deposits is the proof which they furnish that, from at least as far back as the beginning of the Paleozoic era, fully five hundred million years ago, to the present time, the two great deep ocean basins—the Atlantic and the Pacific—have maintained essentially the same positions on the earth. This is proved by the fact that nowhere, on any continent among the rocks of all ages, as old at least as the early Paleozoic, do we find any really typical deep-sea deposits. There is then no evidence that a deep sea ever spread over any considerable part of any continent, and this in spite of the fact that marine deposits of shallow water origin furnish abundant evidence of former sea extensions. The shallow seas have at various times spread over large portions of the continents.

On many rocky coasts the waves are incessantly pounding and wearing away the rocks. In such places the sea, like a mighty horizontal saw, is cutting into the borders of the lands. The finer materials produced by the grinding up of the rocks are carried seaward by the undertow. But, if the land remains stationary with reference to the sea, this landward cutting by the waves reaches a limit. Since even

big waves have very little effect in water 100 or 200
feet deep, a shelf is cut by the waves and this shelf,
not many miles wide, is covered by shallow water.
The finer ground-up rock materials carried out by
the undertow are dumped just beyond the edge of
the shelf which is thus built out seaward as a terrace.
In traveling over this shelf and terrace, the waves,
due to friction, lose their power. With gradually
sinking land, a much wider shelf may be cut, because
the power of the waves is then allowed to continue.

It might be of interest to cite a few cases of relatively rapid coast destruction by the waves which
have come under human observation. A remarkable
example is the island of Heligoland on which is (or
was) located the powerful German fort which guards
the entrance to the Kiel Canal. In the year 800 A. D.
this island had 120 miles of shore line; in 1300 it
had 45 miles of shore; in 1649 only 8 miles; and in
1900 but 3 miles of shore line remained. In southeastern England "whole farms and villages have
been washed away in the last few centuries, the sea
cliffs retreating from 7 to 15 feet a year." A church
located a mile from the sea shore near the mouth of
the Thames river, in the sixteenth century, now
stands on a cliff overlooking the sea. An island in
Chesapeake Bay covered over 400 acres in 1848, and
the waves have since reduced it to about fifty acres.
Study showed that the relatively soft unconsolidated
strata of the Nashaquitsa Cliffs on the island of
Martha's Vineyard, were cut back at the rate of 5½
feet per year, between 1846 and 1886.

If part of the relatively smooth sea bottom should
be raised into land, the resulting shore line would
of course, be regular and free from indentations or
sharp embayments. Examples of such coasts which

are very young are at Cape Nome, Alaska; the northern coast of Spain; and the west coast of northern South America. Soon, however, such a shore line is attacked, and, either where the waves are greatest or the rocks are weakest, indentations will result and the whole coast is gradually eaten back until the power of the waves is largely spent in traveling across the shallow water shelf. Sand bars are then built across the mouths of the bays or indentations which later the rivers gradually fill up with sediment. The result is a relatively straight or regular shore line. Finally the whole land mass attacked by the sea may be reduced to base level of wave erosion.

If a portion of the relatively rugged land surface should become submerged under the sea, a very irregular, deeply indented shore line would result, due to the entrance of tidewater into the valleys. The deeply indented coast of Maine is a fine example of a very irregular youthful shore line produced by geologically recent sinking of a rugged, hilly region so that tidewater backs for miles into the lower reaches of the river valleys. The promontories and islands are undergoing rapid wear, and the development of bars across the inlets has scarely begun. Other excellent examples are the coasts of Norway and southern Alaska. Such a coast is then attacked by the ocean waves and the promontories are cut back until the broad shallow water shelf is formed, after which sand bars are built across the remaining embayments and the shore line becomes relatively regular.

It is, then, a remarkable fact that, whether shore lines originate by emergence of sea bottom, or by sinking of land, there is a very strong tendency on the part of nature to develop regular shore lines. It should be stated that the principles of wave work

58   GEOLOGY

and shore-form development just outlined apply almost equally well to lakes, especially large ones.

Before leaving this subject of shore-line development, mention should be made of the fact that bars and beaches are often built part way or wholly across embayments of the coast with surprising rapidity. To illustrate, Sandy Hook, New Jersey, is advancing northward, while Rockaway Beach, New York, is extending westward, the tendency being to close up the entrance to New York harbor and to make the line of seashore more nearly regular. Records show that Rockaway Beach actually advanced westward more than three miles between the years 1835 and 1908.

CHAPTER V

GLACIERS AND THEIR WORK

A GLACIER may be defined as a mass of flowing ice. The motion may not be that of flowage in the usually accepted sense of the term. A discussion of the various theories of glacier motion will not here be attempted. Glaciers form only in regions of perpetual snow, but they commonly move down far below the line of perpetual snow of any given region. In the polar regions they may form near sea level, while in the tropics they form at altitudes of two to three miles, and there only rarely. In southern Alaska, the lower limit of perpetual snow is about 5,000 feet above sea level, and many of the glaciers come down to sea (Plate 5a), while in the Alps, the lower limit of perpetual snow is at about 9,000 feet, and the glaciers descend as much as 5,000 feet below it.

In regions of perpetual snow there is a tendency for more or less snow to accumulate faster than it can be removed by evaporation or melting. As such snow accumulates it gradually undergoes a change, especially in its lower parts, first into granulated snow (so-called "névé") and then into solid ice. Snow drifts in the northern United States often undergo similar transformation, after a few months first to névé, and then to ice. This transformation seems to be brought about mainly by weight of overlying snow which compacts the snow crystals; by rain or melting snow percolating into the snow to

freeze and fill spaces between the snow crystals; and
by the actual growth of the crystals themselves.
When ice of sufficient thickness has accumulated
(probably at best several hundred feet), the spreading action or flowage begins and a glacier has developed. Renewed snowfalls over the gathering
ground keep up the supply of ice.

There are several types of glaciers: valley or alpine glaciers; cliff or hanging glaciers; piedmont
glaciers; ice caps; and continental ice sheets. A
valley or alpine glacier consists essentially of a
stream of ice slowly flowing down a valley and fed
from a catchment basin of snow within a region of
perpetual snow. In the Alps, where glaciers of this
sort are very typically shown, they vary in length
up to eight or nine miles. Perhaps the grandest display of great valley glaciers is in southern Alaska
where they attain lengths up to forty or fifty miles
and widths of one or two miles (Plate 5).

Hanging or cliff glaciers are in many ways like
valley glaciers, but they are generally smaller; they
develop in snow-filled basins above the snow line
usually on steep mountain sides; and they do not
reach down into well-defined valleys. Most of the
glaciers of the Glacier National Park in Montana
and many of those in the Cascade Mountains are of
this type. Mount Rainier in Washington is one of
the most remarkable single large mountain peaks in
the world, in regard to development of glaciers over
it. Great tongues of ice, starting mostly at 8,000 to
10,000 feet above sea level, flow down the sides of the
mountain for distances of to four and even six miles.
The total area of ice in this remarkable system of
radiating glaciers on this one mountain is over forty
square miles. These Mount Rainier glaciers are in

general best classified as intermediate in type between valley and hanging glaciers.

In some high latitude areas, as in Iceland and Spitzbergen, snow and ice may accumulate on

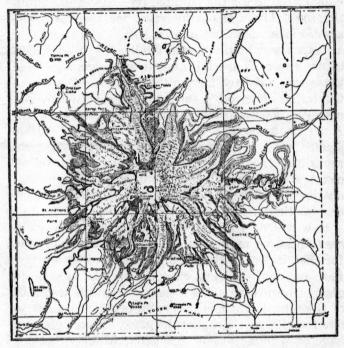

Fig. 6.—Map of Mount Rainier, Washington, showing its wonderful system of glaciers which covers more than 40 square miles. Dotted portions represent moraines. (U. S. Geological Survey.)

relatively level plains or plateaus and slowly spread or flow radially from their centers. These are called ice caps. Ordinary ice caps usually do not cover more than some hundreds of square miles.

Continental glaciers or ice sheets are, in principle, much like ice caps, but they are larger. Greenland is buried under an ice sheet of moderate size (about 500,000 square miles), the motion being outward in all directions toward the sea. Tongues of ice, like valley glaciers, are commonly sent off from the main body of ice across the land border of Greenland into the sea. The size of the great ice sheet of Antarctica is not definitely known, but it covers probably at least several million square miles. Two continental ice sheets of special interest to the geologist are those which existed during the great Ice Age of the Quaternary period. One of these then covered nearly 4,000,000 square miles of northern North America, while the other covered about 2,000,000 square miles of northern Europe. The main facts regarding the Ice Age are given in a succeeding chapter. The facts brought out in the present discussion of existing glaciers will greatly aid in understanding the Ice Age.

How fast do glaciers flow? Based upon many observations, we may say that an average rate of flow for the glaciers of the world is not more than a few feet per day. A very exceptional case is a large glacier, branching off as a tongue from the ice sheet of Greenland, which is said to move sixty to seventy-five feet per day. Some of the great Alaskan glaciers have been found to flow from four to forty feet per day. Most glaciers of the Alps move only one to two feet per day. A glacier advances only when the rate of motion is greater than the rate of melting of its lower end and vice versa in the case of retreat. Thus it is true, though seemingly paradoxical, to assert that a glacier has a constant forward motion even when it is retreating by melting.

By watching the changing position of marked objects placed in the ice, it has been proved that, in a valley glacier, the top moves faster than the bottom; the middle moves faster than the sides; the rate of motion increases with thickness of ice, slope of floor over which it moves, and temperature.

Ice, like molasses candy, tends to crack when subjected to a relatively sudden force, and where the ice rides over a salient on the bed of the glacier, transverse cracks or fissures often develop. Due to more rapid motion of the central part of a valley glacier, stresses and strains are set up and crevasses are formed, usually pointing obliquely upstream. Where the ice tends to spread laterally in a broad portion of a valley, longitudinal cracks may develop. Crevasses vary in size up to several feet in width and hundreds of feet in depth. Owing to the forward motion of the ice, old fissures tend to close up and new ones form, and, aided by uneven melting, the surface of a glacier is generally very rough.

Like running water, ice may have considerable erosive power when it is properly supplied with tools. The total erosive effect which has been, and is now being, accomplished by ice compared with that of running water is, however, slight. One of the main processes by which ice erosion is accomplished is "corrasion" due to the rubbing or grinding action of hard rock fragments frozen into the bottom and sides of the glacier. Thick ice, shod with hard rock fragments and flowing through a deep, narrow valley of soft rock, is especially powerful as an erosive agent because the abrasive tools are supplied; the work to be done is easy; and the deep ice causes great pressure on the bottom and lower sides of the valley. Rock surfaces which have been thus subjected to ice erosion are characteristically smoothed and more or less scratched, striated, or grooved due to the corrasive effects of small and large rock fragments. This affords one of the best means of proving the former presence of a glacier over a region or in a valley. A typical V-shaped stream cut (eroded) valley is changed into one with a U-shaped profile or cross section by glacier erosion (Plate 6).

Another important process of ice erosion is "plucking," which consists in pushing along already more or less loosened joint blocks by the pressure of the moving ice. The pressure thus exerted, especially by a deep valley glacier, may be enormous. This process was an important factor in the development of the famous Yosemite Valley, a very brief account of whose history it will now be instructive to give.

The Yosemite Valley, about 7 miles long, less than one mile wide, and from 2,000 to 4,000 feet deep, lies on the western slope of the Sierra Nevada Mountains of California. Great cliffs of granite, mostly from 1,000 to over 3,000 feet high, bound the valley on either side. The floor of the valley is wide and remarkably flat (Plate 7). Just prior to the Ice Age, by the processes of erosion already set forth, the Merced River had carved out a great steep-sided V-shaped canyon commonly from 1,000 to 3,000 feet deep. During the Ice Age, two glaciers joined to form an extra deep powerful glacier, which flowed through a deep part of the Merced Canyon and modified it into the Yosemite Valley, essentially as we see it to-day. Because the ice was shod with many fragments of hard rock (granite), and the pressure at the bottom and lower sides of the glacier (several thousand feet thick) was so great, the V-shaped stream-cut canyon was changed to a U-shaped canyon with very steep to even vertical walls. A factor of great importance which notably aided the erosive

PLATE 5.—(a) DAVIDSON GLACIER, ALASKA. This glacier is at work
slowly grinding down the valley floor and cutting back its walls,
thus changing the original stream-cut, V-shaped profile, like that
of Plate 5. (*Photo by Wright, U. S. Geological Survey.*)

PLATE 5.—(b) NISQUALLY GLACIER, MT. RAINIER, WASHINGTON.
Part of a lateral moraine left recently by a retreating glacier.
(*Photo by the author.*)

PLATE 6.—SWIFT CURRENT VALLEY IN GLACIER NATIONAL PARK, MONTANA. This was once a deep V-shaped canyon carved out (eroded) by stream action. Then a great valley glacier slowly plowed its way through it during the Ice Age and, by ice erosion, the present nearly straight U-shaped canyon has resulted. (*Photo by Campbell, U. S. Geological Survey.*)

power of the glacier in this case was the existence of an unusual number of large vertical joint cracks in the granite in this local region. The plucking action of the ice was thus very greatly facilitated and great slabs of rock, separated by the vertical joints, especially toward the lower sides and bottom of the valley, were pushed away one after another by the ice. When the ice disappeared, great precipitous joint faces from 1,000 to 3,000 feet high were left along the valley sides. At its lower end the glacier left a dam of glacial débris (moraine) across the valley, thus causing a lake to form over the valley floor. The wide flat bottom of the valley was caused by filling up of the lake with sediment. The uniqueness of the Yosemite Valley is, then, due to a remarkable combination of several main factors; one, the presence of a large swift river well supplied with tools which carved out a deep V-shaped canyon; two, a mighty glacier which plowed its way through this canyon and converted it by erosion into a U-shaped canyon; three, the weakening of the rock by many joint cracks, thus greatly facilitating the ice erosion; and four, a post-glacial lake covering the valley floor which became filled with sediment. As a result of the ice work, several streams, tributary to the main stream (Merced River) which flows through the bottom of the valley, were forced to plunge over great vertical rock walls (joint faces), thus producing high and beautiful true waterfalls, including the very high Upper Yosemite Fall where Yosemite Creek makes a straight drop of 1,430 feet. A tributary valley like that of Yosemite Creek, which ends abruptly well above the main valley, is known as a "hanging" valley. The valley of Bridal Veil Creek is another good example. (See Plate 7.) Valleys which were once occupied by active glaciers are generally characterized by their U-shaped cross sections and their hanging (tributary) valleys, but the great height and steepness of the valley walls in Yosemite are exceptional.

A type of glacial erosion which is of special interest is the sculpturing of so-called "cirques" or "amphitheaters" in mountains within the region of perpetual snow. Where the main mass of snow and ice in the catchment basin or gathering ground of a valley glacier pulls away from the snow and névé on the upper slopes, the rock wall is more or less exposed in the deep crevasse. During warm days water fills the joint cracks in the rocks down in this crevasse (so-called "Bergschrund"), and during cold nights the water freezes and forces the blocks of rock apart. This is greatest toward the bottom of the crevasse and so, by this excavating or quarrying process, vertical or very steep walls are developed around a great bowlike basin or cirque. Such cirques, now free from glacial ice, with precipitous walls 500 to 2,000 feet high and one-fourth of a mile to one-half of a mile across, are common in the Sierra Nevada and Cascade Ranges and in the Rocky Mountains.

What becomes of the materials eroded by the ice? An answer to this question involves at least a brief discussion of the deposition of glacial débris, this constituting an important feature of the work of ice. The débris transported by a glacier is carried either on its surface or within it, or pushed along under it. It is generally heterogeneous material ranging from the finest clay through sand and gravel, to bowlders of many tons' weight. Various types of glacial deposits are abundantly illustrated by débris left strewn over much of the northeastern United States and some reference to these will be made.

Most valley glaciers carry considerable débris on their surfaces, this representing material which falls or is carried down from the valley walls upon the margins of the ice, thus forming marginal moraines. When two glaciers flow together, one marginal moraine from each will coalesce to form a medial moraine. The material carried along at the bottom of a glacier is called the ground moraine. Where it contains much very fine grained material with pebbles or boulders scattered through its mass, it is called "till" or "boulder clay." The pebbles or boulders of the ground moraine are commonly faceted and striated as a result of having been rubbed against the bedrock on which the glacier moved. Ground moraine material is the most extensively developed of all glacial deposits. It is so widely scattered over the glaciated northeastern portion of the United States that most of the soils consist of it, having been left strewn over the country during the melting of the vast ice sheet.

When a glacier remains practically stationary for some time, more or less material which it carries is piled up at its lower end to form a terminal moraine. Repeated pauses during general glacier retreat permit the accumulations of so-called recessional moraines. A wonderful display of recessional moraines occurs from the Great Lakes south, where they are festooned one within another and remain almost exactly as they were formed during pauses in retreat of great lobes of ice during the closing stages of the Ice Age. A great terminal moraine marks the southernmost limit of the ice sheet during the Ice Age, a very fine illustration being the ridge of low irregular hills extending the whole length of Long Island. Some of the material in that morainic ridge was transported by the ice from northern New England.

Considerable rock débris is transported within the ice, and such "englacial" material in part results from rock débris which falls on the surface in the catchment basin and becomes buried under new snowfalls which change to ice, and in part from material which falls into the crevasses in the glacier farther down the valley. Marked objects thrown into the catchment basin have, after many years, emerged at or near the end of the glacier; thus the rate of motion can be very accurately told. A very remarkable case of transportation through the body of a glacier is the following: In 1820, three men were buried under an avalanche in the catchment basin of the Bossons Glacier in the Alps. Forty-one years later several parts of the bodies, including the three heads together with some pieces of clothing, emerged at the foot of the glacier after traveling most of its length at the rate of eight inches per day. The heads were so perfectly preserved after their remarkable journey in cold storage that they were clearly recognized by former friends!

Where a valley floor slopes downward away from the end of a glacier, waters emerging from the ice, heavily loaded with rock débris, cause more or less deposition of the débris on the valley floor often for miles beyond the ice front. Such a deposit is called a "valley train." When the ice front pauses for a considerable time upon a rather flat surface, the débris-laden waters emerging from the ice develop an "outwash plain" by deposition of sediment rather uniformly over the flat surface. A very fine example is the plain which constitutes most of the southern half of Long Island just beyond the southern limit of the great terminal moraine ridge.

A type of glacial deposit of particular interest is the "drumlin" which is, in reality, only a special form of ground moraine material (commonly till), and, therefore, essentially unstratified. Typical drumlins are low, rounded mounds of till with roughly elliptical bases and steeper fronts facing the direction from which the ice flowed. Their long axes are always parallel to the direction of ice movement. In height they commonly range from 50 to 200 feet. Their mode of origin is not yet definitely known, but they form near the margins of broad lobes of ice either by erosion of earlier glacial deposits, or by accumulation beneath the ice under peculiarly favorable conditions, as perhaps in the longitudinal crevasses. One of the finest and most extensive exhibitions of drumlins in the world is in western New York between Syracuse and Rochester. Thousands of drumlins there rise above the general level of the Ontario plain, the New York Central Railroad passing through the very midst of them. Drumlins are also abundant in eastern Wisconsin.

Another type of glacial deposit in the form of low hills is the "kame" which, unlike the drumlin, always consists of more or less stratified material. Kames are seldom over 200 feet high, and they are of various shapes. In many cases they form irregular groups of hills, and in other cases fairly well defined kame ridges. Kames form as deposits from débris-laden streams emerging from the margins of glaciers, the water sometimes rising as great fountains because of the pressure. Such deposits are now actually in process of formation along the edge of

the great Malaspina Glacier of Alaska. Kames are
commonly associated with terminal and recessional
moraines. "Eskers" are similar except that they are
long winding low ridges of stratified material deposited by débris-laden streams, probably in longitudinal fissures in the ice near its margin. (See
Plate 18.)

Glacial boulders, or "erratics" are blocks of rock
or boulders left strewn over the country during the
melting of the ice. They vary in size from small
pebbles to those of many tons of weight, and most
of them were derived from ledges of relatively hard,
resistant rocks. (See Plate 18.) Erratics have very
commonly been carried a few miles from their parent
ledges, while more rarely they have traveled even
hundreds of miles. They are extremely abundant in
New York and New England, many occurring even
high up on the mountains. In some cases erratics
of ten or more tons' weight have been left in such
remarkably balanced positions on bedrock that a
child can cause one of them to swing back and forth
slightly. Such a boulder is literally a "rocking
stone." In the Adirondack Mountains the writer
recently observed a rounded erratic of very hard
rock fourteen feet in diameter resting in a very remarkably balanced position on top of another large
round glacial boulder.

CHAPTER VI

THE ACTION OF WIND

ONLY during the last quarter of a century have geologists come to properly appreciate the really important geological work of the wind. One reason for this is the fact that people live mostly in humid regions where the soils are largely effectually protected against wind action by the vegetation. But even in such regions, wind action is by no means negligible. One has but to observe the great clouds of dust raised by strong wind from freshly cultivated fields during a little dry weather in the late spring. Much of this dust is carried considerable distances, often miles, and in some cases young crops are injured by removal of soil from around the roots, while in other cases young plants are buried by deposition of the wind-blown material over them. In humid regions, the action of the wind is perhaps most strikingly exhibited along and near shores of sea and lakes, where loose dry sands are picked up and transported in great quantities, often depositing them as sand dunes, which may form groups of hills covering considerable areas. Very conspicious examples are the sand dunes of Dune Park in northern Indiana, and the dunes along the coast of New Jersey.

But the action of wind is most strikingly effective in desert and semiarid regions. The importance of the work of wind is made more impressive when we

realize that about one-fifth of the land of the earth
is desert.

In deserts some of the ordinary agents of weathering and erosion are either absent or notably reduced
in effectiveness. Thus, chemical action is, in general,
reduced to a minimum; weathering effects due to
moisture in the air are notably reduced, and either
frost action, or wedge work of ice, is relatively unimportant due to lack of water. Change of temperature between night and day is, however, unusually
important as a process whereby rocks are broken
up due to relatively rapid expansion and contraction in deserts because such temperature changes
are exceptionally great, and rocks and soils are
almost everywhere directly exposed, being free
from vegetation.

The finer grained materials, especially sand grains,
in deserts are picked up by the wind and driven,
often with great velocity, against barren rock ledges
and large and small rock fragments. By this process
(corrasion) the rocks are worn and often polished
by the materials blown against them. The principle
is that of the artificial sand-blast, used in etching
glass, or cleaning and polishing building and decorative stones. Under favorable conditions wind-driven
sand accomplishes noticeable erosion in a surprisingly short time. Thus, in a hard wind storm, a plate
glass window in a lighthouse on Cape Cod was worn
to opaqueness, while in a few weeks or months the
directly exposed window glass may there be worn
through.

The great erosive effect of wind-driven sand is
relatively close to the ground because the larger and
heavier fragments are not lifted to very considerable
heights. For this reason ordinary telegraph poles

are difficult to maintain in desert regions because, unless they are specially protected, they are soon cut down by sand swept against their bases. In the desert regions of our Southwestern States cliffs rising above the general level of the country are often undercut by wind erosion, sometimes with the development of large caverns. (See Plate 8.) Even the high portions of great ledges are there more or less fantastically sculptured by wind erosion, the softer portions being more deeply cut into than the harder. The famous sphinx of Egypt has been notably roughened by action of this kind.

The enormous power of high winds to transport rock material in desert regions is strikingly illustrated by the great sand storms of the Sahara Desert, where sand and dust, forming clouds with cubic miles of volume, sweep for many miles across the country. Some one has estimated that every cubic mile of air in such a storm contains more than 100,-000 tons of rock material. It is said that an army of 50,000 men under Cambyses was buried under the sands of a storm in the desert of northern Africa.

Dust from some of these storms is known to be driven hundreds of miles out over the Atlantic Ocean, there to settle in the sea. In mountainous desert regions, like the Great Basin of our Western States, the general tendency is for the rock materials wind-eroded from the mountains to be carried into the intermontane basins or valleys. Some basins of this sort are believed to contain depths of hundreds of feet of wind-blown material.

A special kind of wind-blown material called "loess," is a sort of fine-grained yellow, or brown loam which, though relatively unconsolidated, has

a remarkable property of standing out as high steep
cliffs or bluffs along the banks of streams. Many
thousands of square miles of northern China are
covered with loess. Among many other regions,
thousands of square miles of parts of the States of
Iowa, Nebraska, and Kansas are covered with loess,
which, in this case, is believed to be fine material
gathered by winds from the region just after the retreat of one of the ice sheets of the great Ice Age,
when there was very little vegetation to hold down
the loose soils of glacial origin.

Much as snowdrifts are formed, so, in many
places, the wind-driven sands are built up into
sand hills or so-called "dunes." Dunes are very common in many places, as for example, along our middle Atlantic coast; in Dune Park of northern Indiana;
and in the great arid and semiarid regions of the
Western States. Where there is a distinctly prevailing direction of wind, the sand is blown to the lee-
ward side from the windward side, and the dunes are
caused to migrate in the direction of the wind. The
burial and destruction of forests, and the uncovering
of the dead trees is not uncommonly caused by migration of sand dunes, all stages of this phenomenon being well exhibited in Dune Park, Indiana. The rate
of dune migration is very variable, but study in a
number of places has shown a rate of from a few feet
to more than 100 feet per year. Arable lands, buildings, and even towns have been encroached upon
and buried under drifting sand. An interesting example is a church in the village of Kunzen, on the
Baltic seashore which, in a period of sixty years,
became completely buried under a dune and then
completely uncovered by migration of the dune.
Much destruction has been wrought by shifting

sands on the Bay of Biscay, where farms and even villages have been overwhelmed. The ruins of the ancient cities of Babylon and Nineveh are buried mostly under wind-blown sand and dust. There is good reason to believe that the climate of central and western Asia is now notably drier than it was a few thousand years ago, and this may help to explain the burial of many old cities and villages there under wind-blown deposits.

CHAPTER VII

INSTABILITY OF THE EARTH'S CRUST

THE crust of the earth is unstable. To the modern student of geology the old notion of a "terra firma" is outworn. The idea of an unshakable, immovable earth could never have emanated from the inhabitants of an earthquake country. In general we may recognize two types of crustal movements—slow and sudden. To most people the sudden movements accompanied by earthquakes are more significant and impressive because they are more localized and evident, and often accompanied by destruction of property, or quick, though minor, changes in the landscape. But movements which take place slowly and quietly are often of far greater significance in the interpretation of the profound physical changes which have affected the earth during its millions of years of known history.

A few well-known examples will serve to prove that upward, downward, and differential movements of the earth's crust have actually taken place not only in the remote ages of geologic time, but also that such movements took place in geologically recent time, and that similar movements are still going on. It is very important that the reader thoroughly appreciate the fact that crustal disturbances, often profound ones, do take place, because this is one of the most fundamental tenets of geologic science. Let us consider the case of the Hudson-Champlain-St. Lawrence Valley region. That the whole region was once notably higher (at least 1,000 feet) than at present is proved by the drowned character of the Hudson Valley, in which tidewater extends northward for 150 miles to near Troy. Where the New York City Aqueduct passes under the

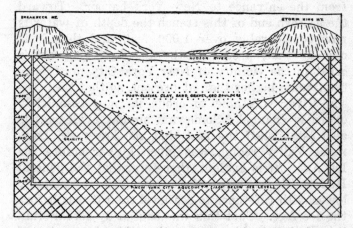

FIG. 7.—Structure section across the Hudson River Valley near West Point, New York. The shafts and tunnel, 1,200 feet below sea level, in solid rock, show the position of the New York City aqueduct from the Catskills. The Preglacial valley has been submerged and filled with Postglacial sediment to a depth of nearly 800 feet. (Redrawn by the author after Berkey, from New York State Museum Bulletin.)

Hudson River near Newburgh, the bedrock bottom of the old river channel is now about 800 feet below sea level as determined by drilling. This old channel is there filled up nearly to sea level with glacial and postglacial rock débris, which shows that the old channel must have been cut before the oncoming of the ice of the great Ice Age. Before the Ice Age, then, the lower Hudson Valley must have been considerably more than 800 feet higher than at present, because it then contained a river with sufficient current to be an active agent of erosion, carving out the canyonlike valley in the vicinity of West Point. This conclusion is strongly reenforced by the fact that the old valley of the Hudson River has been definitely traced as a distinct trench across the shallow sea bottom for about 100 miles eastward from the entrance to New York harbor. Toward the eastern end of this trench the depth of water is now considerably over 1,000 feet, and thus it is obvious that, preceding the Ice Age, the earth's crust in the vicinity of New York City must have been much higher than at present, so that the Hudson River was able to erode its now completely drowned channel. Somewhat similar evidence has also established the fact that the lower St. Lawrence Valley region was much higher before the Ice Age. It is evident, therefore, that the general Hudson-St. Lawrence Valley region is now notably lower with reference to sea level than it was before the Ice Age. That this was caused by actual sinking of the earth's crust rather than by a rise of sea level is proved by the fact that similar changes of level between land and sea did not take place at the same time even along the Atlantic and Gulf coast of our Southern States.

We shall now proceed to the next step in the geologically recent history of earth-crust movements in the Hudson-Champlain-St. Lawrence Valley region by asserting that, since the Ice Age, the land was actually notably lower than at present. In fact, the land was enough lower to allow tidewater to extend up the St. Lawrence Valley into the Ontario basin, and all through the Champlain-Hudson Valley. Many beaches, bars, and delta deposits formed in these arms of the sea are still plainly preserved, in some cases with shells and bones of marine animals in them, now hundreds of feet above sea level. These marine deposits are highest above sea level in the northern portion of the Champlain Valley, where they lie at an altitude of 700 feet or more and their altitude steadily diminishes southward to about 300 to 400 feet in the general vicinity of Albany, and to near sea level in the general vicinity of New York City. Obviously, then, the land stood lower during part or all of the interval of not more than a few tens of thousands of years since the Ice Age than at present. This leads us to the third important conclusion regarding earth movements in this region, namely, that still later the land has undergone a differential uplift, the rate having steadily increased toward the north where the total uplift is many hundreds of feet. We have discussed this region somewhat in detail because the principles of slow up and down movements of the earth's crust are there so plainly recorded.

Among many other regions where earth movements similar to those above described have taken place, brief mention may be made of Norway. The great fjords of Norway were, just before the Ice Age, stream-cut valleys which were then more or less modified by glacial erosion, and after the Ice Age the rivers in them were drowned due to land subsidence. The kind of evidence is like that above given for the lower Hudson River. Since the subsidence there has been partial reelevation, as proved by the fact that along the sides of the larger fjords marine terraces and beaches may be traced with gradually increasing altitude for many miles (150 or more) back into the country where they are hundreds of feet above tidewater.

Scandinavia is of still further special interest because very appreciable earth movements have there come under human observation. Marks carefully placed along the shores of Sweden by the government have proved that during the last 175 years the southern end of the country has actually subsided a little, while from Stockholm north the land has risen in increasing amount, reaching a maximum of seven or eight feet. In southern Sweden, at Malmo, a certain street now at times becomes covered by wind-driven high water, and during excavations made some years ago an older street eight feet below the present one was found.

A theory which appears to be in perfect harmony with the facts to account for the subsidence and partial reelevation of central eastern North America and Scandinavia since the beginning of the Ice Age is that the great weight of ice during the Ice Age pressed the land down, and that since the removal of the ice there has been an appreciable tendency for the land to spring back.

Certain crustal movements which have occurred about the Bay of Naples are of very special interest because actual human history dates can be placed upon them. Most remarkable are the records in connection with the temple of Jupiter Serapis which was built near the shore before the Christian era. The land sank about five feet and a new pavement had to be constructed; then, by the middle of the third century A. D., the temple rose to well above sea level. By about the ninth century the land had subsided fully thirty feet, so that marble columns of the temple were bored full of holes as high as twenty-one feet above their bases by marine-shelled animals, species of which still live in the bay. Then a slow uplift of twenty-three feet began, bringing the bases of the columns two feet above sea level by 1749. Since that time a slight sinking has taken place and this seems to be still going on. Three of the marble columns with the borings still stand in upright position.

While the movements just described were taking place, the island of Capri, twenty miles across the Bay of Naples, has slowly sunk to an amount estimated at thirty or forty feet as proved by evidence from the famous Blue Grotto. About the beginning of the Christian era a large ancient wave-cut cave, part of which is now called the Blue Grotto, had its floor above sea level, and it was used by certain Romans as a cool place to retire to from the heat. In order to obtain better light an opening was cut through its upper portion. The land has sunk so much that at the present time even part of the artificial opening (through which tourists pass) is now under water.

By way of illustrating remarkable contrasts in direction of crustal movements on very considerable scales in a given region, we shall briefly mention some facts regarding part of the coast of southern California and the neighboring islands of Santa Catalina and San Clemente, respectively twenty-five and fifty miles offshore. Those movements were not, however, checked up by human history records. The mainland at San Pedro has clearly risen 1,240 feet, as proved by the presence of unusually perfect coast terraces (so-called "raised beaches"), while San Clemente has risen 1,500 feet as proved by the raised beaches into which deep, youthful V-shaped stream-cut valleys have been sunk, and a shore line characteristic of recent notable uplift. It is a remarkable fact that at the same time the intervening island (Santa Catalina) has notably sunk, as proved by the nature of its shore line, and the distinctly more mature character of its topography.

We are, however, by no means dependent upon lands along sea shores for evidences of slow rising and sinking of land. Thus, by careful measurements it has been shown that the general region of the Great Lakes is now differentially rising toward the northeast at the rate of about five inches per 100 miles per century. At Chicago the rise of water is estimated at about nine inches per century, which means increase of flowage through the Chicago Canal. At this rate the upper lakes would, in some thousands of years, drain through this canal to the Mississippi. A well-preserved shore line of the large ancestor of Lake Ontario shows a steady increase in altitude at the rate of several feet per mile toward the northeast from near Niagara to the St. Lawrence Valley, thus proving a tilting of the land since the shore line was formed.

Shore lines of the great ancestor of Great Salt Lake also show warping of the earth's crust, some parts of a definite shore line being several hundred feet higher than others.

Very significant evidence pointing to profound crustal movements consists in the finding of fossil remains of marine animals in the strata high above sea level, very commonly from one to three miles, in many parts of the world, especially in the high mountains. In Wyoming, nearly horizontal strata of the Mesozoic Age carrying marine fossils lie two miles or more above sea level. The fact that given formations, carrying marine fossils representing certain definite portions of geologic time, are found at various altitudes up to several miles in many parts of the world, shows that the land in those places has really risen relative to sea level.

It should not be presumed from the above discussion that the sea level itself has never changed. Thus, the vast areas of thick ice sheets in both North America and Europe during the Great Ice Age represented sufficient water withdrawn from the sea to very appreciably lower its level. All land-derived materials, carried into the sea mainly by rivers, displace sea water, with consequent rise of its level. If all existing lands were worn down and carried into the sea, its level would be raised some hundreds of feet. Subsidence of any part of the ocean bottom would cause a lowering of sea level. There is a strong reason to believe that some such shiftings of sea level have occurred during the vast lapse of geologic time. During certain periods erosion of the land predominated, and during other periods building up of the land predominated, as pointed out in the chapters on geologic history. It is not thought that shifting of sea level has ever amounted to more than a few hundred feet, at least not during the millions of years of the more clearly recorded earth history.

We have thus far considered slow upward and downward movements of the earth's crust without notable structural changes in the rocks. Another type of crustal disturbance causes more or less profound changes in the structures of the rocks themselves. Just how the earth originated is a matter of uncertainty, but we can be sure that for many millions of years it has been a shrinking body. The outer, or crustal, portion of the earth, in adjusting itself to the contracting interior, has had many pressures, stresses, and strains set up within it. As results of such forces the rocks at and near the earth's surface have in various places, and at various times, been broken (faulted) and subjected to sudden movements (see discussion beyond), while those well within the crustal portion, that is to say a few miles or more down, have, in many cases, been bent (folded), or even crumpled. For these reasons the surface and near-surface crustal portions are called the "zone of fracture," while the more deeply buried portions comprise the "zone of flowage." In the zone of flowage the rocks, where subjected to great lateral pressure, act like plastic materials and therefore bend rather than break, because of the great weight of overlying materials. Laboratory experiments have confirmed the findings of geologists in this regard. Small masses of rocks properly inclosed in nickel-steel cylinders have been subjected to slow differential pressures equivalent to those which obtain twenty to forty miles within the earth. Under such conditions rocks have been made to change shape very notably without fracturing. Both geological observations and experiments have led us to conclude that not even small fractures or crevices can remain open at a depth greater than ten or twelve miles even in the hardest rocks.

From time to time, during the long history of the earth, forces of lateral pressure have been slowly exerted along more or less localized zones or belts within the earth's crust, and the rocks have been deformed chiefly by bending or folding, especially in those regions where mountains of the folded type have developed. Movements of this type are considered beyond in the chapter on mountains. Rock folds vary in size from microscopic to miles across, and they exhibit many shapes. Plate 7 will give the reader a good idea of actual rock folds of common sizes and shapes in various places. Folded structures are most clearly discernible in sedimentary rocks, because of their stratified (layered) arrangement. Since folds in hard rocks rarely, if ever, develop except at a depth of some miles within

FIG. 8.—An outcrop of stratified crystalline limestone (or marble) exhibiting two small sharp folds—a syncline on the left and an anticline on the right—near Lenox, Mass. These folds developed during the great mountain-making disturbance at the end of the Ordovician period fully 400,000,000 years ago. (After Dale, U. S. Geological Survey.)

the earth, they show at the surface only where great thicknesses of overlying materials have been stripped off by erosion.

From the standpoint of our consideration of slow earth-crust movements, it is important to bear in mind that lateral pressure in the zone of flowage has not only notably deformed rocks, but that, as a result of the buckling forces, given rock masses have, in many cases, been notably shifted downward or upward—mainly upward—from their original positions. Folded strata carrying shells of sea animals are commonly found thousands of feet above sea level in many of the great mountain ranges of the world. During the process of folding on a large scale the crust of the earth is very appreciably shortened at right angles to the direc-

tion of applied pressure, due to squeezing or bending
of the strata. In the case of the Appalachian mountains of Pennsylvania it has been estimated that
such shortening amounts to about twenty-six miles
or, in other words, that the strata originally spread
out horizontally across an area whose width was

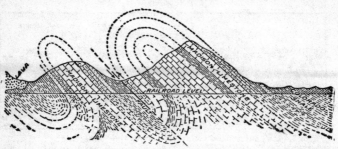

FIG. 9.—Structure section showing the profile of the mountains
and relations of rocks below the surface near Livingston, Montana.
The strata were crowded together until they bent into great sharply
defined folds at the time of the Rocky Mountain Revolution fifty
million years ago. Then the rocks broke along the fault fracture and
the mass on the right was shoved over upon the mass on the left.
(After U. S. Geological Survey.)

about 100 miles have been squeezed or folded into an
area whose width is twenty-six miles less.

We shall now turn to a consideration of sudden
earth movements and some of their effects, including earthquakes. Mention has already been made
of the fact that, when pressures and strains are set
up in the outer portion ("zone of fracture") of the
earth's crust, the rocks yield mainly by breaking or
fracturing because the rocks not being under a great
load of overlying material are there brittle. The
earth's crust has been fractured on small and large
scales in many places during the long space of
geologic time. Where one block of earth's crust has
slipped or moved past another along a fracture we

have what is called a "fault." Such displacements of rock masses vary in amount from less than an inch to some miles, and they constitute one of the most important features of the architecture of the outer portion of the earth. There are two types of faults fundamentally different as to cause. In one type (so-called "normal fault") the rocks suddenly yield to a force of tension; a fracture develops and the earth block on one side of the fracture or fault drops with reference to that on the other. In the other type (so-called "thrust faults") the rocks yield suddenly to a force of compression or lateral thrust, and one block of earth is pushed or thrust partly over another along the surface of fracture or fault. (See Figure 10.)

Faults range in length up to hundreds of miles, those from one to twenty miles in length being very common. Where an earth block has been displaced thousands of feet along a fault surface, it is not to be understood that the whole displacement resulted from a single movement, but rather from a series of sudden movements separated by greater or less intervals of time. Each sudden movement along a fault surface produces a vibration of the earth near by. Many such sudden movements are known to have caused violent earthquakes. Displacements of twenty to fifty feet, as a result of single movements, are definitely known to have taken place in various regions during the last fifty years; and rarely, if ever, has any sudden displacement of as much as several hundred feet occurred. Cliffs and steep slopes very commonly result from faulting, but, because of the long lapse of time required for the repeated movements in the case of great faults, the cliffs or steep slopes begin to wear back and become

more or less subdued long before the last of the
movements take place. In regions where movements along great faults have long since ceased,
the original steep slopes may be completely obliterated by erosion.

How does the geologist determine the actual
amount of displacement, especially in the case of
a large fault in stratified rocks? First, the various
formations of the region, where unaffected by fault-

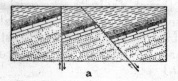 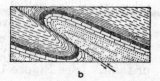

FIG. 10.—Vertical sections through strata illustrating common kinds
of faults: a, "normal faults" where one mass simply sinks below
another; b, a "thrust fault" where one mass is shoved over another.
(After U. S. Geological Survey.)

ing, are carefully studied, especially in regard to the
character and thickness of each, and their relative
geologic ages or normal order as they were deposited one layer above the other. Then, in the
simple case of a normal-fault surface at right angles
to horizontal strata, it is only necessary to find out
what two formations or parts of formations come
together along the fault fracture, and the actual
amount of displacement is readily determined.
Where strata and normal fault surfaces lie at
various angles, and also in thrust faults, those
angles must be determined in addition to the data
above named. In many mining regions, where valuable deposits are affected by faulting, accurate
knowledge of the direction and amount of displacements of faults is of great economic importance.

A few examples of normal faults from well-known districts will now be briefly described. The whole eastern front of the central and southern Sierra Nevada Range of California is a great, steep fault slope, from a few thousand to ten thousand or more feet high and hundreds of miles long, of such recent geologic age that it has been only moderately affected by erosion. In fact, it is well known that the southern two-thirds of the range is a great tilted fault block, the total displacement having resulted from repeated sudden movements since about the middle of the present geologic era. A great fault also extends along the eastern base of the great Wasatch Range of Utah and the steep slope thousands of feet high is a fault scarp only slightly modified by erosion. Renewed movements along this profound fault have very recently taken place as proved by the presence of fresh fault scarps in loose deposits which have accumulated across the mouths of some of the canyons, as, for example, near Ogden. In fact, practically all of the north-south ranges of the Great Basin from Utah to California are essentially a series of tilted fault blocks. Another great fault, less conspicuous from the topographic standpoint, is hundreds of miles long in the Coast Range Mountains of California. At the time of the San Francisco earthquake of 1906 there was a renewed sudden movement along this great fracture. The eastern one-half of the Adirondack Mountains of New York is literally a mosaic of hundreds of fault blocks. Many of these faults are from two to thirty miles long and they commonly show displacements of from a few hundred to 2,000 or more feet. A glance at the geological map (in colors) of the vicinity of the great copper mines at Bisbee, Arizona, shows most of that region to contain a network of normal faults which separate it into a mosaic of fault blocks. In each of the examples of faults just given a block of earth has sunk relative to the other, or in other words, each is a "normal fault."

We shall now turn to some large scale cases of faults in which great masses of earth have been pushed one over another—so-called "thrust faults." In the southern Appalachian Range, and especially well exhibited in the vicinity of Rome, Georgia, one portion of the mountain mass has literally been shoved over another, at a low angle over a fault surface many miles long, for fully seven miles westward. Both the tremendous weight of rock material actually translated and the number of sudden movements required in the operation stagger the imagination. It is safe to say that during the long time of this great operation violent earthquakes were not uncommon. In the Rocky Mountains of the northern United States and southern Canada there is the greatest known thrust fault on the continent. It is hundreds of miles long, and the actual displacement is commonly at least several miles. In the Glacier National Park of Montana it has been established that the front range portion of the Rockies has actually been pushed at least seven miles, and possibly as much as twenty miles, eastward over a fault surface, and out upon the Great Plains. In some cases rocks of the Prepaleozoic Age have there been pushed upon rocks of the late Mesozoic Age, thus locally upsetting the geologic column.

The Wasatch Range of Utah, in addition to the great normal fault along its western base, contains a remarkable system of thrust faults. In the

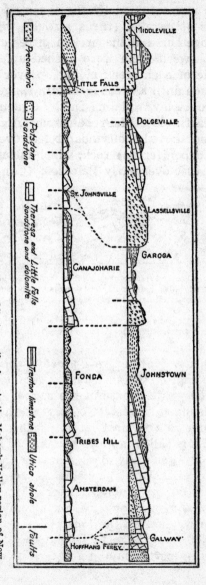

FIG. 11.—East-west profile and vertical structure sections fifty-two miles long in the Mohawk Valley region of New York, showing numerous tilted fault blocks which notably influence the topography. Vertical scale exaggerated. The rocks are Prepaleozoic and early Paleozoic in age. (Modified by the author after Darton, New York State Museum.)

region now occupied by the Wasatch Mountains a number of parallel (thrust) faults were developed close together and the broken pieces of the earth's crust between them were pushed up, the rocks on one side of each crack riding up over those on the other side until a great mountain range was formed where once lay a plain. In the Ogden Canyon one great earth block of Prepaleozoic (Algonkian) Age has been shoved thousands of feet over late Paleozoic (Carboniferous) rock, which latter has in turn been thrust over early Paleozoic (Cambrian) rock.

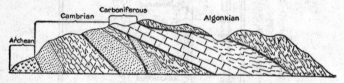

Fig. 12.—Vertical (structure) section through a part of the earth's crust several miles long in Ogden Canyon, Utah, showing the system of great thrust faults. Prepaleozoic (Algonkian) rocks have been pushed far over upon late Paleozoic (Carboniferous) strata, which latter have in turn been shoved over early Paleozoic (Cambrian) strata, etc. (After U. S. Geological Survey.)

This thrust faulting was accomplished before the development of the geologically recent normal fault along the western base of the range.

Any sudden movement of part of the crust of the earth, due to a natural cause, produces a trembling or shaking called an earthquake. Though earthquakes are generally classed among the most terrifying of all natural phenomena, those which have occurred during human historic times have had scarcely any geological or topographical effects of real consequence on the face of the earth. Locally, the effects may be notable and the destruction of life and property may be great. The earth may be locally cracked and rent, small fault scarps may develop, landslides and avalanches may result from the shaking of the earth, buildings may be demolished, and sea waves may be rolled upon the land. On the other hand, many earthquakes, called "tremors," are too slight to be noticed by people, though they are recorded by specially constructed instruments called "seismographs." We have already stated that actual sudden displacements causing earthquakes have amounted to twenty or even fifty feet right along fault fractures, but during the vibrations or quakings, which are often so destructively sent out into the neighboring country, the earth's surface rarely actually moves more than a small fraction of an inch. Because of the suddenness of the movement objects on the surface may be moved inches or even feet. Violent shocks may last one or two minutes and cause the whole earth to tremble, though at distant points only seismographs record the movement. It is probably true that some part of the earth is shaking all the time.

Studies during the last fifty years have made it certain that the main cause of earthquakes is the sudden slipping of earth blocks past each other along fault fractures, the sudden slipping furnishing the impulse which sends out the vibrations into the surrounding more or less elastic crust of the earth. The low rumbling to roaring sound, which sometimes immediately precedes an earthquake, is probably due to the grinding of the rocks together below the surface.

Earthquakes generally accompany volcanic outbursts of the violent or explosive type, and in such cases subterranean explosions cause both the eruptions and the quakings of the earth.

It is well known that the principal volcanic districts or belts of the earth are also the belts of most frequent earthquakes, but this does not mean that volcanic action causes most of the earthquakes. Active volcanoes and earthquakes are so commonly associated in the same belts because those belts no doubt represent portions of the crust which are now most actively yielding to the forces directly resulting from the shrinkage of the earth. Within the volcanic belts many earthquakes take place unaccompanied by any volcanic action, and many others take place far from volcanoes. Some earthquakes have been caused by the impact of great landslides or avalanches, or by the sudden caving in of underground openings.

Brief descriptions of a few typical carefully studied earthquakes during recent years will serve to make the main features of earthquakes still clearer to the reader.

The violent Japanese earthquake of 1891 was caused by the sinking of a block of earth forty miles long from two to thirty feet below that on the other side of a fault fracture. There was also considerable horizontal shifting, and cracks developed in the adjacent region. A distinct fault scarp, fifteen to twenty feet high, developed, and in some cases extended right across cultivated fields.

The San Francisco earthquake of 1906 was produced by renewed movement along the great fault which extends lengthwise through the Coast Range Mountains for several hundred miles. It is literally correct to say that, for 250 miles along this great earth fracture, one part of the Coast Range region suddenly slipped from two to twenty-two feet past the other. More or less of the movement extended

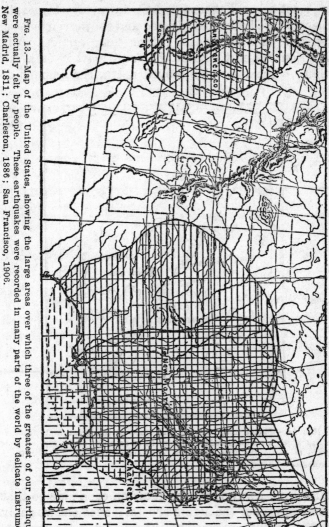

FIG. 13.—Map of the United States, showing the large areas over which three of the greatest of our earthquakes were actually felt by people. These earthquakes were recorded in many parts of the world by delicate instruments: New Madrid, 1811; Charleston, 1886; San Francisco, 1906.

at least several thousand feet down into the earth. In this case both sides slipped and the movement was very largely horizontal rather than vertical. The land on the east side of the fault moved south and that on the west side moved north, the amount di-

FIG. 14.—Sketch map showing the trace of the great fault fracture along which a renewed sudden movement of as much as twenty feet took place to cause the San Francisco earthquake of 1906. (After U. S. Geological Survey.)

minishing away from the fault on each side so that some miles out the actual crustal movement was only a few inches. When one thinks of the tremendous volumes of earth material involved in this shifting of the earth's crust, is it any wonder that such destruc-

PLATE 7.—VIEW IN THE YOSEMITE VALLEY FROM NEAR THE WESTERN ENTRANCE. The great rock called "El Capitan," on the left rises 3,500 feet above the river, and Bridal Veil Falls on the right is 620 feet high. All the rock is granite, the nearly vertical walls of which have resulted from the action of a great glacier which plowed its way through the valley during the Ice Age; the valley walls have been cut back by the removal of large vertical joint blocks. The flat bottom of the valley has resulted from the filling with sediment of a postglacial lake in the valley. (*Photo by F. N. Kneeland, Northampton, Mass.*)

PLATE 8.—(*a*) LOOKING-GLASS ROCK, UTAH. The rock is stratified sandstone sculptured partly by wind erosion, that is, by the wind driving particles of sand against it. (*Photo by Cross, U. S. Geological Survey.*)

PLATE 8.—(*b*) A SERIES OF SMALL ANTICLINES AND SYNCLINES, NEAR DAGGETT, CALIFORNIA. (*Photo by the author.*)

tive earthquake waves were produced? Many buildings were wrecked, several hundred people were killed, the disastrous San Francisco fire resulted, water mains were broken, and fences and roads crossed by the fault were dislocated as much as fifteen to twenty feet.

During the great earthquake on the coast of Alaska in 1899 notable changes took place along the

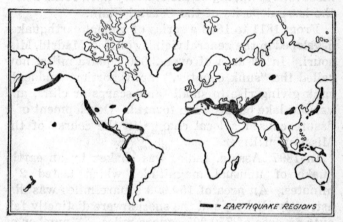

= EARTHQUAKE REGIONS

FIG. 15.—Map showing the principal earthquake regions of the world.

shore for some miles, one portion having suddenly risen as much as forty-seven feet, while another portion sank below sea level.

In 1886 the earthquake centering near Charleston, S. C., was preceded by rumbling and roaring noises and the slight quaking increased to violent shaking which lasted more than a minute. Eight minutes later a rather violent earthquake shock took place, followed during the next ten or twelve hours by less severe shocks. Most buildings in the city were wrecked or more or less badly damaged, and some people were killed. The shocks were so violent that the quaking was actually felt by people over an area of more than 2,000,000 square miles, the disturbance having spread at the rate of about 150 miles per minute. Near Charleston openings and fissures were formed through which sand and muddy water were ejected, but the cause of the disturbance was most likely slipping of the old very hard rocks below the loose deposits of the Coastal Plain.

From 1811 to 1813 a series of violent earthquakes developed in the general vicinity of New Madrid, Missouri. In an area of over 2,000 square miles, now called the "sunk country," many portions suddenly sank giving rise to small fault scarps or cliffs, and various lake basins were formed. Development of a fissure caused a local change in the course of the Mississippi River.

In 1897, Assam, India, was shaken by an earthquake of unusual magnitude, which lasted $2\frac{1}{2}$ minutes. An area of 150,000 square miles was disastrously shaken, and the shocks were distinctly felt over an area of 750,000 square miles. A number of notable fault scarps developed, the movement on one having been thirty-five feet.

In 1923 a terrific earthquake, followed by great fires, overtook the region including Tokyo and Yokohama in Japan. It lasted five minutes. Many thousands of people were killed and large sections of the cities were destroyed. It was caused by a sudden shifting of the earth's crust at the bottom of Sagami Bay.

CHAPTER VIII

IGNEOUS ACTION

NOT only because of the great power and terrifying grandeur of violent eruptions, but also because of their destruction of life and property, volcanoes stand out in the popular mind as among the most real and important of all geological phenomena. But great volcanic outbursts, like violent earthquakes, are in truth only outward, sensible, relatively minor manifestations of the tremendous earthchanging forces below the surface. They are far less important as geological agencies than the mighty interior forces which cause parts of continents to be slowly upraised and the rocks folded, or even than the incessant action of streams whereby the lands are cut down. Even as an igneous agency, volcanoes are notably less important than the development and shifting of molten materials within the earth's crust. Volcanic action is, however, not only conspicuous, but it is also of real significance as a means of changing the earth, such action having taken place since very early known geologic time. After bringing out the main facts and principles of volcanoes, aided by descriptions of specific eruptions, we shall turn to a consideration of igneous activity within the earth's crust.

Mount Vesuvius in Italy is perhaps the most famous active volcano in the world. Its eruptions have

been more or less carefully studied for a longer time
than any other. The eruption in the year 79 A. D.
was really a tremendous explosion causing a large
part of the old crater to be blown away, and sending
immense volumes of rock fragments, mostly finely
divided (so-called "ashes") into the air which completely buried the small city of Pompeii. Water
from the great clouds of condensing steam, mixed
with "ashes," formed muddy floods which overwhelmed Herculaneum. Little or no lava was
erupted. Since that time the crater has been more
or less active and the present cone, 4,000 feet high,

Fig. 16.—Map showing the distribution of active and recently active
volcanoes of the world.

has been built up. During the last seventy-five years
the greatest eruptions took place in 1872 and 1906,
when streams of molten rock flowed down the sides
of the mountain.

One of the greatest volcanic explosions ever recorded was that of the island of Krakatoa, between
Sumatra and Java, in 1883. The greater part of the

island was blown away and there was water 1,000 feet deep, where just before the island stood hundreds of feet high. About a cubic mile of rock material was sent into the air mostly in the form of fine dust—some of it for seventeen miles—and com-

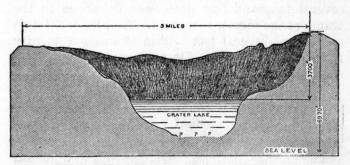

FIG. 17.—The great hole left after the top of Mt. Katmai in southern Alaska was blown off in 1912 by one of the most tremendous volcanic explosions in the annals of human history. The water in the lake is hot. (After Griggs, National Geographic Magazine.)

pletely hid the sun, causing total darkness during the eruption. Dust fell over an area of several hundred thousand square miles. Several days after the explosion ships more than 1,000 miles away were dust covered. Such enormous quantities of a light porous lava called "pumice" fell and floated upon the sea that navigation was badly obstructed many miles from the volcano. Extremely fine dust gradually spread through the whole earth's atmosphere, causing the extraordinary red sunsets for several months. The sound of the explosion was heard for hundreds of miles. Great sea waves 50 to 100 feet high were stirred up and they swept inland for several miles over the low-lying coast lands of neighboring Java and Sumatra, overwhelming hundreds of villages and drowning tens of thousands of people.

One of the greatest explosions on record was that of Katmai volcano, seven thousand feet high, on the coast of Alaska, in June, 1912. Not only was the top of the mountain completely blown off, but also a great crater pit, three miles wide across the top and several thousand feet deep, was developed in the stump of the former mountain. Volcanic dust fell to a depth of several feet within twenty-five to fifty miles of the mountain. Dust accumulated to a depth of nearly a foot in the village of Kodiak, 100 miles

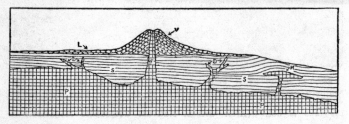

FIG. 18.—Diagrammatic vertical or structure section through a portion of the earth illustrating the common modes of occurrence of igneous rocks. P, deep-seated (plutonic) igneous rock; S, strata; D, dikes; M, mass of igneous rock forced between strata bending them upward; F, feeding channel of volcano; V, volcano; L, lava sheets. (By the author.)

east of the mountain, where total darkness prevailed for more than two days. A lake of very hot water now occupies the bottom of the great new crater. The noise of the explosion was heard for at least 750 miles.

One of the most frightful volcanic catastrophes of recent years was the eruption of Mont Pelée, island of Martinique, West Indies, in 1902. In this case, also, no lava was poured out, but violent explosions sent great clouds of very highly heated gases and vapors, mingled with incandescent dust, thousands of feet into the air.

One of these great clouds rushed down the mountain at hurricane speed and destroyed the city of St. Pierre with its 30,000 inhabitants. After the main eruption a spine or core of hard rock began to rise out of the crater and it slowly grew to a height of 1,000 feet in several months, after which it began to crumble away. This spine probably represented nearly frozen lava which solidified as it was gradually forced out of the mountain.

Of special interest to us, though not of great importance is the only active volcano in the United States. In May, 1914, Mount Lassen (or Lassen Peak), a long inactive volcano in northern California, suddenly burst forth explosively and during the next several years hundreds of eruptions occurred. Little or no lava appeared, but great clouds of steam and dust often shot into the air from one to three miles above the top of the mountain, which lies over 10,000 feet above sea level. (Plate 12.) Great quantities of dust have accumulated for miles around the mountain. There may be no new activity for many years, yet it is unlikely that Mount Lassen has become an extinct volcano.

It should not be presumed, however, that all, or nearly all, volcanoes are of the explosive type. Others of the more quiet type are well exemplified by the two great Hawaiian volcanoes, Mauna Loa and Kilauea. Any but relatively very minor explosions rarely, if ever, occur, the product of such volcanoes being almost wholly lava, which flows down the mountainsides in molten streams. The Hawaiian Islands have, in fact, been almost entirely built up by successive eruptions of lava, the building-up process having begun well below sea level. Mauna Loa rises to nearly 14,000 feet above the sea, but,

due to the fact that the streams of lava have spread
so far, the mountain has an exceptionally low angle
of slope which makes it difficult to realize that it is
so high. Considering its submarine portion, Mauna
Loa really rises nearly 30,000 feet above the sea
floor. Although Kilauea lies nearly 4,000 feet
above sea level on the flank of Mauna Loa, and only
twenty miles distant from it, the two volcanoes are
singularly independent in regard to their eruptions. Each mountain has a crater irregularly oval
in shape, nearly three miles long, bounded by almost
vertical walls of hard lava, in some cases arranged
in terraces. The floors of the great crater pits are
relatively level, and consist of black lava in which
are lakes of molten and even boiling lava. The
black lava floor is, in each case, only a frozen or
hardened crust upon a great column of molten lava
extending down into the mountain. Prior to an
eruption of Mauna Loa the lava column rises hundreds of feet in the crater, but during recent years
the lava seldom, if ever, flows out over the crater
rim. Instead, it breaks through the mountainsides
at various altitudes, the great flow of 1919 having
started at an altitude of about 8,000 feet. This
stream of liquid rock, fully one-half of a mile wide,
flowed for weeks down the mountainside and into
the ocean, the waters of which, in contact with the
highly heated lava, were thrown into terrific com-
motion. In 1885 a stream of lava several miles wide
flowed forty-five miles. In one case, lava traveled
the first fifteen miles in two hours, but this is an unusually great rate of speed. Lava streams in general seldom move faster than one or two miles per
hour, and as the liquid rock gradually cools and becomes more and more viscous, the speed diminishes

to zero. Almost incredible volumes of steam emanate from streams of molten lava.

In 1840 an outflow of lava took place from the side of Kilauea Mountain and ran into the sea. Since that time the floor of the great crater pit (quoting Professor W. H. Hobbs) "has been essentially a movable platform of frozen lava of unknown and doubtless variable thickness which has risen and descended (hundreds of feet) like the floor of an elevator car between its guiding ways. The floor has, however, never been complete, for one or more open lakes are always to be seen, that of Halemaumau, located near the southwestern margin, having been much the most persistent. Within the open lakes the boiling lava is apparently white hot at a depth of but a few inches below the surface, and in the overturnings of the mass these hotter portions are brought to the surface and appear as white streaks marking the redder surface portions. From time to time the surface freezes over, the cracks open and erupt at favored points along the fissures, sending up jets and fountains of lava, the material of which falls in pasty fragments that build up driblet cones. Small fluid clots are shot out, carrying threadlike lines of lava glass behind them, the well-known 'Pelée's hair.' Sometimes the open lakes build up congealed walls, rising above the general level of the pit, and from their rim the lava spills over in cascades to spread out upon the frozen floor."

In some regions, like the Columbian Plateau of the northwestern United States and the Deccan of India, each covering about 200,000 square miles, vast quantities of lava have been poured out layer upon layer to depths of even thousands of feet. Distinct volcanic cones or mountains in those regions are either absent or too scarce to look to as sources of so much lava. Such lava floods were probably mostly erupted from great fissures in the earth's crust, the flows generally retaining a high enough degree of fluidity to spread many miles.

Some idea of the quantitative geological importance of volcanism may be conveyed to the reader when we assert that, according to a conservative estimate, fully one-half of a million cubic miles of molten rocks have been poured out upon the surface of the earth through volcanic action in relatively recent geological time! The Cascade Range with its lofty peaks, including Mount Shasta and Mount Rainier, each rising more than 14,000 feet above the sea, has been built up very largely by volcanic action during the last era of geologic time. Many other mountain peaks and various ranges have been similarly developed either wholly or in part. The great chain of Aleutian Islands extending hundreds of miles into the sea, is the scene of much volcanic activity where a great mountain range is now literally being born out of the sea by the processes of vulcanism.

Before this the reader has more than likely wondered about the source of the heat, vapors (mainly water), and power involved in volcanic action. Answers to these questions are closely tied up with the precise cause (or causes) of volcanic action which remains one of the most uncertain of the larger problems of geologic science. Before briefly discussing the causes, a few additional facts should be stated. First, in regard to the heat, a careful determination of the temperature of the molten lava of Kilauea in 1911 showed it to be 1,260 degrees Centigrade, or 2,300 degrees F. This is, however, a relatively high temperature, because many lavas from other regions show melting points all the way down to at least 800 degrees Centigrade (1,472 degrees F.). Water in the form of steam is quantitatively one of the greatest products of volcanoes. A fair idea of the tremendous volumes of water involved may be gained from the statement that a careful estimate shows that fully 460,000,000 gallons of water in the form of steam erupted from a single secondary cone of Mount Etna during a period of 100 days. Among other gases which are given off in greater or less amounts during volcanic activity are carbonic acid gas, sulphureted hydrogen, sulphur dioxide, and hydrochloric acid. Some idea of the power back of volcanoes may be gained not only from the tremendous explosions such as those above described, but also from the fact that the pressure necessary to raise the column of lava from sea level to the top of Mauna Loa (nearly 14,000 feet) is about 1,150 atmospheres, or about 17,000 pounds per square inch. The actual pressure must there be much greater because the lava is forced up from far below sea level.

A long-held idea that a relatively thin crust covers a molten interior, and that downward pressure of this crust due to earth contraction causes molten rocks to be forced out, has been too thoroughly disproved to now be at all seriously entertained. The fact that near-by volcanoes commonly erupt entirely independently, as in the case of Mauna Loa and Kilauea, shows that there can be no universal liquid beneath a relatively thin crust. Other arguments against liquidity of the earth's interior are that the earth acts like a body nearly as rigid as steel against the powerful tide-producing forces, and that earthquake waves which pass through the earth to a depth of at least 2,000 miles are the kind which require a solid medium for transmission.

Let us then briefly consider more plausible views regarding the cause of volcanic action. First of all we may be sure that the earth is highly heated inside. Measurements in many deep borings show that the temperature increases at the rate of about 1 degree F. for each 50 to 60 feet downward, to depths greater than a mile. Accordingly, on the basis of 1 degree rise in 50 feet, at depths of 20 to 35 miles, the temperature must be great enough (2,120 degrees to 3,590 degrees F.), to cause all ordinary rocks to melt *if they were at the surface*. At such depths, however, the downward pressure upon the rocks is so great that their melting points are notably raised, and there is every reason to believe that under ordinary conditions the rocks 20 to 35 miles down are not molten. If we adhere to the older (nebular) hypothesis of earth origin, the interior heat of the earth is left over from the cooling, once molten, earth. On the basis of another (planetesimal) hypothesis, the earth's heat is due to the steady, powerful action of gravity causing the earth to contract. In any case, the earth is hot inside as proved by deep well records and igneous phenomena in general, and it is a contracting or shrinking body as proved by the many large scale zones of wrinkling or folding of rocks. If, then, highly heated solid rocks at reasonable distances down in any part of the earth are subjected to relief of pressure by an earth movement such as upward crumpling of the crust, or by readjustment of large fault blocks, such heated solid rocks would become molten. The very earth movement which brings about relief of pressure and melting may very reasonably be regarded as the power which forces some of the newly formed molten material higher up into the earth's crust, and even out upon the surface. This view harmonizes with the well-known fact, already mentioned, that the main belts of active volcanoes are also the main belts of active earth movements, such as earthquakes.

Another source of power behind volcanic action is steam pressure. We have already mentioned the fact that vast amounts of water in the form of steam escape from volcanoes or even from streams of molten lava. The violent volcanic explosions are quite certainly all, or nearly all, direct results of sudden giving way of volcanoes to steam pressure which accumulates during greater or less periods of time, and with little or no possibility of escape, without rupturing the mountain. Steam alone, or combined with some of the other gases so common as volcanic products, may also aid in forcing out molten rock. What is the source of the steam and other gases or vapors? According to one view they were originally in the earth, while according to another view the water at least has been absorbed by molten rocks from surface waters which have worked their way downward. At least two arguments oppose the second hypothesis: first, that not a few volcanoes are really many miles from the sea or other bodies of water, while downward percolation of rain water would fall far short of supplying the tremendous quantities of water ejected, and second, any water taken up by molten rock must be absorbed within a very few miles of the surface because, as we have learned, farther down there are no openings large enough to permit the downward passage of water, but, as a matter of fact, the very upper part of the earth's crust is just the place where molten rocks begin to give up their water, often with terrific violence.

We may now turn to a consideration of the other very important kind of igneous activity, namely, the rise and transfer of molten materials within the earth's crust, but not to the surface. The quantity of such deep-seated (so-called "plutonic") igneous rock material which has been intruded into the earth's crust within known geologic time, is far greater than that which has been forced to surface, that is the so-called "volcanic" material. The plutonic rocks are always thoroughly crystallized, and they are generally coarser grained than the volcanic rocks.

Where molten materials have been forced into cracks or fissures in the crust of the earth and there congealed, we have a very common mode of occurrence called "dikes" (Plate 11b). In many regions often one set of dikes was formed, after which one or more succeeding injections from the same of different deep-seated bodies of molten rock took place, and some of the later dikes were forced to cut across earlier ones. Dikes of all lengths up to at least thirty miles, and of all widths up to many hundreds of feet, are known, but they are generally less than a mile long and not more than a few feet or rods wide. They have been intruded into all kinds of rock formations—igneous, sedimentary, and metamorphic. Dikes are common in many parts of the world and they often excite the interest of laymen. They are wonderfully displayed along the southern coast of Maine. Plate 9 shows small dikes where the molten material was forced from a larger mass into a body of older dark rock. The Palisades of the Hudson River, just north of New York City, consist of a layer of igneous rock several hundred feet thick which, in the molten condition, was forced nearly horizontally between layers of sandstone millions of years ago, that is in the early Mesozoic era. The palisade or columnar structure was caused by cracking of the rock during the cooling and contraction. This is the explanation of most columnar structures of igneous rocks, exceptionally fine exhibitions being at the Giant's Causeway in Ireland, and Devil's Tower, Wyoming (Plate 12b).

A type of occurrence not so common, but of special interest, is where a body of molten rock rising in nearly horizontal strata becomes cooler and therefore stiffer or more viscous and, losing its power to penetrate, forces its way between the layers causing the strata to be arched or domed over it. Sufficient removal of overlying material by erosion has revealed many fine examples of this type of occurrence.

Another type of interest is the volcanic neck, which is the core or plug filling the feeding channel of a volcano. In certain regions, like parts of Arizona and New Mexico, extinct volcanic mountains may be all cut away by erosion, except the central cores or necks which, both because they are more resistant and are last to be reached by erosion, stand out conspicuously as great towers on the landscape (Plate 12b).

Most important of all from the quantitative standpoint, however, are the great bodies of igneous rocks, ranging up to many miles across, which, in a molten condition, were forced irregularly into the earth's crust from unknown depths.

The common rock called granite belongs in this category of rocks, which are the best and most extensively developed of all igneous types. The roots or cores of great mountain ranges often consist of such rocks which are exposed to view only after removal of great thickness of overlying material. Immense areas of granite and other plutonic rocks of extra deep-seated origin are exposed, because of removal of overlying material by erosion, in southeastern Canada, the Adirondack Mountains, New England, the Piedmont Plateau of the Atlantic Coast, and in the Sierra Nevada Mountains. All the rock forming the lofty walls of Yosemite Valley is granite, which was forced into the earth's crust in relatively late Mesozoic time, and which has since been laid bare by erosion.

CHAPTER IX

WATERS WITHIN THE EARTH

IT has been estimated that approximately 1,500 cubic miles of water fall upon the surface of the United States each year. About one-half of this goes back into the atmosphere by evaporation; about one-fourth of it flows away in surface streams; and the remaining one-fourth enters the crust of the earth. Considerable water which enters the earth returns to the surface as springs, by capillarity of soils and rocks, or by being drawn up into plants and evaporated. Some idea of the amount of ground water may be gleaned from the statement, based upon a careful estimate, that all the water in the rocks and soils of the first 100 feet below the surface of the United States would make a layer seventeen feet thick. In most humid regions the soils and loose rock formations are saturated with water at greater or less depths (usually less than 100 feet) below the surface. The surface of this saturated layer is called the ground-water level, or more familiarly the "water table." The water table shifts up and down more or less according to variation in rainfall.

In addition to the water held in the loose rocks and soils near the earth's surface, large quantities occur in definite layers (usually strata) of porous rocks which very commonly extend at various angles, hundreds or even thousands of feet into the earth. A very fine illustration of this principle is the case of the Dakota sandstone formation of Nebraska. Almost anywhere across the State a well drilled through a bed of clay and into the porous sandstone layer encounters water. (Figure 19.) Another principle is also well illustrated, namely, that water in such a porous layer may actually travel hundreds of miles, water obtained from a well sunk to the Dakota sandstone having actually traveled under the surface of the State all the way from the eastern face of the Rocky Mountains, where rain and melting snow entered the upturned and exposed porous rock layer. Another good example is Iowa, where certain porous rock layers outcropping in the northwestern and northeastern corners of that and adjacent States gradually bend down under the State, reaching the greatest depths (up to 3,000 feet) far in the interior. From wells 3,000 feet deep near Boone, Iowa, it is, therefore, a fact that some of the water pumped out of the earth actually traveled underground all the way from beyond the corners of the State. This sort of travel of underground water is common in many parts of the world. It should be clearly understood that such water does not flow freely as in a pipe along subterranean passageways, but rather it slowly works its way between the grains of porous rock. Where such water moves distinctly downward, and the porous layer has both above and below it an impervious rock layer like shale or clay, it gradually gets under greater and greater pressure. In some cases such pressure has actually been found by deep drilling to be equivalent to that of a column of water several thousand feet high. The rate of motion of water in porous underground rock layers is very slow, data from various sources indicating a rate of speed of not

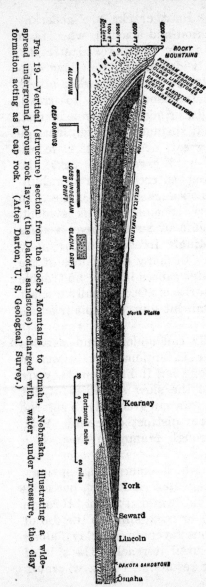

FIG. 19.—Vertical (structure) section from the Rocky Mountains to Omaha, Nebraska, illustrating a widespread underground porous rock layer (the Dakota sandstone) charged with water under pressure, the clay formation acting as a cap rock. (After Darton, U. S. Geological Survey.)

more than one-fifth of a mile a year in coarse porous sandstone, while in many rocks it cannot be more than ten to fifty feet per year.

We still have to consider a t h i r d mode of occurrence of waters within the earth. Many formations, like granite and other types of crystalline rocks are neither in definite layers, nor are they sufficiently porous to allow water to really flow through them. Where such r o c k s extend far down from or near the s u r f a c e, how does rain water descend? It does so along cracks or fractures (both joints and faults) which we have learned are almost universally abundantly present in all hard rocks in the upper (or zone of fracture) portion

of the earth's crust. Joint cracks are generally
very irregular in direction and spacing, while fault
fractures are usually fairly regular and straight.
Many cracks are not wide enough to allow anything like good passageways for water, while others
are sufficiently open to allow water to travel
along them for hundreds, or even thousands of feet.
In canyons of the West, springs not rarely emerge
from the bottoms of great, nearly vertical ledges
of granite and other hard crystalline rocks, the
waters certainly having entered the rocks hundreds, or even some thousands of feet, higher. In
rocks of the kind here considered it is evident,
then, that the movements of subterranean waters
must be mostly exceedingly irregular and usually
not in great quantities. In many deep mines of the
world, underground water causes little or no trouble
except often near the surface. Occasionally a shaft
or tunnel strikes a prominent joint or fault fracture
filled with water.

What we might really call underground streams
may occur only under exceptional conditions in
rocks other than limestone, but in limestone they are
not uncommon because the slow solubility of the
rock allows underground waters gradually to enlarge
the passageways to form distinct channels. Echo
River, which flows through Mammoth Cave, is a
fine case in point.

Most water by far which emerges as springs,
was at one time surface water. A simple, but common case is where rain water soaking through
porous soil (e. g., sand) or rock, sinks to the top of
an underlying impervious layer (e. g., clay) along
whose surface it flows until it reaches the side of
a valley where a spring results. In fact, wherever

the water table is crossed by the surface of the ground, water must either seep or flow out. Where underground streams which are common in limestone regions reach the surface on hill or valley sides, springs result. Another source of springs is where under proper conditions of slope a porous rock layer, charged with water well below the surface, appears at a lower level than its source of water. Still another type of spring is where a fissure or fracture crosses a water-bearing layer in which the pressure is great enough to cause the water to rise to the surface along the relatively open fissure or fracture.

In various localities we hear of springs in seemingly paradoxical situations on tops of hills and even mountains. Such a mystery is not difficult to clear up. In the first place, such springs are rarely at the summit of the hill or mountain. A case well known to many persons is the small, but never-failing spring a little below the summit of Mount Whiteface, a peak in the Adirondacks, rising 3,000 feet above the general level of the immediately surrounding country. In this case, a mass of highly fractured rock, subjected to much rainfall and lying above the level of the spring, is sufficiently large easily to contain and give forth enough water to account for several such springs. In rare cases, however, springs or flowing wells are located on summits, and in such places it is only necessary to bear in mind some of the principles above set forth, but mainly the facts that water may travel under pressure long distances underground, and that the point of emergence may be on a hill which is actually lower than the source of the water far away.

The economic significance of underground waters is forcibly brought to our attention when we realize that 75 per cent of the people of the United States depend upon wells for their water supply. Many city supplies, most farm supplies, and much irrigation water come from wells. The 3,000,000 people of Iowa, for example, are dependent upon under-

FIG. 20.—Ideal section illustrating the chief requisite conditions of artesian wells. A, a porous stratum; B and C, impervious beds below and above A, acting as confining strata; F, the height of the water level in the porous bed A, or, in other words, the height of the reservoir or fountainhead; D and E, flowing wells springing from the porous water-filled bed A. (After U. S. Geological Survey.)

ground waters from wells varying in depth from a few feet to several thousand feet.

Most wells are simply dug to depths a little below the water table. In humid climate regions the depths seldom exceed fifty feet. The water encountered in such wells is rarely under pressure. In some regions of deep soils or loose formations, wells are actually bored with an auger to depths of as great as 200 feet. Deep wells in relatively hard rocks are always drilled to depths of even thousands of feet. In such cases the purpose is to strike either a porous rock layer charged with water, or a crack or fissure filled with water, the water almost always being under pressure (sometimes very great), under such conditions. These are called artesian wells whether the water under pressure actually flows out at the surface or not.

We may now inquire as to the necessary conditions for artesian wells. This may best be done by the aid of diagrams. Figure 20 illustrates a very common case where a porous layer, lying between impervious layers, passing under a valley, comes to the surface of the hills on each side where the water enters the porous layer. On sinking a well to the water-charged layer, the water rushes through the hole to a greater or less distance above the surface. In Figure 21 the porous and impervious layers are simply tilted, and the water under pressure rises through the free opening to the surface. Wells of this kind are also common in the Atlantic Coastal Plain of the United States. In another case, less comprehensible to the layman, the porous water-bearing stratum curves downward under a hill or mountain, water entering it where it is exposed on each side. Under such conditions a flowing artesian well cannot be drilled at or near the summit, but since the water is under pressure it will rise in the hole to a level approaching that of the lowest part of the outcrop of the porous layer on either side of the hill or mountain. This is essentially

FIG. 21.—Section illustrating the thinning out of a porous water-bearing bed, A, inclosed between impervious beds B and C, thus furnishing the necessary conditions for an artesian fountain at D. (After U. S. Geological Survey.)

the condition of things toward the interior of Iowa, where water from the deeper wells rises 2,000 feet or more in the holes, but does not reach the surface.

The drilling of deep wells, where records, including samples of rock materials brought up, have been kept, has been a great aid to the geologist in determining, or rendering more precise, the knowledge of not only the kinds of rocks underground, but also the thicknesses and structural relations of the formations.

In yet another way deep wells are of special significance, that is in regard to the light which they throw upon the subterranean temperature of the earth. A very deep well in eastern United States was drilled near Fairmont, West Virginia, to a depth of 7,579 feet, in quest of oil or gas. At a depth of 7,500 feet, the temperature was found to be 168 degrees F. Allowing for a near-surface temperature of 50 degrees, this means an average rate of increase downward of 1 degree in 62 feet. There is a very deep well near Clarksburg, West Virginia, sunk to a depth of 7,386 feet, with a temperature of 172 degrees at the 7,000-foot level, or at the rate of one degree in 57 feet, allowing for a near-surface temperature of 50 degrees. It is a remarkable fact, that little or no water was encountered all the way down. A well 7,348 feet deep in southeastern Germany gave a temperature of 186 degrees at the bottom, or a rate of increase of 1 degree in 54 feet. These three records are about the average for the deep holes of the world. Some of the deepest mining shafts in the world are in the copper mining region of northern Michigan, where over 5,000 feet (counted vertically, not down the slope) down the temperature is nearly 90 degrees the year round. The rate of increase is here less than in most wells of such depth, because of the cooling air currents. Many years ago a rather remarkable experiment in well drilling was tried by the city of Budapest, Hungary, the attempt being to get a supply of water at the brewing temperature of 176 degrees in order to encourage the manufacture of beer. After getting a good supply of water at a depth of 3,120 feet and a temperature of 158 degrees, work was stopped. In building the two great tunnels (St. Gotthard and Simplon) through portions of the Alps, such high temperatures were encountered that work was continued only under great difficulties. In the famous Comstock gold and silver mine of Nevada, over forty years ago, temperatures as high as 157 degrees were encountered in the shafts at a depth of only 2,000 feet or a little over, the exceptional temperature for such depth no doubt being due to occurrence of the ores in geologically recent igneous rocks which have not yet cooled to the normal temperature for the depth of 2,000 feet.

From the sanitary standpoint, wells are of very great significance, especially in view of the fact that such a large proportion of people depend upon well water. It is generally understood that typhoid fever is more common in the country than in cities, in spite of what might reasonably be expected. What are some of the causes leading up to such a situation? The idea that water purifies itself after flowing a relatively short distance is, in many cases, far from being true, especially when we are dealing with underground water. Actual observations prove that germ-laden water may travel surprisingly far underground. Germ-laden water from barns, cesspools, or outhouses spreads notably on sinking to the water table and it is easy to see how so many wells become contaminated. On general principles, a geologist is especially wary of water from a well in a barn yard. The well for human use at least should be located out of reasonable range of such contamination. Under the condition of the diagram a well or spring some distance down the side of the hill may actually be unfit for use, though a serious situation is much less likely to develop there. Nor should one assume that by locating the well on the uphill side of the house, and the outhouses or cesspool on the downhill side, safety is assured. From what we have learned in regard to earth movements, and the tilting of strata from their original positions, we know how the movement

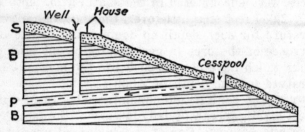

Fig. 22.—Diagram illustrating a danger of contamination of wells by impure underground water. S, soil; B, bedrock; P, porous stratum. Impure water from cesspool moves through porous layer to bottom of well. (By the author.)

of water in the saturated zone near the surface may be downhill roughly following the hill slope, while in a tilted porous layer of rock farther below the surface the movement of water may be in just the opposite direction. A well drilled into the solid rock for safety on the uphill side of a house might derive its water from this very same porous layer, whose water has been contaminated from a cesspool or other source down the side of the hill. Such a case is by no means a theory or a rarity. There is also real danger of contamination in cases where the water flows more like streams underground through cracks or fissures in hard or dense rocks, or through channels developed by solution in limestone. It may happen that water becoming contaminated from barn sites, cesspools, or outhouses finds its way along such a channel to the side or bottom of a well. The author well remembers the case of a farmer whose house, barn, and well were close together on a little limestone terrace and who continued to use the well water although he complained of its disagreeable taste, especially after a rain when he could "taste the barn in it."

Finally, in this connection, it may be said that wells should be located in the light of the principles above explained, best of all upon the advice of some one with geological training, and that, to insure safety to health from the well water, sanitary analyses (at small cost) should be made once or twice a year. A bad well should be abandoned and a new one sunk.

A large amount of money has been wasted upon, and much mystery and superstition have surrounded so-called "water witches," or those who claim some special or supernatural power of locating supplies of underground water. Most common of all devices used is the so-called "divining rod," which is a forked stick of willow, witch-hazel, or other wood, according to the seemingly special requirement of the operator. Certain mechanical and electrical devices are also employed. With one fork of the divining rod grasped in each hand and the main part of the stick upright, the operator walks about until, due to some "mysterious" influence, a place is found where underground water pulls the upright portion of the stick downward in spite of the grasp of the holder. Some operators even claim to know just how deep a well must be sunk. Without any attempt to question the honesty of all operators, geologists are in full accord with the following quotation from a paper published by M. L. Fuller, for the United States Geological Survey: "The uselessness of the divining rod is indicated by the facts that it may be worked at will by the operator, that he fails to detect strong water currents in tunnels and other channels that afford no surface indications of water, and that his locations in limestone regions where water flows in well-defined channels are no more successful than those dependent upon mere guesses. In fact, its operators are successful only in regions in which ground water occurs in definite sheets in porous material, or in more or less clayey deposits, such as pebbly clay or till. In such regions (which are extremely common) few failures can occur, for wells can get water almost anywhere. Ground water occurs under certain definite conditions, and just as surface streams may be expected wherever there is a valley, so ground water may be found where certain rocks and conditions exist. No appliance, either mechanical or electrical, has yet been devised that will detect water in places where plain common sense will not show its presence just as well. The only advantage of employing a 'water witch,' as the operator of the divining rod is sometimes called, is that crudely skilled services are thus occasionally obtained, since the men so employed, if endowed with any natural shrewdness, become, through their experience in locating wells, better observers of the occurrences and movements of ground water than the average person."

It should not be assumed, however, from the above statement that the location or foretelling of underground water is mostly hopeless from a scientific point of view. In most regions the kinds of rocks which would be pierced by wells can be more or less accurately foretold by careful studies of the rocks exposed at the surface. But foretelling the underground water is often much more uncertain. Where the geologic structure or arrangement of rocks in a region is fairly regular, as in the case of most sedimentary rocks, and a few scattering deep wells have been drilled, with records preserved, the geologist, by combining such data with his surface studies, can do much toward putting the facts regarding the underground waters of the region on a scientific basis. There are many such regions, an excellent case in point being Iowa, regarding which State the United States Geological Survey has published a report containing data by the use of which it is possible to foretell almost exactly what formations would be pierced by drilling from 1,000 to 3,000 feet or more, the thickness of each, which ones are water-bearing and, in many cases, even the character of the mineralization of the water for almost any part of the State. Such knowledge, through the years, is worth untold millions of dollars to the State. Where the rocks are igneous and rather uniformly dense, usually little or nothing can be accurately foretold about the underground water supplies, because in such rocks the water follows exceedingly variable and irregular cracks and fissures. In metamorphic rocks the difficulties are usually about as great. In limestone regions, with humid climate, much water travels in channels underground, but these are so exceedingly irregular that there is no way of locating them by surface studies. In humid climates it seldom happens, however, that a well does not reach at least a fair supply of water within a few thousand feet even in rock formations in which the water travels along irregular cracks and channels.

Certain other important features of the geological work of underground water should be brought to the attention of the reader. One of these is its power to dissolve mineral substances of many kinds more or less rapidly. As already pointed out, limestone is especially susceptible to solution in water, both surface and underground.

The carbonate of lime taken into solution from limestone is the principal substance which causes so-called "hard water." Most of the solution takes place in the upper part of the zone of fracture of the earth's crust and the dissolved substances are carried along generally to the lower levels where they tend to deposit (and crystallize), filling fissures, cracks, and even tiny spaces between mineral grains. Cracks and fissures thus filled by mineral matter from solution are called "veins." In many mining regions valuable ores and other substances have been deposited from underground water solutions and concentrated in veins. In many places underground waters with certain substances in solution travel through various rocks or encounter solutions of other substances and, as a result of chemical action, many new mineral combinations result. Such actions through the millions of years of geologic time have effected great changes in many rock formations. In the case of petrification, like that of petrified wood, the buried organism slowly decomposes cell by cell, and particle by particle it is replaced by mineral matter from underground water solutions. In this manner the remarkable so-called petrified forests (not really forests) of Arizona and the Yellowstone Park were

formed, the petrifying material there having been
the very common substance called silica which is
the same in composition as the familiar mineral
quartz.   Mineral matter carried in solution in surface streams is derived from ground waters which
reach the surface.   An idea of the tremendous quantity of mineral matter thus removed may be gained
from the statement that by careful determination
the Mississippi River carries 120,000,000 tons in
solution into the Gulf of Mexico each year.

One interesting effect of the dissolving power of
underground water in limestone regions is the de-

FIG. 23.—Structure section and part of landscape in a limestone region
showing how caves and natural bridges are formed by the dissolving
action of underground water. AA, limestone; BB, sink holes; DD,
caves and galleries; and an arch (natural bridge) which is the remnant
of a large cave. (After Shaler, U. S. Geological Survey.)

velopment of caves or caverns.   Most remarkable of
all is Mammoth Cave, Kentucky, with its hundreds
of miles of passageways and galleries.   This marvelous work of nature is all a result of the action of
underground water which has dissolved and carried
away vast quantities of limestone.   Echo River,
which flows through the cavern, is still carrying on
the work aided by various underground tributaries.
The stalactites and stalagmites, which are so strikingly displayed in many caves, as at Luray, Virginia, are made by lime-charged water which drips or
oozes from the roof and, due mainly to evaporation,
deposits the lime.   Many wonderful and fantastic

effects are thus produced. Where part of the roof
of a cave is dissolved out, or falls in, a "sink hole"
results. Where all but a portion of the roof of a
cave or underground channel has fallen in, a natural
bridge, like the famous one in Virginia, results,
though natural bridges are also formed by other
means.

In concluding this chapter we shall briefly discuss
hot underground waters, hot springs, and geysers.
There are two well-known ways by which underground waters may become heated. One is by the
movement of water downward into the normally
heated portion of the earth, the rate of increase
downward being, as above stated, 1 degree F. for
about 50 to 60 feet. Water descending two miles
would, therefore, attain a temperature of about 200
degrees F. In some regions such a temperature
may be reached at depths considerably less. Such
water (under pressure) taking a short course to the
surface (forming springs) at a lower level would
retain much of its heat taken up far below the
surface. In regions where there are great down-
folds of the strata (i. e., synclines), as in the central
to southern Appalachians, conditions appear to be
favorable for such warm or hot springs, as, for example, at Hot Springs, Virginia. A second cause of
the heating of underground water is by the descent
of surface waters into contact with masses of still
hot igneous rock of relatively recent geologic age. In
some such cases the water does not go more than
some hundreds of feet down and when, under proper
conditions, it returns to the surface hot and even
boiling springs may result.

Geysers are periodically eruptive hot springs
found only in a few of the volcanic regions of the

PLATE 9.—AN UPBEND FOLD (*anticline*) IN THE APPALACHIAN MOUNTAIN STRATA NEAR HANCOCK, MARYLAND. The strata were deposited in horizontal layers upon the sea bottom, covering the region many millions of years ago in middle Paleozoic time. At the time of the Appalachian Mountain revolution, near the end of Paleozoic time, this and many other folds developed well below the surface. Removal of overlying material by erosion has laid bare the fold as we see it to-day. (*Photo by Russell, U. S. Geological Survey.*)

PLATE 10.—(*a*) A LEDGE OF IGNEOUS ROCK (GRANITE) IN NORTHERN
NEW YORK. This illustrates so-called "joints" or natural cracks,
commonly separating most hard rock masses into more or less
prismatic blocks. (*Photo by the author.*)

PLATE 10.—(*b*) A FAULT FRACTURE IN A LEDGE AT EAST CANADA
CREEK IN THE MOHAWK VALLEY, NEW YORK. The Ordovician limestone formation in thin layers on the right has sunk hundreds of
feet along the vertical fault to the left of the middle, bringing it
sharply against the older (Cambrian) massive formation on the left.
The hole is artificial. (*Photo by Darton, U. S. Geological Survey.*)

world. They are most wonderfully displayed in the Yellowstone National Park, where they send columns of hot water to all heights up to 250 feet at various intervals of time. Almost incredible amounts of hot water are sent into the air every day in the geyser basins of Yellowstone Park. The single geyser "Old Faithful," which erupts at intervals of about seventy minutes, sends a column of water several feet in diameter to heights of from 125 to 150 feet. During each eruption about 1,500,000 gallons of water are sent forth, or every day enough to supply the need of a fairly large city. A very brief explantion of the cause of geyser eruptions may be stated as follows: The very irregular, narrow, geyser tube extends nearly vertically downward into yet uncooled lava. The tube is more or less rapidly filled by underground water. The bottom, or near-bottom, portion of the water gradually becomes heated by the lava until finally the boiling point is reached for that depth. But, because of the pressure of the overlying water column, the boiling point at that depth is considerably greater than for the surface. A little steam develops far down and this causes the whole column of water above it to lift slightly, thus relieving the pressure on the superheated water far down. This relief of pressure allows much of the superheated water far down to flash into steam, which violently forces the column of water out of the geyser tube.

CHAPTER X

HOW MOUNTAINS COME AND GO

MOUNTAINS constitute the grandest relief features of the earth, and some of the most profound lessons of earth changes may be learned by studying them. To the layman who views great mountains in all their grandeur and massiveness, the expression "everlasting hills" seems appropriate. But the geologist knows that even the loftiest mountains are only temporary features on the face of the earth. Like organisms, they come and go. For example, where the great Rocky Mountains now stand was only a few million years ago (in late Mesozoic time) the bottom of an interior sea. Where the Appalachians now stand there were no mountains late in the Paleozoic era (not less than ten or twelve million years ago), but instead sea water covered the district. Then the Appalachians were formed, lifting their heads much higher than at present, after which they were cut down almost to sea level, and then once more upraised. The Coast Range Mountains of our Pacific Coast have come into existence since the middle of the present (Cenozoic) geologic era. Every mountain, like every organism, has a life history, in some cases simple, and other cases complex. All pass through stages of birth, youth, maturity, old age, and death. Some rear their heads and disappear after a short (geological) existence. Others continue their growth and persist much longer, while still others undergo periods of profound rejuvenation.

Among the various processes by which mountain ranges have been formed, the folding and accompanying general uplift of strata are the most important. In fact, in most of the great mountain ranges of the world the folded structure is conspicuously developed, so much so that they may well be called "folded mountains." Very commonly, however, mountains of this type have also been subjected to more or less fracturing of the rocks (faulting), and not uncommonly they have also been subjected to igneous activity, including both intrusion and extrusion of molten material. It is among the folded mountains of greater or less degree of complexity that the "greatest exhibitions of geologic phenomena are seen and the lessons which geology as a sciences teaches may be learned. If one desires to know the history of a region, one turns naturally to its mountain ranges, for here may be found the upturned and dissected strata, a study of whose kinds, thickness, and fossils throws light upon past events, while their foldings and dislocations show the nature and results of those great dynamic agencies which, from time to time, have operated upon the outer portion of the earth, and given to it the broad distinctive features which characterize it today." (L. V. Pirsson.) Among the great mountains we may also see wonderful exhibitions of the results of weathering and erosion, especially the work of rivers and glaciers.

We can, perhaps, best convey to the reader some of the main facts and principles regarding folded mountains by considering certain observations which may be readily made in a short trip across a folded range of not too complex kind—for example, across the Appalachian range along the line of the Baltimore and Ohio Railroad, west of Washington, or the Pennsylvania Railroad, west of Philadelphia. It would be most evident that the mountains consist of strata, that is sedimentary rocks, such as sandstone, shale and limestone, which were deposited under water. A few measurements would reveal the fact that thousands of feet in thickness of strata are represented. Careful measurements by geologists have, in fact, shown that the strata were originally piled up layer upon layer to a thickness of 25,000 to 30,000 feet. The fact that they are strata of such great thickness proves that sediments must there have accumulated under water for some millions of years at least. Closer examination of a few good exposures (i. e., outcrops) would further reveal the presence of fossil shells and impressions of marine organisms, thus definitely leading us to conclude that the strata were laid down under sea water, which, of course, means that the present site of the mountain range was once sea floor.

Examination of the rock materials also establishes the fact that the strata are such as were deposited in relatively shallow sea water—that is to say, none are at all of the sort which are now forming under really deep ocean water. Most of the strata represent original sands (and even gravels) and muds which could have accumulated only relatively near shore, that is within about 100 miles, which harmonizes with a statement made in a preceding chapter to the effect that very little land-derived sediment is at present depositing more than 100 miles out from shore. The coarse materials (sands and gravels) could not, of course, be carried many miles out, while many of the strata are covered with ripple marks, thus positively proving their shallow-water origin. We conclude, therefore, that the Appalachian strata are of marine, shallow-water origin. But we have already stated that these strata are at least 25,000 feet thick. How, then, do we reconcile these two seemingly paradoxical statements? All that is necessary is to realize that the floor of the shallow sea, in which the sediments eroded from adjacent land were being deposited, slowly, though more or less irregularly, subsided or sank during the long ages (millions of years) of their accumulation. It would carry us too far afield to really attempt an explanation of this remarkable type of geologic phenomenon, and it must suffice to suggest that, starting with the earth's crust in equilibrium, the very weight of accumulating strata would tend to destroy that equilibrium and so cause subsidence.

In our trip across the mountains it would be strikingly evident that the strata are no longer in their original horizontal position, as they were piled up layer upon layer, but that they have been notably disturbed and thrown into folds (Plate 9), large and small, some masses of the strata having been bent upward (anticlines) and others downward (synclines). Such folded structures could have been developed only by a great force of lateral compression in the earth's crust within the zone of flowage. Under compression the strata were mashed together, notably bent into curves (folds), and more or less upraised. It would also be readily observed that the main axes of the folds extend essentially parallel to the main trend of the mountain range, thus proving that the force of compression was exerted at right angles to the trend of the range.

Using a biological analogy, a brief history of a typical folded mountain range may be stated as follows: First, there is the prenatal or embryonic

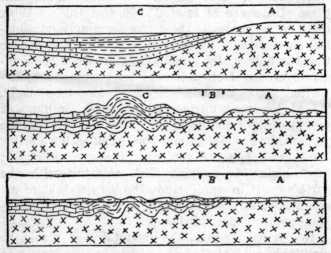

FIG. 24.—Diagrammatic sections illustrating the development of a typical folded mountain range. Upper figure: A, the old land eroded to furnish sediments deposited under the adjacent sea at C. Middle figure: strata (C) folded as they would appear if unaffected by erosion, and a downwarp (B) between A and C. Lower figure: condition after profound erosion, and filling of B with sediment. (Drawn by the author.)

stage when the materials of the range are gathering, that is when the sediments are piling up layer upon layer relatively near shore on a sinking sea bottom. Next comes the birth of the range when, due to the great lateral compressive force, the strata are thrown into folds and forced to appear above sea level, the range thus literally being born out of the sea. During the next, or youthful stage, the range grows (with increasing altitudes) because of continued application of the compressive force. Even during the youthful growing stage weathering and erosion attack the range and tend to reduce it. Then comes the stage of maturity, when the up-building (compressive) force and the tearing down (erosive) force about counterbalance each other. At this time the range has reached its maximum height and ruggedness of relief, with ridges and valleys higher and deeper than at any other time. The old-age stage sets in when the upbuilding power wanes or actually ceases, and erosion dominates or reigns supreme. Slowly but surely, unless there be a renewal by an upbuilding power, the range is cut down until little or nothing of it remains well above sea level, or, in other words, until a peneplain is developed. This last stage may truly be called the death of the range. Usually, however, some local portions of the disappearing range, which are more resistant or more favorably situated against erosion, are left standing to at least moderate heights above the general level of the plain of erosion.

The above normal order of events may be disturbed at any stage, especially after maturity, by renewed uplift when the streams are revived in activity and increased ruggedness results. Even after the whole range as a relief feature has been planed away, the site of the range may be uplifted and a new cycle of erosion started.

By the use of two well-known examples we shall not only illustrate the above principles of mountain history, but also show that no less than a few million years must be allowed for the growth and decay of a great folded range. During the last (Permian) period of the Paleozoic era the Appalachian strata began to buckle and the yielding to pressure continued till well into the succeeding (Triassic) period. The climax was reached about the close of the Permian. Then, throughout the Mesozoic era, erosion reduced the central Appalachians to a great plain (peneplain) near sea level, after which, in the earlier part of the present (Cenozoic era), the site of the former range was distinctly upraised (without folding of the rocks), causing the revived streams to begin their work of carving out the present ridges and valleys, this work still being in progress.

In the case of the Sierra Nevada, the strata were folded into a lofty mountain range relatively late in the Mesozoic era and, by the middle of the Cenozoic era, the old-age stage of erosion was well advanced when the range was not more than a few thousand feet high. Then (in the latter part of the Cenozoic) uplift, accompanied by faulting on a large scale, but not by folding, took place, and the range was notably rejuvenated to about its present height. All the remarkably deep canyons of the Sierra have been carved out since the rejuvenation.

How is the geological birthday of a mountain range determined? In the preceding paragraph we stated that the Appalachians were folded and born out of the sea about the close of the Paleozoic era. This is readily proved by calling attention to two facts. First, the youngest strata involved in the folding are of Permian, or late Paleozoic Age in the geologic column, as proved by their fossil content, etc., and obviously the folding must have taken place after they had been deposited. Clearly, then, the folding could not have taken place before very late Paleozoic time. Second, the oldest strata resting upon the folded rocks are of early (not the very

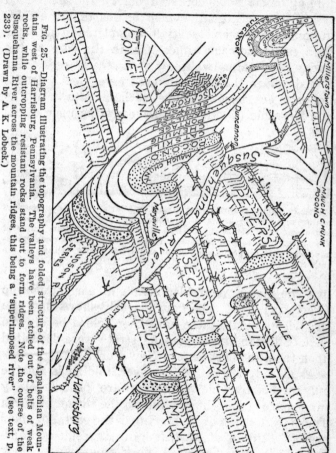

FIG. 25.—Diagram illustrating the topography and folded structure of the Appalachian Mountains west of Harrisburg, Pennsylvania. The valleys have been etched out of belts of weak rocks, while outcropping resistant rocks stand out to form ridges. Note the course of the Susquehanna River across the mountain ridges, this being a "superimposed river" (see text, p. 233). (Drawn by A. K. Lobeck.)

earliest) Mesozoic Age, and these strata are somewhat tilted but not folded. Obviously, then, the folding must have occurred before the nonfolded strata were deposited, which means that the folding must have been essentially completed in not later than early Mesozoic time. Or, in the case of the Rocky Mountains, we know that strata were there folded late in the Mesozoic era or very early in the Cenozoic era, because folded rocks as late in age as late Mesozoic (Cretaceous) have resting upon them,

FIG. 26.—Only slightly tilted strata of Silurian and Devonian ages resting upon folded strata of Cambrian and Ordovician ages in an east-west section across the Catskill Mountains and Hudson Valley of New York. The folding took place at the time of the Taconic Mountain Revolution toward the end of the Ordovician period. (Drawn by the author.)

in some places, nonfolded strata of early Cenozoic (Tertiary) Age. The figure clearly shows how the Ordovician strata must have been folded before the next (Silurian and Devonian) strata were deposited upon them in southeastern New York.

As already suggested, however, folding is not the only method by which mountains are formed. Many ranges are either entirely due to the tilting of earth blocks by faulting or fracturing of the earth, or their present altitude, at least, is a direct result of faulting. Such may be called block mountains. They are wonderfully represented by the various north-south ranges rising some thousands of feet above the general level of the Great Basin region of Utah and Nevada. These ranges are, in short, somewhat eroded edges of approximately parallel-tilted fault blocks lying between the Sierra Nevada Range and the Wasatch Range. In southeastern Oregon a series of nearly parallel block mountains, up to forty miles in length and over 1,000 feet in height, show very steep eastern fronts only slightly modified by erosion.

Another mode of origin of mountains is by the rise of molten material to the surface, especially where a chain of volcanoes is located. Thus the Cascade Mountains from northern California through Oregon and Washington, including Mounts Lassen, Shasta, Pitt, Baker, St. Helens, and Rainier, are very largely the result of volcanic action. The long chain of Aleutian Islands of Alaska, referred to in our study of volcanoes, is an excellent example of a great mountain range now being built up out of the sea by volcanic action. More locally molten rocks under pressure may not reach the surface but instead simply bulge or dome the strata over them, as in the case of the group known as the Henry Mountains of Utah, and also in other parts of the West.

In still other cases mountains of considerable area and altitude have resulted from erosion of uplifted regions where the uplift has been practically unaccompanied by either folding, faulting, or igneous activity. Any low-lying area, regardless of the character of its rocks, structure, or previous history, may be notably upraised and simply subjected to erosion. An excellent illustration is afforded by the Catskill Mountains of New York, where numerous deep valleys and narrow ridges have been carved out of upraised nearly horizontal strata. The so-called "Bad Lands" region of parts of South

Dakota and Wyoming is also essentially of this type, where deep, narrow valleys and sharp ridges have been etched out of high, relatively soft, nearly horizontal strata, resulting in an almost impassable maze of mountains. In the high, recently upraised Colorado Plateau of parts of Arizona, New Mexico, Colorado, and Utah, nearly horizontal strata are being etched out, the result being numerous buttes, mesas (flat-topped hills and mountains) and deep canyons, including the Grand Canyon with its maze of peaks and pinnacles, many of them rising like mountains out of the canyon depths.

Mountains of the pure types just described are not the prevailing ones of the earth. Most mountains and their structures, as we see them to-day, are products of two or more of the processes of folding, faulting, igneous action, and erosion. A few well-known examples will suffice to make this matter clearer. Thus, the Appalachian Mountains originally developed by severe folding of thick strata. After considerable erosion, numerous small and large thrust faults developed, some of the dislocations amounting to miles. Then the whole range was cut down nearly to sea level by erosion, after which the district was upraised (without folding) mostly from 2,000 to 4,000 feet, and the present long, narrow mountain ridges and valleys have been carved out by stream erosion. Thus folding, faulting, and erosion all enter into the height and structure of the Appalachians.

A lofty mountain range still more complex in its history is the Sierra Nevada of California. First, thick strata were highly folded, upraised, and intruded by great masses of molten granite. Erosion then proceeded to cut the range down to hills, after which a great fracture (fault) developed along the eastern side and the Sierra Nevada earth block was notably tilted with steep eastern front and long western slope. Erosion has considerably modified the eastern fault face, and the deep canyons like Yosemite, King's River and American River, have been carved out of the western slope of the great tilted fault block. Geologically recently the central to northern portion of the range has been affected by volcanic action, streams of lava in some cases having flowed down the valleys.

CHAPTER XI

A STUDY OF LAKES

LAKES are ephemeral features on the face of the earth. Compared to the tens of millions of years of known earth history, lakes, even large ones, are very short lived. They may, in truth, be regarded as merely results of the temporary obstructions to drainage. Lake basins are known to originate in many ways, and there are various means by which they are destroyed. Not attempting an exhaustive, scientific treatment of the subject, our present purpose may be well served by describing and explaining some of the better known and more remarkable lakes of the world.

Even a cursory examination of a large map of the world reveals the fact that the regions of most numerous lakes are those which were recently occupied by glaciers—either the vast ice sheets of the Glacial epoch or mountain (or valley) glaciers. This is because more lakes of the present time have come into existence as direct or indirect results of glaciation than by any other cause. A considerable number of these lakes occupy rock basins which have been eroded or excavated by the direct action of flowing ice. Small lakes of this sort are commonly found in the upper parts of valleys formerly occupied by mountain or so-called Alpine glaciers, because there the excavating power of such glaciers was especially effective. More rarely rock basins have been scoured out by glaciers farther down their valleys. Many lakes occupy rock basins excavated by ice in the high Sierra Nevada and Cascade Ranges, in the Rocky Mountains from Colorado into Canada, in the Alps, and in the mountains of Norway. Few, if any of them are, however, large or famous. Other lakes, some of very considerable size, occupy rock basins scoured out by the passage of the great ice sheets of the Glacial epoch in North America and Europe, though they are less common than formerly supposed. Some of the many lake basins of Ontario, Canada, are quite certainly of this origin, as might well be expected, because the power of the great ice sheet was there in general notably greater than south of the Great Lakes where the tendency was to unload or deposit the eroded materials as shown by the great accumulations of glacial débris (moraines).

Where the ice walls of certain existing glaciers form dams across valleys, waters are ponded, a small lake of this kind occurring alongside the Great Aletsch Glacier of the Alps, where its wall is slowly moving past a tributary valley. Lakes of this kind also occur in Greenland and in Alaska, but none are of considerable size. During the Great Ice Age, however, literally thousands of large and small lakes were formed, both during the advance and the retreat of the ice, wherever the glacier wall blocked valleys which sloped downward toward the ice. New York State furnishes many fine examples of large and small lakes of this sort. Thus, when the great glacier was melting in northern New York, waters hundreds of feet deep and many miles long were ponded between two ice lobes—one retreating eastward and the other westward from the Mohawk

Valley. An ice dam lake was also formed a little later, when an ice wall blocked the northern part of the Black River Valley just west of the Adirondack Mountains and caused a lake covering about 200 square miles. One of the largest of all known ice dam lakes has been called Lake Agassiz, which attained a maximum length of over 700 miles and a width of 250 miles in the Red River of the North region of eastern North Dakota, western and northwestern Minnesota, and northward into Canada, most of its area having been in Canada. It began as a small lake with southward drainage into the Mississippi when the great northward retreating ice sheet formed a dam across the valley of the Red River of the North. The retreating ice continued to block the northward drainage until the vast lake, covering a greater territory than all of the present Great Lakes combined, was developed. Beaches, bars, deltas and the outflow channel of this remarkable lake are wonderfully well preserved. Lake Winnipeg is a mere remnant of great Lake Agassiz.

Many ponds and small lakes occupy basins formed by irregular accumulations of glacial (morainic) materials. Still others lie in depressions which formed by the melting of masses of ice which became wholly or partly buried by ice deposits, or by sediments washed into bodies of water which were held up by ice dams. Depressions of the latter kind are commonly found as pits or so-called "kettle holes" below the general level of sand flats or sand plains of glacial lake origin.

Most common of all lake basins of glacial origin are those formed by accumulation of glacial débris or morainic materials acting as natural dams across valleys. This is, in fact, the most common of all ways by which existing lake basins, some of them very large, have been formed. Most of the thousands of ponds and lakes of Minnesota, Wisconsin, and northern New York belong in this category.

In the Adirondack Mountains, for example, most of the lakes, like the well-known Lake Placid, Saranac Lakes, Long Lake, and Schroon Lake, have their waters ponded by single dams of glacial débris across valleys. In some cases a series of such dams blockades a valley and forms a chain of lakes like the well-known Fulton Chain in the Adirondacks. Less commonly the lake may have its waters ponded by two natural dams of glacial débris, one across a valley at each end of a lake. A very fine, large scale example of the last-named type is the famous Lake George in the southeastern Adirondacks. It is over 30 miles long and from 1 to 2½ miles wide. It lies in the bottom of a deep, narrow mountain valley, mountain sides rising very steeply from a few hundred feet to 2,000 or more feet above its shores. There are many islands, especially in the so-called "Narrows," thus greatly enhancing the scenic effect. The valley itself has been produced by a combination of faulting and erosion. There was a preglacial stream divide at the present location of the "Narrows." This divide was somewhat reduced by ice erosion when the deep, narrow body of ice plowed its way through the valley during the Ice Age. During the retreat of the ice heavy morainic accumulations were left as dams across the valley at each end of the lake.

Another remarkable body of water, similar to Lake George in its origin, is Chautauqua Lake of western New York, famous for its Chautauqua assemblies. It lies 1,338 feet above sea level, with its northern end near the edge of the steep front of the plateau overlooking Lake Erie. Chautauqua Lake really consists of parts of two valleys, one sloping north and the other sloping south, each dammed by glacial deposits.

The famous Alpine lakes—Garda, Como, and Maggiore—have resulted from deposition of glacial morainic materials under conditions different from those above described. In these cases great mountain or valley glaciers once flowed down the valleys and spread out part way upon the Italian plain. Great accumulations of glacial débris took place around the borders of the glacier lobes, and, after retreat of the ice, the glacial deposits acted as dams ponding the waters far back into the mountain valleys.

The origin and history of the Great Lakes constitutes one of the most interesting and remarkable chapters in the recent geological history of North America. Most of the salient points have been well worked out and they may be very briefly summarized, as follows: Before the Ice Age the Great Lakes did not exist, because the region, prior to that time, had been land subjected to erosion for millions of years—a time altogether too long for any lake to survive. Their sites were occupied by broad, low, stream-cut valleys which were quite certainly locally somewhat deepened by ice erosion during the Ice Age. Ice erosion is, however, altogether insufficient to account for the great closed basins. The two most important factors entering into the formation of the basins of the Great Lakes were doubtless the great glacial (morainic) accumulations acting as dams along the south side, and the tilting of the land downward on the north side of the region. In support of this explanation it has been established that the great dumping ground of ice-transported materials from the north was in general along the southern side of the Great Lakes and southward. It has also been well established that, late in the Ice Age, the land on the southern side of the Great

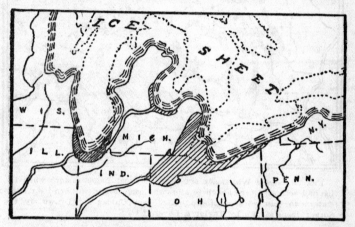

Fig. 27.—Sketch map showing a very early stage in the history of the Great Lakes when two relatively small lakes in front of the ice wall separately drained into the Mississippi River. (Drawn by the author from map by Taylor & Leverett.)

Lakes region was lower than at present, as proved by the tilted character of beaches of the well-known extinct glacial lakes which were the ancestors of the present lakes. Such a down-warp of the land must have helped to form the closed basins by tending to stop the southward and southwestward drainage of the region.

We shall now very briefly trace out the principal stages in the history of the Great Lakes during the final retreat of the vast ice sheet. This may best be done by the aid of maps which need only brief explanation. When the ice sheet had retreated far enough northward to uncover the very southern end of the Lake Michigan basin and a little beyond, a

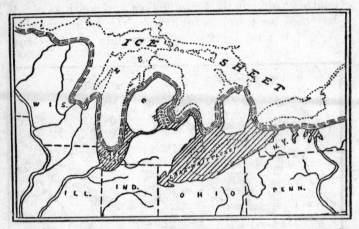

FIG. 28.—Lake Whittlesey stage of the Great Lakes history when the ice had retreated far enough to allow the eastern and western ice margin waters to join with a single outlet past Chicago. (Drawn by the author from a map by Taylor & Leverett.)

small glacial lake (Lake Chicago) developed against the ice wall. Its outlet was through the Illinois River and thence into the Mississippi. At the same time a larger glacial lake, held up by the ice wall, developed over the western part of the Erie basin and beyond. Its outlet was through the Wabash River. With further retreat of the ice a large lake (Whittlesey) covering considerably more than the area of Lake Erie developed, with outlet westward across Michigan into the enlarged Lake Chicago which continued to drain into the Illinois River. During a still later stage of ice withdrawal the remarkable set of three glacial lakes existed—Lakes

Duluth, Chicago, and Lundy. Each of these large
lakes had its own outlet. Lake Duluth covered
about half of the Lake Superior basin and drained
through the St. Croix River into the Mississippi.
Lake Chicago expanded to cover nearly all of the
Michigan basin and continued to drain through the
Illinois River. Lake Lundy covered not only more
than the area of the Erie basin, but also considerable territory north of Detroit, and drained eastward alongside the ice lobe of the Ontario basin
through the Mohawk and Hudson valleys of New

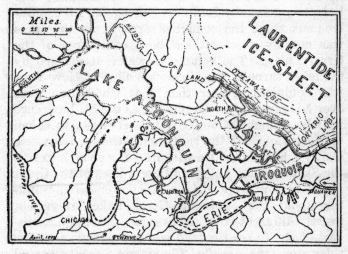

Fig. 29. — The Algonquin-Iroquois stage of the Great Lakes when
their whole area was ice-free, and all their waters drained through
the Mohawk-Hudson Valleys of New York into the Atlantic Ocean.
(After Taylor, published by New York State Museum.)

York, and into the Atlantic Ocean. Just after the
ice completely withdrew from the area now occupied
by the Great Lakes, but still blocked the St. Lawrence Valley, the vast body of water called Lake

Algonquin more than covered the sites of the present Superior, Michigan, and Huron. At this time the land was distinctly lower toward the northeast than at present, causing the outlets to the west to be abandoned. The great Lake Algonquin poured its waters eastward through the Trent River channel of Ontario, Canada, into glacial Lake Iroquois, which was the great ancestor of Lake Ontario. Lake Iroquois, in turn, had its outlet eastward through the Mohawk and Hudson Valleys of New York. For part of the time at least, Lake Erie maintained a separate existence discharging into Lake Iroquois near Buffalo. During the Algonquin-Iroquois stage the combined area of all the lakes was notably greater than the present area of the Great Lakes. The volume of water discharged by the lakes through the Mohawk Valley of New York was doubtless greater than that which now goes over Niagara Falls. Gradually, as the St. Lawrence ice lobe waned, the outlet waters of the lakes began to move alongside the ice through the St. Lawrence Valley. Finally the ice withdrew far enough to free the St. Lawrence Valley and the waters of the Great Lakes region dropped to a still lower level, bringing about the Nipissing Great Lakes stage not greatly different from the present. East and northeast of the Lakes the land was low enough to allow tidewater (the so-called Champlain Sea) to extend through the Hudson, Champlain, and St. Lawrence Valleys, and possibly into the Ontario basin, as proved by the occurrence of marine beaches and fossils. The waters in the Erie and Ontario basins covered about the present areas, while the Nipissing Lakes, which covered a little more than the present areas of the three upper Great Lakes, had their out-

let through the Ottawa River channel into tidewater (Champlain Sea). Postglacial warping of
the land has brought the whole region to the present
condition.

Many lakes, including some remarkable ones,
occupy basins which are directly due to movements
of the earth's crust—either faulting or warping.

FIG. 30.—Map showing next to the present stage of the Great Lakes
history when the land was lower on the north and the upper (Nipissing)
lakes drained through the Ottawa River Valley into an arm of the sea
(Champlain Sea) which reached through the Champlain and Hudson
Valleys. (After Taylor, published by New York State Museum.)

An example of a lake occupying part of a fault
basin is the famous Dead Sea of Palestine. This
lake lies in the lowest part of the Jordan Valley,
which has geologically recently come into existence
by the sinking of a long, narrow block of earth for
several thousand feet between two great earth fractures (faults). The Dead Sea covers about 500
square miles and its surface lies about 1,300 feet

below sea level, which makes it the lowest lake in the world. Almost equally remarkable is the fact that its depth is about 1,300 feet, so that the lowest part of the lake basin is 2,600 feet below sea level. The lake contains approximately 24 per cent salt, mostly common table salt, causing it to be a thick brine in which there is neither plant nor animal life —hence the name "Dead Sea." At one time, probably just after the Ice Age, the lake was much larger and deeper, when it filled a considerable part of the Jordan Valley and had an outlet to the south. During the high-level stage the water was fresh, but gradually, as the climate became drier, evaporation was greater than intake, the outlet was abandoned, and the mineral matter (mostly chloride of magnesia and common table salt) carried by the streams in solution into the shrinking lake steadily accumulated until the high degree of salinity of the present time has been reached.

Great Salt Lake, Utah, is a remarkable lake whose history has been carefully studied. It occupies the lowest position of an extensive basin which, in turn, forms but part of the whole great district of Utah which has geologically recently sunk thousands of feet on the west side of the great fault already described as occurring along the western base of the Wasatch Mountains. At present the lake covers about 2,000 square miles, but its area fluctuates considerably. It is scarcely believable that this big lake has an average depth of only fifteen feet and a maximum depth of only fifty feet. It lies 4,200 feet above sea level, and it carries about 18 per cent salts in solution. Most abundant by far is common table salt, of which there are no less than 5,000,000,000 tons in solution. The waters also contain other salts in very large quantities. Should the lake completely disappear by evaporation, these salts would be deposited. There is, indeed, so much saline matter in solution in the lake, that it is impossible for a person to sink in its dense waters. What has been the source of these salts? Great Salt Lake is not, as supposed by some, a remnant of an ocean once covering the region. Briefly, the explanation is as follows: At one time, when the climate was moister, the basin now only in part occupied by the lake was filled to overflowing with an outlet north into the Snake and Columbia rivers. That great body of water (called "Lake Bonneville") covered nearly 20,000 square miles and its depth was about 1,000 feet deeper than now, the present depth being very small. Because it had an outlet that lake was, of course, fresh. Beaches and shore lines 1,000 feet above the present lake, and at various lower levels, are still wonderfully well preserved. When, due to climatic change, evaporation exceeded intake by streams, the outlet was cut off. But slowly, as the lake shrank, streams (especially the Jordan River) carried a little salt in solution, the percentage of salt increasing until the present stage has been reached. In a real sense, much of the salt was once in the sea, because it has been dissolved out of the strata which accumulated under sea water long before the basin of Great Salt Lake came into existence.

Another famous lake, which also occupies part of a basin due to faulting, is Lake Tahoe in the Sierra Nevada Mountains, near Truckee, California. This lake, whose length is 21 miles, and width 12 miles, lies 6,225 feet above sea level. On almost all sides steep mountains rise several thousand feet above its waters. Its great depth of 1,635 feet makes it, so far as known, the second deepest lake in North America, Crater Lake, Oregon, only outranking it. The water is exceedingly clear. An experiment some years ago showed that a white disk eight inches in diameter could actually be seen through a thickness of 216 feet of its water. "The statement sometimes made that 'Tahoe is an old volcanic crater' is not true. The region about the lake shows evidences of volcanic activity of various kinds, and the lake waters themselves have probably been dammed at times by outpourings of lava. A lava flow appears to have temporarily filled the outlet channel below Tahoe City. The lake, however, lies in a structural depression—a dropped (fault) block in the earth's crust." (U. S. Geological Survey.)

The basin of the largest lake in the world—the Caspian Sea—has resulted from warping of the earth's crust. It has an area of 170,000 square miles, a maximum depth of 3,200 feet, and its surface is about 90 feet below sea level. The composition of its water and some of its animal life indicate that it was once an arm of the sea. It has been detached or cut off by an upwarp of the land between it and the Black Sea region. If this great lake is a cut-off arm of the sea, with no outlet, how do we explain the fact that its salinity is much less than that of the ocean? Toward the north, where it is shallow and fed by so much river water, it is, in fact, almost fresh water. Even the southern one-half carries not over 1 per cent of salt. The explanation is that a steady current passes through a narrow passageway into a gulf or bay on its eastern side where evaporation is much greater than over the general surface of the Caspian. The salt is, therefore, gradually accumulating at the estimated rate of 350,000 tons per day in this gulf, while the sea itself is becoming fresher.

The basin of Lake Champlain, about 100 miles long, was occupied by tidewater geologically very recently (that is, since the Ice Age), but it has been cut off by uplift of the land on the north, since which time the waters of the lake have been completely rinsed out and freshened.

Many lake basins directly result from volcanic action. In many parts of the world lakes, usually of small size, occupy craters of volcanoes as, for example, in the Eifel region of Germany, the Auvergne district of France, and near Rome and Naples in Italy. Such a lake of exceptional interest fills part of the great crater, several thousand feet deep, which resulted from the explosion of Mt. Katmai, Alaska, in 1912. The water of this lake, more than a mile wide and of unknown depth, is hot.

One of the most unique and beautiful lakes of the world is Crater Lake in the Cascade Mountains of southern Oregon. It partly fills a great, nearly circular hole, six miles in diameter, with a maximum depth of about 4,000 feet, in the top of a mountain (Plate 13b). The lake is over five miles in diameter and nearly 2,000 feet deep, making it the deepest in North America. Its surface is about 6,200 feet above sea level. Precipitous rock walls rising 500 to 2,000 feet completely encircle the lake, the main body of whose water is of a marvelous deep, sapphire-blue color, while the shallow portions around some of the shore are of emerald-green. Crater Lake has very little intake except direct rainfall and snowfall, and its water is fresh. The great hole was not produced by an explosion like that of Katmai, but rather by the sinking of the top of a once much greater mountain. That the mountain was once about the size and shape of Mt. Shasta is proved by the fact that deep glaciated valleys lead up the slopes and end abruptly at the very rim of the present mountain. Obviously these valleys were scoured out in recent geologic time by glaciers whose sources were several thousand feet up on a former cone-shaped mountain. That the mountain top sank rather than exploded is proved by the absence of volcanic débris over the sides and base of the mountain.

Still another way by which lakes are formed by volcanic action is by streams of lava blocking valleys. The famous Sea of Galilee in Palestine was thus formed by a stream of lava, which geologically recently flowed down from the east into the Jordan Valley and across it, where it cooled to form a dam ponding the waters of the Jordan River. Because the river flows through the lake, its water is fresh. One of the most remarkable facts about this lake is that its surface lies nearly 700 feet below sea level. A number of lava-dam lakes are known in the Sierra Nevada and Cascade Mountains.

A very interesting case of a lake basin, formed by cutting off an arm of the sea without any movement of the earth's crust, is the Salton Sink of southern California. This basin, many miles long and wide, lies below sea level, its lowest point being 287 feet below tide. The Gulf of California formerly reached much farther north and into California where it covered the site of the Salton Sink. Gradually the Colorado River, always loaded with sediment, built a broad delta deposit right across the gulf, the northern end of which thus became cut off, leaving a big salt lake. But the river flowed into the gulf, while in the dry climate the evaporation was great enough to gradually dry away the salt lake. This was the condition of things until 1904, when much of the river at a time of flood got out of control and, following the general course of a great irrigating canal, it flowed for several years into the lowest part of the Salton Sink, partly filling it to form a lake 45 miles long, 17 miles wide, and 83 feet deep. Since 1907 the lake has been notably decreasing in size, and it may entirely disappear.

Other ways by which lakes, mostly relatively small ones, may develop are by landslides blocking valley drainages; by streams cutting across winding curves leaving so-called "oxbow lakes" which are common, for example, along the lower Mississippi River; by wave and wind action along shores of lakes or sea; by filling so-called "sink holes" which result from dissolving or falling in of roofs of caves; and by beavers through whose industry dams are built across valleys or streams.

Some of the most common ways by which lakes may be destroyed are the following: by being filled with sediment carried in by streams, or by vegetation, or by both; by cutting down outlets; by evaporation due to a change in climate; by removal of the ice dam in certain types of glacial lakes; and by movements or warping of the earth's crust.

CHAPTER XII

HOW THE EARTH MAY HAVE ORIGINATED

THE problem of the origin of the earth is essentially astronomical rather than geological, because geological history is considered to have begun when common earth processes, such as erosion, deposition, and transportation of sediments, etc., were brought into play. It is quite certain, however, that the earth in its pregeologic state gradually merged into its geological condition. For this reason the geologist is interested in the more important doctrines or hypotheses which have been put forth to account for the origin of the earth. In fact, one of the few hypotheses which must be taken seriously is largely the work of a geologist. The most acceptable hypothesis not only best satisfies the facts regarding the earth's astronomical relationships, but also best harmonizes with our knowledge of the oldest known rocks and their history.

Since the problem of the origin of the earth is an essential part of the problem of the origin of the solar system, the following well-known facts should be clearly in the mind of the reader. Nine planets, including the earth, revolve in nearly circular paths around the central sun, whose diameter is 866,000 miles. The radius of the solar system is at least several billion miles, considering the distance of the outermost known planet (Pluto) from the sun. Neptune requires 164 years for a trip around the sun, while Earth, which averages about 93,000,-000 miles from the sun, makes its circuit once a year. The planets all revolve around the sun in the same direction, and in nearly the same plane. The sun and all eight planets rotate on their axes in the same direction, the earth's rotation being accomplished every twenty-four hours. Most of the planets have one or more smaller bodies called satellites revolving about them, such as Earth, with its one satellite (the moon), and Saturn, with its eight satellites, etc. It is well known that this solar system is only a very small part of the vast universe, as shown by the facts that no star is nearer the earth than several trillion miles, and that some stars are so far away that light traveling at the rate of 186,000 miles per second requires a thousand years to reach the earth!

Toward the end of the eighteenth century the famous nebular or ring hypothesis was set forth by the astronomer named Laplace. This assumes an original very hot incandescent mass of gas spheroidal in shape and greater in diameter than the present solar system. This mass rotated in the direction of rotation of our sun and its planets. Loss of heat by radiation caused the mass to shrink, and this in turn not only made it rotate faster, but also caused the centrifugal force (i. e., the force whose direction was from the center) in its equatorial portion to gradually become stronger. Finally a time came when the force of gravity (i. e., the force whose direction was toward the center) and the centrifugal force became equal and a ring was left (not thrown) off, while the rest of the mass of gas continued to shrink. After a time the material of the ring collected to form the outermost planet. The other planets were similarly formed from other rings which were left off as contraction of the great mass of gas went on. The sun represents the remainder of the great mass of rotating gas.

What is the bearing of this nebular hypothesis upon the early geological history of the earth? According to the hypothesis the earth must once have been much more highly heated and larger than now. It condensed to a liquid and then it cooled enough to permit the formation of a solid crust over a liquid interior. It then had a hot dense atmosphere containing all the water of the earth in the form of vapor, and this atmosphere steadily became thinner due to absorption by the earth. When the pressure and temperature conditions became favorable, much of the water vapor condensed to form the ocean and the atmosphere gradually changed to its present condition. According to this view the oldest rocks of the earth must have been igneous because they resulted from the solidification of the outer part of the molten globe.

Within recent years certain serious objections to the nebular hypothesis have been raised, and Chamberlin and Moulton have formulated the planetesimal or spiral hypothesis as an attempt at a more rational explanation of the origin of the solar system. Some of the objections to the older doctrine are that among the many thousands of known nebulæ in the universe very few only are of the Laplacian or ring type, while spiral forms are abundant. Spectroscopic study shows that the nebulæ are not gaseous, but made up of either liquid or solid particles, and that the leaving off of rings would necessitate the assumption of an intermit-

PLATE 11.—(*a*) MOLTEN LAVA FLOWING OVER A CLIFF INTO WATER IN THE HAWAIIAN ISLANDS. (*After Diller, U. S. Geological Survey.*)

PLATE 11.—(*b*) DIKES OF GRANITE (LIGHT GRAY) CUTTING AN OLD DARK ROCK. While the granite on the right was being forced in molten condition upward into the earth's crust, tongues of it (dikes) were sent off into the adjacent rock.

(*Photo by Howe, U. S. Geological Survey.*)

PLATE 12.—(a) LASSEN PEAK, NORTHERN CALIFORNIA, IN ERUPTION AUGUST 22, 1914. The great cloud of steam and volcanic ash rose several miles. This is the only active volcano in the United States proper, and it is now included in Lassen Volcano National Park. (By permission of R. E. Stinson, Red Bluff, Cal.)

PLATE 12.—(b) DEVIL'S TOWER, WYOMING. This great mass of rock was forced in molten condition through strata which, because of their weakness, have been eroded away all around the hard igneous rock. This is probably the core or neck of a former volcano. (Photo by Darton, U. S. Geological Survey.)

tent process which could scarcely have operated under the conditions of the hypothesis.

Anything like a full understanding of the planetesimal hypothesis would be difficult to obtain, and, in the brief space at our disposal, we shall attempt to make clear only a few of the salient points.

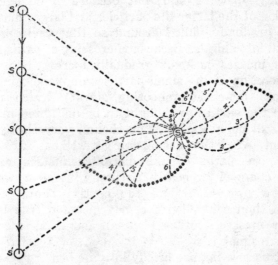

Fig. 31.—Diagram showing the origin and character of a spiral nebula according to the planetesimal hypothesis of the origin of the solar system. (Modified after Moulton.)

According to this hypothesis the solar system was, during a previous stage of its evolution, a great, flat, spiral nebula, made up of finely divided solid or possibly liquid particles called planetesimals, among which were scattered some larger "knots" or masses. Each tiny particle and larger mass or knot is considered to have traveled in its own particular orbit or path about a central very large mass—the future sun. It is even suggested that the spiral nebula originated by disruption of one star by a swift-moving passing star. The planets began as a series of hot gas-bolts shot out from the sun, and, in cooling, each bolt condensed to a nuclear body associated with myriads of planetesimals. Each disrupted particle and large mass at first started straight for the large passing star, but because of change of position of the latter the particles and larger masses were gradually pulled around so that their paths curved into spirals. Because of crossing of paths, the larger masses or knots gradually increased in size by accretion of the small particles or planetesimals. Meteors (so-called "shooting stars") which now strike the earth are thought to be disrupted materials still being gathered in, though very slowly at present. After the passing star got well out of range, the spiral paths of the disrupted masses gradually changed to nearly circular, due to a wrapping-up process around the central body (sun) which then controlled the movements of the both larger masses (future planets) and small masses (planetesimals).

Let us now inquire briefly into the bearing of this hypothesis upon the early geological history of the earth. Except in its very early nuclear stage the earth was never in the form of a highly heated gas, nor was it ever necessarily hotter than now. Instead of beginning as a much larger body which has gradually diminished in size, the earth steadily grew, up to a certain stage, by ingathering of planetesimals. Increase in size caused the force of gravity to increase and this caused not only steady contraction of the earth's matter, but also a development of greater internal heat. The earth has been getting smaller ever since the force of compression has predominated over the building-up process, because of the diminishing supply of planetesimals. Due to steadily increasing internal pressure and heat the various gases, including water vapor, have been driven out of the earth to form an atmosphere which has gradually become larger and denser. After sufficient accumulation of water vapor, condensation and rainfall took place; the waters of the earth began to gather to form the oceans; and the ordinary geologic processes of erosion and deposition of strata were initiated. According to this view stratified rocks could have been formed very early in the history of the earth, and in this connection it is interesting to note that the oldest known rocks are actually of sedimentary origin.

According to the Jeans and Jeffreys modification of the planetesimal hypothesis, instead of gas-bolts shot out from the sun from time to time, a long streamer of very hot gas was steadily pulled out of the sun by a passing star and drawn forward by the star. The streamer became disrupted into spheres (planets), which, in the course of time, began to revolve around the sun. As one of these spheres, the earth cooled to full-size molten condition, and then to the present-day largely-solid earth. This theory has been further modified by assuming both a passing star and one striking a glancing blow.

CHAPTER XIII

VERY ANCIENT EARTH HISTORY

(*Archeozoic and Proterozoic Eras*)

WE shall now consider the older rocks of the earth, including those of Archeozoic, Protero- zoic, and Paleozoic ages. What are the salient points in the very early history of the earth (not including the evolution of organisms) shown by these very ancient rocks? Beginning with the oldest known rocks, it will be our purpose to trace out the principal recorded events of earth history in the regular order of their occurrence. As in human history, so in earth history the recorded events of very early times are fewest and most dif- ficult of all to understand. In spite of this dif- ficulty it is best to begin with the oldest known rocks or, as Le Conte has said, "to follow the natural order of events. This has the great advantage of bringing out the philosophy of the history—the law of evolution." Because of limitation of space we shall give special attention to the physical history of North America, but the general principles brought out apply almost equally well to the other continents.

The Archeozoic rocks contain the earliest known records of geological history, or, in other words, the oldest recorded ordinary geological processes such as weathering and erosion, deposition of strata, igneous activity, etc. Although we are here dealing with the most obscure records of any great rock system, partly because the rocks have been so profoundly altered (metamorphosed), and partly because of the absence of anything like definitely determinable fossils, it is, nevertheless, true that certain very important conclusions have been reached regarding this very ancient geological era.

Among the very oldest of all known rocks of North America are the Grenville strata, so named from a town in the St. Lawrence Valley. In fact, no rocks elsewhere in the world have been proved to be more ancient. The Grenville series consists of a great mass of sediments (strata)—original muds, sands, and limes—which were deposited layer upon layer under water (Plate 14). The widespread extent and character of the series in southeastern Canada and the Adirondacks, and more than likely far beyond these limits, make it certain that the Grenville strata were laid down on the bottom of a relatively shallow sea very much as sediments are now piling up on shallow sea bottoms. Thus, the most ancient definitely known condition of the region where the Grenville strata are exposed was an expanse of the sea covering the whole area. Wherever, in other parts of the world, the Archeozoic rocks have been studied, stratified rocks also seem to be the very oldest which are recognizable, but up to the present time no such rocks have been proved to be any older than, or even as old as, the Grenville series.

It may occur to the reader to ask, how long ago did the Grenville ocean exist? There are grave difficulties in the way of answering this question in terms of years since we have nothing like an exact

standard for such a measurement or comparison.
Although we must concede that not even approxi-
mate figures can be given, it can, nevertheless be
demonstrated by several independent lines of reasoning that the time must be measured by hundreds of millions of years, a very conservative
estimate of the minimum time which must be allowed being about 1,500,000,000 years. In any case,
the time is so utterly inconceivable to us that the
important thing to bear in mind is that the great
well-known events of earth history, which have
transpired since the existence of the Grenville ocean,
require a lapse of many millions of years, as shown
by revolutionary changes in geographic and geologic conditions such as the long periods of erosion,
the enormous accumulations of sediment, the repeated spreading out and disappearance of sea
water over many portions of the earth, and the
building up and tearing down of great mountain
ranges at various times. The ideas here expressed
will be much better appreciated by the reader after
following through the salient points in the history
of North America as set forth in the succeeding
pages.

Again, the reader may ask, by what line of
reasoning do we conclude that these stratified rocks
are so exceedingly ancient? All rocks of Archeozoic
Age, including strata as well as certain younger
igneous rocks (see below), invariably occupy a basal
position in relation to all other rock systems. They
constitute a complex lot of crystalline metamorphic
rocks, combining certain characteristics which lie
below the base of the determined sedimentary succession. Where rocks with the characteristics of the
Archeozoic are separated from the oldest Paleozoic

(Cambrian) strata by the great sedimentary or metamorphic system known as the Proterozoic (see below), we may be sure that we are dealing with Archeozoic rocks. If the series of rocks in question belongs in the Archeozoic system, all that remains is to determine its age position in that system. This can usually readily be done because wherever they have been studied the Archeozoic rocks may be subdivided into two groups of rocks, a sedimentary and an igneous. Where the igneous rocks, mainly granites and related types, occur associated with the sedimentary rocks (e. g., Grenville), they very clearly were forced or intruded, while molten, into the sedimentary rocks, thus proving these latter to be the older.

Since the Archeozoic strata of the Adirondack Mountains, southeastern Canada, and also all, or nearly all, other known districts are mostly badly disturbed, tilted, and more or less bent or folded, and since neither top nor bottom of the piles of strata has ever been recognized as such, it is impossible to give anything like an exact figure for the thickness of the series. Continuous successions of strata have, however, been observed in enough places to show that they were commonly deposited layer upon layer to a thickness of at least some tens of thousands of feet. A thickness of over 100,000 feet has been reported from southeastern Canada. The clear implication is that the Archeozoic sea which received sediments must have existed for a vast length of time which must be measured by at least some millions of years, because in the light of all our knowledge regarding the rate of accumulation of sediments a very long time was necessary for the piling up of such thick masses of strata. It does not, however, necessarily follow that the Grenville ocean was many thousands of feet deep where deposition took place. In fact, the very character of the original sediments (muds, sands, and limes) clearly indicates that the Archeozoic sea in which they accumulated was, for most part at least, of shallow water because such sediments have rarely, if ever, been carried out into an ocean of deep water. The great ocean abysses of to-day are not receiving any appreciable amount of land-derived sediment. Thus we are forced to conclude that in Archeozoic time, as well as many times in later ages, the shallow sea bottom gradually sank while the sediments accumulated. Even more conclusive proof of such subsidence has been obtained from the study of so-called "folded" mountain ranges of Paleozoic and later time, an excellent example being the Appalachian Range.

Having established the sedimentary origin and great antiquity of the Grenville series, we are led to the interesting and important conclusion that these oldest known rocks are not the most ancient which ever existed, because the Grenville strata must have been deposited layer upon layer, upon a floor of still older rocks. If such still older rocks are anywhere exposed to view, they have never been recognized as such. Again, the fact that the most ancient known rocks were deposited under water carries with it the corollary that there must have been lands at no great distances from the areas of deposition because, then as now, such sediments as muds and sands could have been derived only from the wear or erosion of lands, and have been deposited in layers under water adjacent to those lands. But we are utterly in the dark regarding any knowledge of the location or character of such very ancient lands.

The most ancient known strata, as we see them to-day, do not look like ordinary sediments such as shales, sandstones, and limestones. They have been profoundly changed from their original condition, that is to say, they have undergone metamorphism. The Archeozoic strata now exposed to view were formerly buried at least some miles below the earth's surface, the overlying younger rocks having since been removed by erosion through the millions of years of time. Far below the earth's surface, under conditions of relatively high temperature, pressure, and moisture, the materials of the strata were completely crystallized into various minerals. The surfaces of separation of the very ancient layers of sediment are still usually more or less clearly present (Plate 14). Original limestone has been changed into crystalline limestone or marble; sandstone has been changed into quartzite, and shale, sandy shale, and shaly sandstone have been changed into various schists and gneisses.

In western Ontario there are also stratified rocks (called the Keewatin series) which seem to be of about the same age as the Grenville strata farther east. A point of special interest in connection with the Keewatin strata is the presence of layers of lava in portions of the series, thus proving that molten rock materials were poured out on the earth's surface during the most ancient known era of the earth's history.

After the accumulation of the very ancient Archeozoic sediments igneous activity took place on grand scales when great masses of molten rock were forced (intruded) into the sediments from below. Masses of molten materials are known to have been thus intruded at several different times, but of these the most common by far cooled to form a great series of granite and closely related rocks. The general effect was to break the old strata up into patches or masses of varying sizes as clearly shown by the present distribution and modes of occurrence of these igneous rocks. In most cases the strata were pushed aside by, or tilted or domed over, the upwelling molten floods—in many cases the molten materials were, under great pressure, intimately forced or injected into the strata; numerous large and small masses of strata were caught up or enveloped (as inclusions) in the molten floods; in some cases there was local digestion or assimilation of the strata by the molten materials, while in still other places large bodies of strata seem to have been left practically intact and undisturbed. Such igneous rocks, which are very widespread, are all of the plutonic or deep-seated types; that is, they were never forced up to the earth's surface like lavas, but they solidified at considerable depths (at least some thousands of feet) below the surface. We see them exposed today only because a tremendous amount of overlying rock materials has been removed by erosion. These igneous rocks are generally easily distinguished from the old sediments of Grenville age because of their more general homogeneity in large masses, and their lack of sharply defined bands or layers of varying composition. The fact that the minerals have always crystallized to form medium to coarse-grained rocks shows that these rocks solidified under deep-seated conditions, since it is well known that surface flows (lavas) are much finer grained commonly with more or less of the rock not crystallized at all. Slow cooling under great pressure favors more complete crystallization with growth of larger crystals.

As we have just learned, the very character and structure of the Archeozoic rocks now exposed to view show conclusively that they were formerly deeply buried, and the inference is perfectly plain that the overlying rock materials were removed by erosion. Profound erosion of any land mass means that the land must have stood well above sea level, and thus we come to the important conclusion that the great mass of Archeozoic rocks (both strata and igneous rocks) were upraised well above sea level. Just when the uplift occurred cannot be positively stated, but in every region where the matter has been studied it took place before the strata of the next geological era began to deposit as shown by the fact that such later strata rest upon the profoundly eroded surface of the Archeozoic rocks. Such an erosion surface, called an "unconformity," marks a gap in the geological record of the district where it occurs. There is much to support the view that the uplift was concomitant with the great igneous intrusions, especially the granite. It is reasonable to believe that the same great force which caused the welling up of such tremendous bodies of liquid rock into the earth's crust might easily have caused a decided uplift of a whole large region, but even so the process must have been geologically slow. In regard to the height of those ancient lands, the character of the topography, and the drainage lines we are as yet utterly in the dark. The fact that many thousands of feet in thickness of materials were removed by erosion to expose the once deeply buried rocks, does not necessarily imply that the lands at any time had great height, because it is possible that while elevation slowly progressed, much material was steadily removed by erosion. In the light of our knowledge of the origin and growth of mountain ranges of later time there is little doubt that at least some of the Archeozoic lands were raised to such mountain heights.

Thus far in our study of the Archeozoic rocks attention has been mainly directed to southeastern Canada and the Adirondack mountains, where careful studies have been made. In all parts of the world where the most ancient known (Archeozoic) rocks have been studied in detail the same general principles apply. Particular attention has been given to the Archeozoic rocks south of Lake Superior, and in the Piedmont Plateau of the eastern United States. On the accompanying map Archeozoic rocks are widely exposed to view within the areas shown in black. It has been estimated that Archeozoic rocks appear at the surface over about one-fifth of the land area of the earth. Where they are not at the surface it is believed that they everywhere exist under cover of later rocks. In other words, Archeozoic rocks are considered to be almost universally present either at or under the earth's surface. This is true of the rocks of no other age. Special mention should be made of the fine exhibitions of Archeozoic rocks in Scandinavia and the Highlands of Scotland.

All known evidence leads us to the remarkable conclusion that the climate of much, or possibly all, of Archeozoic time was not fundamentally different from that of to-day. There must have been weathering of rocks, rainfall, and streams much as at present as proved by the character and composition of the stratified rocks which formed in that remote era. The presence of graphite ("black lead") in crystalline flakes scattered through many of the strata shows that the climate must have been favorable to some form of life, because graphite thus

Fig. 32.—Map showing the surface distribution of Archeozoic and Proterozoic rocks in North America. (Redrawn by the author after U. S. Geological Survey.)

occurring quite certainly represents the remains of organisms, this matter being more fully discussed in a succeeding chapter. In passing it may be stated that climatic zones were then probably scarcely if at all marked off, as they quite certainly were not even during Paleozoic time. One of the great contributions of geology to human knowledge is that during the tens of millions of years from Archeozoic times to the present the earth's climate has undergone no fundamental change or evolution. In the earlier ages there was greater uniformity of climate over the earth, and, during known geologic time there have been rather localized relatively minor fluctuations giving rise to glaciers, deserts, etc., but there has been no real evolution of climate at all comparable to the marvelous evolution of organisms—both animals and plants.

We shall now turn our attention briefly to a consideration of the second great subdivision of geologic time—the Proterozoic era. Rocks of Proterozoic Age comprise all of those which were formed after the Archeozoic rocks and before the deposition of the earliest Paleozoic (Cambrian) strata, these latter being rather definitely recognizable because they contain fossils characteristic of the time. Cambrian strata are, in fact, the oldest rocks which contain anything like an abundance of fossils, so that the separation of rocks of either Archeozoic or Proterozoic Age from the earliest Paleozoic is seldom difficult. But how may we separate the Proterozoic rocks from the Archeozoic? Fossils afford us no aid whatever, because no characteristic fossils have been found in rocks as old even as the earlier Proterozoic. The two great groups of very ancient rocks do, however, show a number of differences which must be considered together. Thus, igneous rocks distinctly predominate in the Archeozoic, while stratified rocks predominate in the Proterozoic. All Archeozoic strata are thoroughly metamorphosed (changed from their original condition), while large masses of the Proterozoic strata are only moderately metamorphosed, or even unaltered, and therefore look much like ordinary strata of later ages. Archeozoic rocks have almost invariably been notably deformed by more or less folding, tilting, etc., while the Proterozoic rocks show relatively much less deformation. Another important criterion is the fact that the Proterozoic rocks, wherever they have been studied in relation to the Archeozoic rocks, always rest upon a profoundly eroded surface of the latter, that is, an unconformity separates the two great sets of rocks. This erosion surface is of still further interest because it is one of oldest known, only one having been recognized within the Archeozoic group itself. Even where the Proterozoic strata have been considerably metamorphosed and deformed, this old erosion surface may be recognized, and if the rocks below that surface possess the characteristics of the Archeozoic rocks as described above, the two great very ancient rock groups may be distinguished. One of the triumphs of geology during the last 25 to 30 years has been the recognition of the great rock group (Proterozoic) between the Archeozoic and Paleozoic, thus bringing to light the records of an era which lasted many millions of years.

The length of time represented by the Proterozoic era is by many believed to have been fully as long as all succeeding eras—Paleozoic, Mesozoic, and Cenozoic—combined. Five hundred millions years is a conservative estimate for the duration of the era. What is the nature of the evidence as recorded in the rocks which lead us to conclude that the Proterozoic era lasted such a vast length of time? The great thickness of Proterozoic strata (over 30,-000 feet in the Lake Superior region), in the light of what we have already learned regarding the present rate of wear (erosion) of lands and deposition of the eroded materials under ordinary conditions, clearly implies millions of years of time for their accumulation. But the Proterozoic strata as we now see them are in most places not a continuous pile, that is they were not laid down layer upon layer without notable interruption. Thus, the thick Proterozoic group of the Lake Superior region has been divided into four distinct, mainly sedimentary series separated from each other by erosion surfaces (unconformities). Each erosion surface represents a long time when the area was elevated and underwent profound wear before the next series of strata accumulated on the worn surface. That such times of erosion were geologically long is proved not only by the profound alteration (metamorphism) of one set of strata before another accumulated, but also by the fact that granite, which, as we have learned, is never exposed except where much overlying material has been eroded, actually formed parts of surfaces of earlier Proterozoic rocks upon which later ones were deposited. In the Lake Superior region there are not only three great erosion surfaces (unconformities) within the Proterozoic group, but also one at the base separating it as a whole from the Archeozoic group, and another at the top separating it from the Paleozoic group. It is, therefore, fair to conclude that the amount of time (millions of years) represented by these great erosion intervals was fully as great as the time needed for deposition of the existing Proterozoic strata.

In the Lake Superior region the older Proterozoic strata are nearly all more or less folded and altered (metamorphosed), and they have been intruded by considerable bodies of molten rock, mostly granite. The later Proterozoic strata have been much less deformed and in many cases they are practically unaltered. In this region a very remarkable event took place in late Proterozoic time. This was volcanic activity on a grand scale. We may gain some idea of the stupendous and long-continued volcanic outpourings from the fact that, based upon actual measurements of thickness, lava sheets, averaging about 100 feet thick, poured out one upon another until a pile about six miles high had accumulated.

In parts of the Grand Canyon of the Colorado tilted Proterozoic strata may be seen resting upon the profoundly eroded surface of the Archeozoic rocks of the inner gorge. The Proterozoic strata, 12,000 feet thick, consist of practically unaltered sandstones, shales, and limestones, associated with some layers of basaltic lava. An erosion surface (unconformity) separates the whole group into two distinct series, and the group is separated from the overlying nearly horizontal Paleozoic (Cambrian) strata in the walls of the Canyon by another erosion surface.

More recently the Proterozoic strata so finely displayed in the Rocky Mountains of Montana and southern Canada have been studied. These strata, at least two or three miles thick, are mostly unaltered sandstones, shales, and limestones, associated with some metamorphic and igneous rocks. As usual, these strata rest upon the eroded Archeozoic. They were more or less upturned and folded before deposition of the succeeding Paleozoic strata. Satisfactory subdivisions have not yet been worked out.

In North America most of the areas shown on the accompanying map contain more or less Proterozoic rocks. Rocks of this age are known to some extent in all continents where their general relationships seem to be much like those of North America. They have perhaps been most carefully studied in Scandinavia and the Highlands of Scotland, where the strata portions are about two miles thick.

The climate of Proterozoic time must, for most part, have been about like that of to-day except, of course, for its much greater uniformity over the earth. About a dozen years ago very typical glacial deposits were discovered within the early Proterozoic rocks of western Ontario, Canada. A climatic condition favorable for the development of glaciers so early in the history of the earth is, to say the least, directly opposed to an idea (based upon the nebular hypothesis) long held that the climate of early geologic time must have been much warmer than that of the present.

CHAPTER XIV

ANCIENT EARTH HISTORY
(*Paleozoic Era*)

BEGINNING with the earliest Paleozoic, the legible records of events of earth history are far more abundant and less defaced than those of earlier times. Stratified rocks of the ordinary kinds greatly predominate over the igneous and metamorphic rocks, and the strata are in general far less disturbed than those of the Archeozoic and Proterozoic groups. From the earliest Paleozoic we have also the first abundant records (fossils) of the life of the earth, so that the ordinary methods of subdividing and determining the relative ages of the Paleozoic and later strata, as well as correlating the subdivisions (formations) in widely separated regions, can be used. From here on in our discussion of earth history we shall be able to trace the salient features of the changing outlines of the face of the earth, the coming and going of the seas over the lands, and the evolution of animals and plants with a considerable degree of definiteness and satisfaction.

First, we shall trace out, in the regular order of their occurrence, the main physical history events of Paleozoic time, leaving a consideration of the evolution of life for other chapters. Because of limitation of space, our attention will be almost wholly centered upon the continent of North America, but the reader should bear in mind that the general principles and facts set forth apply with about equal force to most other continents. In Europe the wonderful records of Paleozoic history are found in strata, whose estimated maximum thickness is about 100,000 feet! It must not be thought, however, that all these strata are piled up in a single locality, but the figure does actually represent the sum total of the greatest thickness of the many subdivisions (formations) of the Paleozoic rocks in different portions of the continent. In North America the maximum thickness of all Paleozoic rocks seems to be no less than 50,000 feet. More than 25,000 feet of strata may actually be observed piled layer upon layer in the highly folded and deeply eroded central Appalachian Mountains. The great thickness of the strata, combined with the facts that the fossils show that many marvelous, mostly progressive, changes took place among living things, that seas came and went repeatedly over many parts of the continent, and that great changes took place in the configuration of the land, force us to conclude that Paleozoic time must have lasted for many millions of years.

Just before the opening of the Paleozoic era practically all of North America appears to have been dry land, which had undergone so much erosion that it was low and far less rugged in relief than at present. This we know, because the rather widespread early Paleozoic (Cambrian) strata almost everywhere rest upon deeply eroded rocks of either Archeozoic or Proterozoic age. Considering both the time involved and the wide area affected, we have no record of anything like such a profound erosion interval since the beginning of the Paleozoic era. It seems that the constructive or upbuilding forces within the earth were then remarkably quiescent, while the destructive forces (erosion) were almost unhampered in their work of cutting down the land.

Have we any definite idea of the relations of land and water in North America during the first or Cambrian period of the Paleozoic era? In the affirmative answer to this question, certain principles will be brought out which the reader should keep in mind as we trace out the succeeding great physical changes in the history of North America. It should, however, be remembered that, in the brief space at our disposal, only the most general, or the most significant localized, physical changes in the long and intricate known history of the continent since the opening of the Paleozoic era can be brought out.

In early Cambrian time a narrow arm of the sea (like a strait) extended from the Gulf of St. Lawrence southward across eastern New York and over the site of the present Appalachian Mountains connecting with the Gulf of Mexico on the south. On the west, a much larger and broader arm of the sea (like a mediterranean) extended from Alaska southward over the site of the Rocky Mountains of Canada and across the sites of the Columbia Plateau to Great Basin of the western United States. All the rest of the continent was land, apparently almost or wholly devoid of high mountains.

By what process of reasoning do we conclude that arms of the early Cambrian sea reached across eastern and western North America? First, wherever marine strata of definitely determined early Cambrian age now occur, the early Cambrian sea must have existed because those strata were obviously deposited in that sea. Second, to those areas we must add others from which it can be demonstrated that early Cambrian marine strata have been removed by erosion. Enough field work along these lines has been done in North America to render it practically

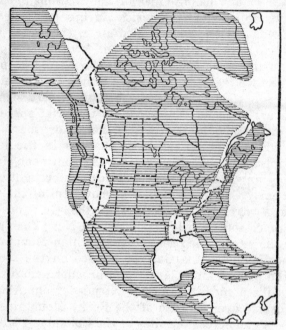

Fig. 33.—Map showing the relations of land and water in North America during early Cambrian time, about 500,000,000 years ago. Lined areas represent land. (Principal data from a map by Willis published in the Journal of Geology.)

certain that the relations of land and water during early Cambrian time were essentially as above outlined.

As Cambrian time went on, the marine waters gradually spread from south to north across most of the Mississippi Valley area, causing the eastern and western arms of the sea to be connected, thus forming an interior continental sea. Otherwise the relations of land and water were much as in early Cambrian time. We know that the sea transgressed northward across the Mississippi Valley district for

FIG. 34.—Map showing the relations of land and water in North America during Middle Ordovician time. Lined areas represent land. (Principal data from a map published by Willis in the Journal of Geology.)

the reason that, on the south, the whole upper Cambrian system of strata is present, while, farther north, only the younger upper Cambrian are to be found, and, farthest north, only the latest Cambrian strata occur. This progressive northward overlap of younger and younger (later) Cambrian strata upon the old rock floor proves, that the Cambrian sea steadily spread farther and farther northward over the Mississippi Valley area. That this spreading sea was shallow is amply demonstrated by the deposits it left, such as shales, conglomerates (i. e., consolidated gravels) and sandstones, often ripple-marked. The Cambrian strata of North America vary in thickness from less than 1,000 feet to about 12,000 feet.

In the Mississippi Valley the Cambrian strata are unaltered and almost undisturbed from their original horizontal position. In the Appalachian Mountains of the east, and the Rocky Mountains of the west, these strata are generally much folded and faulted. In some places, as in western New England, the strata have been notably altered (metamorphosed).

The best estimates for the duration of the Cambrian period range from 30,000,000 to 40,000,000 years. It is a remarkable fact that, during this great lapse of time, North America was unaffected by any great physical disturbances such as mountain making, emergence of large tracts of land, or igneous activity. The great physical event of the late Cambrian was the submergence of a large part of the continent. All was land at the end of the period.

The climate of the earliest Cambrian or latest Proterozoic was favorable for the existence of glaciers, as proved by the occurrences of true glacial deposits in rocks of that age in China, Norway, and Australia. It is a remarkable fact that the glacial materials of China occur along the Yangtse River, thus demonstrating that conditions for glaciers then existed at a latitude as far south as New Orleans. These evidences of glaciation directly refute the old idea, based upon the nebular hypothesis, that the climate of the Paleozoic was distinctly warmer than now. The glacial evidence, added to our knowledge of the character and world-wide distribution of many identical species of animals, leads us to conclude that early Paleozoic climate was not essentially different from that of very recent geologic time, but that the climate was then much more uniform than at present.

In earlier Ordovician time, a condition of considerable flooding gave way to an emergent condition. Then followed a widespread submergence climaxing toward the middle of the period when fully four-fifths of the continent was submerged under shallow sea water. Since middle Ordovician marine strata are more widespread than the rocks of any succeeding age, we can be reasonably sure that so much of the continent was never again covered by the sea. In fact, so far as the records have been interpreted, this came nearest to being a universal flood in the whole known history of the continent. By the very character of the rocks deposited (seldom over a few thousand feet thick), we can be sure that the middle Ordovician continental sea was everywhere far shallower than the great ocean abysses of to-day. Because the lands were so low and restricted, relatively little land-derived sediment washed into the sea. But the shallow sea water was inhabited by millions of animals, the shells of many of which slowly accumulated to build up the thick bodies of limestone strata (Plate 21) which constitute the main bulk of rock of early and middle Ordovician age. The famous Trenton limestone, named from a locality in central New York, with its great abundance of fossils, was formed mostly by the accumulation of shells of animals during middle Ordovician time.

Later in the Ordovician there was a considerable withdrawal of much of the widespread sea. As a result of the generally more elevated lands, erosion proceeded more vigorously, and sands and muds were more abundantly deposited in the restricted sea. Still later, a flooded condition nearly as great as that of the middle Ordovician prevailed. At the close of this period, nearly the whole of North America was land.

A principle above briefly explained in the discussion of the Cambrian may be reëmphasized here. It is as follows: In making a map to show the relations of land and water, say during middle Ordovician time, the geologist is by no means dependent only upon actual surface exposures of middle Ordovician strata. Such exposures fall far short of giving an adequate conception of the former or even present real extent of such strata. In many places originally present Ordovician strata have been removed by erosion. An excellent case in point is the Adirondack region of northern New York. On the west side of the Adirondacks a great pile of marine Ordovician strata 1,500 feet thick end abruptly on the gently sloping flank of the mountains, thus clearly proving that the strata formerly extended at least twenty to thirty miles eastward. Again, in the southern Adirondacks a small area of very typical marine middle Ordovician strata lies fully fifteen miles from the general area of such rocks to the south. This small body of rock is very clearly only an erosion remnant of a general sheet of middle Ordovician rock which once covered the whole intervening district. In many other regions the

middle Ordovician strata are definitely known to be
concealed under cover of later rocks, as in the Mississippi Valley, where the actual surface exposures constitute only a fraction of the middle Ordovician strata
which underlie nearly all the valley, as proved by
deep well drillings, study of the scattering outcrops,
etc.   In still other places, middle Ordovician strata,
associated with other rocks, are highly folded, as in

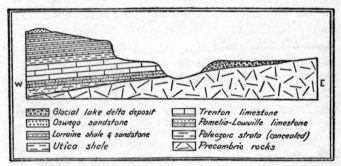

FIG. 35.—Structure section showing rocks representing three geologic
eras separated by millions of years of time.   Length of section 12
miles, vertical scale much exaggerated.   At the bottom are Archeozoic
(Precambric) rocks and resting upon them on the left are early Paleozoic strata 1,500 feet thick.   A glacial lake deposit of late Cenozoic
age lies on the Archeozoic rock toward the right.   It is evident that the
Paleozoic strata formerly extended much farther eastward.   (By the
author as published in a New York State Museum Bulletin.)

the Appalachians, where such strata outcrop in only
narrow belts following the trend of the folds.   In
short, then, wherever it can be proved that middle
Ordovician marine strata are visible at the surface,
or are concealed under other rocks, or were once
present, we can be sure that the middle Ordovician
sea existed.   Exactly this principle applies to any
subdivision of geologic time.

The Ordovician period closed with a great mountain-making disturbance in eastern North Amer-

ica, and at the same time all, or nearly all, of the continent was land. Throughout most of the Cambrian and Ordovician periods, the strata accumulated to a thickness of thousands of feet in the marine waters which spread over the eastern border of New York, the sites of the Green Mountains of Vermont, the Berkshire Hills of Massachusetts, and southward at least as far as Virginia, over the area of the Piedmont Plateau. At, or toward the close of the Ordovician period, a great compressive force in the earth's crust was brought to bear upon the mass of strata and they were tilted, highly folded, and raised above sea level into a great mountain range known to geologists as the Taconic Range. It is quite the rule throughout this region of Taconic disturbance to find the strata either on edge or making high angles with the plane of the horizon. Many of the folds were actually overturned, and in some cases notable thrust faults developed, that is, the upper strata broke across and great masses were shoved over each other. These facts all go to show that the mountain-making compressive force applied to the region was of rather an extreme type. Since the origin of the Taconic Range a tremendous amount of erosion has taken place, so that literally only the roots of the range are now exposed in the Green Mountains, Berkshire Hills, Highlands-of-the-Hudson, and the northern Piedmont Plateau.

How do we know that the Taconic disturbance took place toward the close of the Ordovician period? By way of answer to this question two facts need to be considered. First, relatively late (or young) Ordovician strata are involved with the folds, thus proving that the folds formed after those late Ordovician sediments were deposited. Second, undis-

FIG. 36.—Structure section showing profile and underground relations of the rocks across part of the Highlands-of-the-Hudson region in southeastern New York. Length of section, sixteen miles. The rocks are mostly of Prepaleozoic Age, but with belts of highly infolded early Paleozoic strata toward the middle right. (After Berkey, New York Museum Report.)

turbed strata formed during the middle of the next (Silurian) period, rest upon the eroded edges of the folds, which proves that the folds must have developed well before middle Silurian time because the only time they were subjected to erosion must have been during early Silurian time.

Mention should also be made of the profound metamorphism (alteration) of the Cambrian and Ordovician strata along the main axis of the range, where the intense compression, aided by heat and moisture, caused the deeply buried portions of the strata to become plastic, and hence they became more or less foliated (cleavable) and crystallized into various metamorphic rock types, the limestone having changed to marble, the shale to slate or schist, and the sandstone to quartzite. Thus we explain the rocks of the extensive marble quarries of Vermont and western Massachusetts, the slate quarries of central eastern New York, and the Berkshire schist of the Berkshire Hills of Massachusetts.

One of the grandest and most significant of all the profound geological processes is the birth and history of a great folded mountain range. Since the Taconic Range affords us such an excellent example of a large-scale, well-understood folded range of great antiquity we may do well to consider it in the light of certain other broad relationships. The great compressive force which folded and upraised the Taconic Mountains did not accomplish its work rapidly in the ordinary human history sense of the word. The force was slowly and irresistibly applied, and the strata well below the surface were gradually bulged or folded, or fractured where near the surface, the length of time required for the operation having been, at the very least calculation, some hundreds of thousands of years, and more than likely a million years or more. Such a length of time is, however, so short compared with all known earth history, that we are accustomed to refer to the formation of such a mountain range as simply an event of geological history.

Even before such a range attains its maximum height a very considerable amount of erosion has already taken place. When the first fold appears above sea level, erosion begins its work and continues with increasing vigor as the mountain masses get higher and higher. Thus we have warfare between two great natural processes—the building up and the tearing down. After a time the building-up process wanes and then ceases, while the tearing-down process (erosion) continues either until the whole range has been completely worn down or until some rejuvenating force causes a renewed uplift.

Here is an example of one of the remarkable procedures of nature. After millions of years of work causing the deposition of thousands of feet of strata, piled layer upon layer on the sea floor, a force of lateral pressure is brought to bear and a mountain range is literally born out of the sea. No sooner is the range well formed than the destructive processes (erosion) unceasingly set to work to destroy this marvelous work. But the sediments derived from the wear of the range are carried into the nearest ocean again to accumulate and, perchance, after long ages, to be raised into another range; and so the process may be often repeated. From this we learn that the mountain ranges of the earth are by no means all of the same age. The original Adirondacks were formed long before the Taconics, which originated millions of years before the Appalachians. These last were folded up long before the Sierra Nevada. The Rockies, followed by the Coast Ranges, are each younger than the Sierras as regards their original folding and uplift. Among foreign countries special mention should be made of the British Isles, where Ordovician strata thousands of feet thick were, late in the period, notably folded and upraised, the crustal disturbance having been accompanied by great intrusions of molten rocks and vast outpourings of lavas, so that this region ranks among the greatest of the ancient volcanic areas of Europe.

We shall now turn our attention to a very brief consideration of the salient points in the physical history of North America during the next great period (Silurian) of the Paleozoic era. As a result of the physical disturbance late in the Ordovician the great interior sea was largely or wholly

expelled from the continent, and this was essentially the condition of the continent at the beginning
of the Silurian. Then there began a series of three
great advances and retreats of the sea, much as in
the Ordovician. The greatest of these seas reached

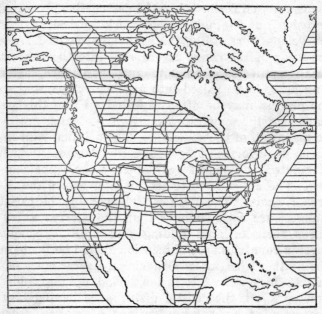

FIG. 37.—General relations of land and water in North America dur-
ing middle and late middle Devonian time, about 350,000,000 years ago.
Lined areas represent water. (From the author's ''Introduction to
Historical Geology.'' Courtesy of D. Van Nostrand Company.)

a climax in about the middle of the period. At this
time the famous and extensive Niagara limestone,
so named from the rock at the crest of Niagara
Falls, was deposited. Except for the newly formed
Taconic Range, standing out as a bold topographic
feature along the middle Atlantic Coast and a

PLATE 13.—(a) PART OF THE MAMMOTH HOT SPRINGS TERRACE IN THE YELLOWSTONE PARK. The view shows the deposit with boiling water flowing over it. The water enters the earth back on the mountain, travels underground in contact with hot lava, rises through limestone, from which the boiling water takes into solution much carbonate of lime which is deposited when the water reaches the surface. (*Photo by Jackson, U. S. Geological Survey.*)

PLATE 13.—(b) VIEW ACROSS PART OF CRATER LAKE, OREGON. This great hole, 3,000 to 4,000 feet deep and 6 miles in diameter and now partly filled with a lake 2,000 feet deep, was formed by a subsidence of the top of a once great cone-shaped volcano fully 14,000 feet high above the sea. The high rock in the distance rises 2,000 feet above the lake which is over 6,000 feet above sea level. The island is a small volcano of recent origin. (*Photo by Russell, U. S. Geological Survey.*)

PLATE 14.—(a) DETAILED VIEW OF PART OF THE VERY OLDEST KNOWN
(ARCHEOZOIC) ROCK FORMATION OF THE EARTH. The rock is distinctly
stratified and represents sands and muds deposited layer upon layer upon
a sea floor at least 50,000,000 years ago. The sands and muds first consolidated into sandstone and shale below the earth's surface. Then, under
conditions of heat, moisture, and pressure, they were notably altered,
mainly by crystallization of minerals, and raised high above sea level.
Finally the strata were laid bare by erosion. (*Photo by the author.*)

PLATE 14.—(b) A TWISTED MASS OF STRATIFIED ARCHEOZOIC LIMESTONE
SURROUNDED BY GRANITE IN NORTHERN NEW YORK. The limestone was
enveloped in the granite while it was being forced in molten condition
into the earth's crust. (*Photo by the author.*)

somewhat wider extent of land, the condition of the continent during middle Silurian time was very similar to that of middle Ordovician time.

Soon after mid-Silurian time the seas became greatly restricted almost to disappearance as such.

FIG. 38.—General relations of land and water in North America during earlier Mississippian time. Lined areas represent water. (From the author's "Introduction to Historical Geology." Courtesy of D. Van Nostrand Company.)

In the eastern United States and southeastern Canada early upper Silurian strata are found only in parts of Ontario, New York, Ohio, Michigan, and from Pennsylvania southward to West Virginia, where they are characterized by red shales and sandstones, and salt and gypsum deposits. Such materials containing few fossils very clearly indicate deposition in either extensive lagoons or more or less cut-off arms of the sea under arid climate conditions rather than in ordinary marine water.

Still later in the Silurian the interior seas were partially restored, as shown by the fact that true marine strata corresponding to that age not only cover the salt and gypsum deposits, but are notably more extensive than they. About the close of the Silurian period almost all of the continent was dry land.

Unlike the Ordovician period, the Silurian closed without any mountain-making disturbance or great uplift of land. The Silurian period, like the preceding Ordovician and Cambrian, seems to have been free from any more than slight igneous activity as, for example, in Maine and New Brunswick. The total thickness of Silurian strata in North America is seldom more than a few thousand feet.

The salient features of the physical history of the next, or Devonian period, are much like those of the preceding Silurian. At the beginning of the Devonian almost all of the continent was dry land, but soon a long, narrow arm of the sea extended across the eastern side of the continent from the Gulf of St. Lawrence southward through western New England, southeastern New York and throughout the Appalachian district, thus reminding us of the long, narrow sound which occupied almost exactly the same territory during the early part of the Cambrian period. In the west the only water was a small embayment reaching across southern California into Nevada. By middle Devonian time these water areas had considerably expanded. During late middle Devonian time the sea was so expanded as to cover much of the Mississippi Valley area, the Appalachian Mountains and St. Lawrence Valley areas, and most of the site of the Rocky Mountains, except for an island of considerable size reaching from New Mexico through Wyoming. The main lands were most of northeastern North America, a large land area extending from Florida to Nova Scotia, and a large area on the western side of the continent from California to Alaska.

A remarkable formation of late Devonian Age should be briefly described. In southeastern New York and the northern Appalachian region there was a tremendous accumulation of sediments which have consolidated into sandstone, together with some shale and conglomerate. This so-called "Catskill" formation is from 1,500 to 8,000 feet thick and is well shown as the main body of rock in the Catskill Mountains. It is largely a shallow-water deposit of essentially nonmarine origin, as proved by coarseness of material, ripple marks, and nonmarine fossils. All evidence points to the origin of this remarkable formation as a great delta deposit built out into the shallow interior sea. Notable thinning toward the west, with increasing fineness of grain of material, shows that the sediment came from the east, no doubt carried by a large river from the small continental land mass (called "Appalachia") on the eastern side of North America.

The maximum thickness of the North American Devonian seems to be about 15,000 feet in the northern Appalachian region, but elsewhere it generally ranges from 1,000 to 4,000 feet thick. In North America the subdivisions of the Devonian strata of New York are taken as a standard for comparison, both because of the wonderful completeness and almost undisturbed character of the rocks there, and because they have been so carefully studied. The Devonian system is there fully 4,000 feet thick, with scarcely a minor subdivision missing, and it covers a wide area (one-third of the State) with many excellent outcrops. There was practically uninterrupted deposition of Devonian strata in southern New York. It is doubtful if there is greater refinement of knowledge regarding the Devonian or any other Paleozoic system of strata anywhere else in North America.

During middle to late Devonian time the region from southern New England to Nova Scotia and the St. Lawrence Valley was notably disturbed by earth movements, the lands having been considerably elevated and the rocks more or less folded. The great delta deposit of late Devonian time, already described as being thousands of feet thick in New York and Pennsylvania, was formed by one or more streams which carved much sediment from the newly upraised lands. Accompanying the uplift and folding of the rocks considerable masses of molten granite were forced into the earth's crust and some molten rock was forced to the surface, producing volcanoes. Much of the granite may now be seen at the surface in various portions of the region, while deeply eroded volcanoes occur near the city of Montreal.

Except for the disturbance of the region extending from New England to the St. Lawrence, the Devonian period seems to have closed rather quietly, but with a very widespread withdrawal of the sea from the land. This is proved by the fact that the early strata of the next period mostly rest upon the eroded surfaces of late Devonian strata.

For many years the term "Carboniferous" period was used to designate a single period of geologic time which, in America at least, is now divided into two periods—the Mississippian and Pennsylvanian —corresponding, respectively, to the earlier and later Carboniferous. In regard to the relations of land and water during the Mississippian period, the general statement may be made that the continent, all land at the beginning of the period, became one-third flooded before the middle of the period, as shown by Figure 38, after which the waters largely withdrew from the land, only to be largely restored in the latter part of the period.

A significant physical change marked the close of the Mississippian. This was the withdrawal of sea water from nearly all of the continent, the emergence of the land having been generally sufficient to allow considerable erosion. The fact that the Mississippian and the next, or Pennsylvanian, strata are separated by the most extensive distinct erosion surface in the whole Paleozoic group of rocks is good reason for considering those two sets of strata to have formed during separate periods of geologic time. Mountains were formed in the regions which now comprise Arkansas and Oklahoma.

In eastern North America the Mississippian strata vary in thickness from a few hundred feet to a maximum of about 5,000 feet in eastern Pennsylvania. In the West, where the thickness is commonly several thousand feet, limestone greatly predominates. There appears to have been vigorous volcanic activity during the period from northern California to Alaska.

Certain profound crustal disturbances marked the close of the period in western Europe, resulting in

upturning and folding of rocks during the process
of mountain forming from Ireland to Germany,
and from Bohemia to southern France. Abundant
intrusions and extrusions of molten rocks accompanied the disturbances.

We turn next to a consideration of the Pennsylvanian period, which is of very special interest, because within the rocks of that age in North America,
Europe, and China occur the greatest known coal
deposits. The period opened with almost all of
North America dry land undergoing more or less
erosion. Early in Pennsylvanian time marine water
began to overspread part of the eastern side of the
United States. Then the water more or less progres-
sively spread westward over the western states and
northwestward over the greater part of Alaska.
Fully one-third of the continent was then flooded by
the sea as shown by Figure 39. Volcanoes were
active along the west coast.

Over the site of the Appalachians and most of the
eastern half of the Mississippi Valley area the land
either stood near sea level and was often swampy or
marshy, or at other times it was a little below sea
level, allowing tidewater to overspread the area.
Such conditions alternated repeatedly, usually more
or less locally, over different parts of the districts in
which the great coal mines of the east are located.
Under such conditions strata from 1,000 to 8,000
feet thick accumulated. Remarkable physical geography of this kind resulted in the growth and
accumulation of vast quantities of vegetable matter
which has changed into the world's greatest coal
beds. Similar conditions prevailed over parts of
Nova Scotia, New Brunswick, and Rhode Island,
where strata fully 13,000 feet thick accumulated.

"Perhaps the most perfect resemblance to coal-forming condition is that now found on such coastal plains as that of southern Florida and the Dismal Swamps of Virginia and North Carolina. Both of these areas are very level, though with slight depressions in which there is either standing water or swamp condition. In both regions there is such general interference with free drainage that there are extensive areas of swamp, and in both there are beds of vegetable accumulations. In each of these areas there is a general absence of sediment and therefore a marked variety of vegetable deposit. If either of these areas were submerged beneath the sea, the vegetable remains would be buried and a further step made toward the formation of a coal bed. Reelevation, making a coastal plain, would permit the accumulation of another coal bed above the first, and this process might be continued again and again." (H. Ries.) But it is not necessary to assume repeated oscillations of a swamp area up and down as the only way of accounting for a succession of coal beds one above another in a given region, because a general, but intermittent, subsidence, with possibly some upward movements, would occasionally cause the prolific plant life of a swamp to be killed, after which sediment would deposit over the site. Shoaling of water by accumulation of sediment would permit the development of more swamp plant life.

In most coal-mining districts there are at least several coal beds, one above another. In Illinois there are nine; in Pennsylvania at least twenty; in Alabama, thirty-five; and in Nova Scotia seventy-six, but not all are important commercially. Each coal bed in such a region represents a swamp which existed in Pennsylvanian time at least ten or twelve million years ago, and in which there grew a luxuriant vegetation. Many individual swamps of that time were of wide extent. The famous Pittsburgh

Fig. 39.—Map showing the general relations of land and water in North America during the middle and late Pennsylvanian period, at least 250,000,000 years ago. Lined areas represent water. (From the author's "Introduction to Historical Geology." Courtesy of D. Van Nostrand Company.)

bituminous coal bed represents probably the largest one of all. It extends from western Pennsylvania into parts of Ohio and West Virginia over an area of fully 15,000 square miles. More than 6,000 square miles of it are being worked and the coal bed averages seven feet in thickness over an area of 2,000 square miles. Among the various anthracite coal beds of the same age in eastern Pennsylvania the Mammoth bed is exceptionally thick, reaching a maximum of fifty feet or more.

In order that the reader may not gain the impression that coal beds make up a very considerable bulk of the strata in coal-mining regions, we should state that, on the average, coal actually constitutes less than 2 per cent of the containing strata.

Some idea of the tremendous length of the geologic ages may be gained by a consideration of the time which must reasonably be allowed for the accumulation of so many coal beds and their containing strata. It has been estimated that a luxuriant growth of vegetation would produce 100 tons of dried organic matter per hundred years. Compressed to the specific gravity of coal (1.4) this would form a layer less than two-thirds of an inch deep on an acre. During the chemical alteration of vegetable matter to coal about four-fifths of the organic matter disappears in the form of gases. On this basis, then, it would take about 10,000 years to accumulate the vegetable matter represented in a coal bed one foot thick. When we realize that the total thickness of the coal beds of the Pennsylvanian system of strata in the great mining regions is commonly from 100 to 250 feet, we conclude that the time they represent is from 1,000,000 to 2,500,000 years. It seems most reasonable that the time necessary for the deposition of the containing strata must have been much longer. It is, therefore, a fair conclusion that the Pennsylvania period lasted many millions of years.

That the climate of the great Coal Age was warm (not tropical), very moist, and uniform, is borne out by such facts as the following, according to D. White: The succulent nature of the plants with their spongy leaves indicates prolific growth in moist, mild climate; lack of yearly rings of growth points to lack of distinct seasons; as in the case of many existing plants the aerial roots signify a warm, moist climate; plants of to-day nearest like the coal plants thrive best in warm, moist regions; vegetable matter at present accumulates best in temperate rather than tropical climates, because there decay is not so rapid; and the remarkable uniformity of climate over the earth is clearly indicated by finding fossil plants of almost or exactly identical types in rocks of Pennsylvanian Age from the Polar regions to the Tropics. The more remarkable plants of the great Coal Age time are described in the chapter on the evolution of plants (Plate 19a).

During the last (Permian) period of the Paleozoic era the marine waters of the west, and the alternating shallow tidewater, swamps, and near sea level lands of the east gradually gave way to dry lands, so that by the close of the period marine water covered only a small part of the Southwest from Oklahoma across central Texas to southern California and northwestern Mexico, where strata as much as several thousand feet thick formed. In the middle western part of the area of the United States, especially from northern Texas to Nebraska and Wyoming, the climate was arid and red strata (so-called "Red Beds"), salt, and gypsum were extensively deposited on land and in great salt lakes or more or less cut-off arms of the sea. Strata commonly from 2,000 to 7,000 feet thick were there de-

posited. Similar conditions prevailed in parts of
Nova Scotia, New Brunswick, and Newfoundland,
where strata 8,000 feet thick accumulated. Over
the site of most of the Appalachians the coal swamp
conditions, with local sea incursions, continued from
the preceding period, as shown by the character of
the strata (1,000 feet thick) containing some coal.

Vigorous volcanic activity which, as already mentioned, began in the Mississippian period from northern California to Alaska continued not only through
the Pennsylvanian and Permian but also into the
early Mesozoic era, as shown by the great quantities of volcanic materials associated with rocks of
those ages.

The Permian presents a puzzling combination of
climatic conditions which causes it to stand out
in marked contrast against the generally mild and
uniform climates of nearly all of preceding Paleozoic time. Most remarkable of all are the records
of a great Ice Age during early Permian time. One
surprising fact is the widespread distribution of the
glacial deposits in both the north and south temperate zones, and even well within the torrid zone.
They are perhaps most extensive and best known
in Australia, South Africa, India, and Brazil. Glacial
deposits almost certainly of the same age on smaller
scales occur in eastern Massachusetts, southern England, eastern Russia and the Caucasus region. Although the areas occupied by the Permian glaciers,
which in many cases must have been extensive ice
sheets, cannot be accurately delimited, it is, nevertheless, quite certain that the ice was notably more
extensively developed than it was during the great
"Ice Age" of late (Quaternary) geologic time.
Another surprising fact is that certain of the

glaciers must have come down to, or nearly to, sea level, as shown by the direct association of marine strata with glacial deposits. Thus, in southern Australia at least eight beds of glacial materials (some of them 100 to 200 feet thick) occur within true marine strata 2,000 feet thick. A third remarkable fact is that the Permian Ice Age, like the Quaternary Ice Age, had interglacial epochs of relatively mild climate, as proved by the occurrences of beds of coal between certain of the layers of glacial materials in Australia, South Africa, and Brazil.

During much of Permian time the climate was arid over large areas as, for example, much of the western interior of the United States, from Ireland to central Germany, and in eastern Russia, as proved by great deposits of salt, gypsum, and red sediments. During late Permian time the greatest salt beds in the world were deposited in northern Germany, a well near Berlin having penetrated a practically solid body of salt associated with certain potash and magnesia salts to a depth of about 4,000 feet without reaching the bottom.

The occurrence of some coal beds, especially in the earlier Permian rocks shows that, temporarily at least, climatic conditions must have favored luxurious growths of coal-forming plants in South Africa, Brazil, Australia, and our own Appalachian district.

From the above facts we see that the Permian represents a remarkable combination of very extensive glaciation, widespread aridity, and warmth and moisture favorable to prolific plant growth all in a single period of geologic time.

The Permian period, and, therefore, the great Paleozoic era, was brought to a close by one of the most profound physical disturbances in the known history of North America. This has been called the Appalachian Revolution because at that time the Appalachian Mountain range was born out of the sea by folding and upheaval of the strata. In fact, "the Appalachian Revolution was one of the most critical periods in the history of the earth, and may have been the greatest of them all in its results." (C. Schuchert). Mountains were brought forth in all the continents, including Australia. All of the mountains which were formed late in the Paleozoic have since been profoundly affected by erosion, and the only ones (e. g., Appalachians) which now show considerable altitudes are those which have been rejuvenated by relatively (geologically) recent earth movements.

We shall now turn our attention to the origin of the Appalachian Range. All through the vast time (probably about 300,000,000 years) of the Paleozoic era a large land mass was remarkably persistent along the eastern side of North America. This land, which has been called "Appalachia," had its western boundary approximately along the eastern border of the sites of the Appalachian Range and the western part of New England. It extended east of the present coast line at least to the border of the continental shelf from 100 to 200 miles out. Concerning the actual altitude and topography of Appalachia we know little or nothing, but the tremendous quantities of sediment derived from its erosion show that it was high enough during nearly all of its history to undergo vigorous erosion.

Barring certain minor oscillations of level, the region just west of Appalachia was mostly occupied by sea water throughout much of Paleozoic time, and sediments derived from the erosion of Appalachia were laid down layer upon layer as strata upon that sea bottom. In general, the coarsest and greatest thickness of sediments accumulated relatively near the land, while finer materials, in thinner sheets, deposited well out over much of the eastern Mississippi Valley area in the shallow seas which were there so commonly present. By actual measurement we know that the thickness of strata deposited over the site of the Appalachians was at least 25,000 feet. Since these latter strata are mostly of comparatively shallow sea-water origin, as proved by coarseness of grain of material, ripple marks, fossil coral reefs, etc., we are forced to conclude that this marginal sea bottom gradually sank while the process of sedimentation was in progress. Otherwise we cannot possibly explain the great pile of strata of shallow water origin. The very weight of accumulating strata may either have aided or actually caused the sinking of the long, relatively narrow trough.

Finally, toward the close of the Paleozoic era, sinking of the marginal sea floor and deposition of sediments gave way to a yielding of the earth's crust by a great force of lateral compression, causing the strata to be thrown into folds well below the surface and more or less fractured in their upper portion. Thus, along the eastern side of the site of the great interior Paleozoic sea, the Appalachian Mountains rose out of what for millions of years had been a long, narrow, sinking sea floor. There was more or less folding from the Gulf of St. Lawrence to central Alabama. Figure 24 diagrammatically represents the principal stages in the history of the Appalachian Range.

While the most pronounced earth disturbance occurred through the long Appalachian belt, the whole eastern side of the continent was profoundly affected. Thus the Mississippi Valley area east of the Great Plains was considerably upraised never again to be submerged except along the Gulf Coast, and an eastern interior sea has never since overspread the region which was repeatedly sea-covered during Paleozoic time.

CHAPTER XV

MEDIEVAL EARTH HISTORY
(*Mesozoic Era*)

WHAT was the condition of North America during the first or Triassic period of the Mesozoic era, about 150 to 200 million years ago? As a result of the Appalachian Revolution the sea was excluded from all the land except along much of the western side from southern California to parts of Alaska. On this western side of the continent the Appalachian Revolution had little or no effect and the Permian conditions continued, essentially without change through the Triassic. The Triassic strata up to 4,000 feet thick are there of typical marine origin. In British Columbia and Alaska there was much igneous activity.

Throughout much of the Rocky Mountains and Great Plains region of the western United States there are extensive deposits of red sediments (so-called "Red Beds"), containing layers of salt and gypsum, from 200 to 1,000 or more feet thick. These strata commonly rest in regular order on Permian Red Beds, so that conditions of deposition of Permian time continued through Triassic time, that is continental deposits formed mostly in salt lakes, fresh lakes, along stream courses, and on land in part by the action of wind.

In the eastern half of North America there is no record of accumulation of any marine strata whatever, because, as a result of the Appalachian Revolution, the land was brought well above sea level. There was, however, deposition of a remarkable series of nonmarine strata in several long, narrow, troughlike depressions whose trend was parallel to, and just east of, the main axis of the newly formed

FIG. 40.—Map showing the general relations of land and water in North America during the late Triassic period. Lined areas represent water; cross-lined area, basin in which partly marine and partly continental deposits formed; and black areas, basins of continental deposition. (From the author's "Introduction to Historical Geology." Courtesy of D. Van Nostrand Company.)

Appalachian Range. These troughs lay between the Appalachians and the very persistent old land mass called Appalachia which we have already described. The facts that these troughs are structural basins; that they so perfectly follow the trend of the Appalachian Mountain folds; and that the strata in them are of late Triassic Age, make it certain that they were formed by great diastrophic forces which must have been a continuation of the Appalachian Revolution. Thus the Appalachian Mountains continued to grow well into the Triassic period, and, while the Paleozoic strata were being folded, the surface of the earth was first down-warped and then down-faulted and thus eventually there were formed the troughs in which the late Triassic strata accumulated. One trough extended through the Connecticut Valley; another (the largest) from southeastern New York through northern New Jersey, southeastern Pennsylvania, Maryland, and into Virginia; while several smaller ones occurred in Virginia and North Carolina.

The troughs, later modified by faulting, were favorably situated for rapid accumulation of thick sedimentary deposits because of their position just between large, high land masses which were being vigorously eroded. The sediments derived from the erosion of the young Appalachians were especially abundant because of the vigorous wearing down of the newly formed high mountains. A thickness of from 5,000 to fully 15,000 feet of mostly red sandstones and shales accumulated in these down-warps, the character and great thickness of the strata strongly pointing to gradual subsidence as the deposition of the sediments went on. It is often stated that these strata were formed in estuaries, but, in the northern areas, at least from Massachusetts to Maryland, many of the layers show ripple marks, sun cracks, rain-drop pits, fossil plants, and fossil bones and tracks of land reptiles. Such strata may well have formed in very shallow water, such

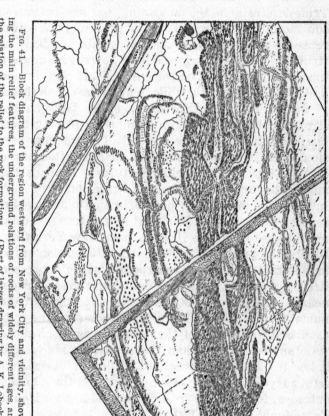

FIG. 41.—Block diagram of the region westward from New York City and vicinity, show-ing the main relief features, the underground relations of rocks of widely different ages, and the relation of the relief to the rock formations. (Part of larger drawing by A. K. Lobeck.)

as river-flood plains or temporary lakes, where changing conditions frequently allowed the surface layers to lie exposed to the sun.

During the time of the accumulation of the late Triassic strata in the subsiding basins there was considerable igneous activity, as proved by the occurrence of sheets of igneous rock within the body of strata. In some cases true lava flows with cindery tops were forced out on the surface and then buried under later sediments, while in other cases the sheets of molten rock were forced up either between the strata or obliquely through them, thus proving their intrusive character. As a result of subsequent erosion, these very resistant lava masses often stand out conspicuously as relief features. Perhaps the most noteworthy example is the great layer of such intrusive igneous rock, part of which outcrops for seventy miles mostly as a bold cliff forming the famous Palisades of the Hudson, near New York City. During the process of cooling and solidification of the molten mass there was contraction which expressed itself by breaking the rock mass into great, crude, nearly vertical columns, and hence the origin of the name "Palisades." The cliff character of the outcrop is due to the fact that the lava is much more resistant to erosion than the sandstone above and below it. In the Connecticut Valley of Massachusetts a layer of lava several hundred feet thick boldly outcrops, forming the crest of the well-known Mount Tom-Mount Holyoke Range.

The close of the Triassic period was marked by enough uplift to leave the whole eastern two-thirds of the continent dry land undergoing erosion. The Triassic deposits of the Atlantic Coast are much broken up into large fault blocks, and this fault-

Fig. 42.—Structure section showing profile and underground relations of rocks across the Connecticut Valley (through Mount Tom) of Massachusetts. Js and Jl are sandstone strata, with included lava sheets (in black) resting upon Paleozoic rocks on either side. The rocks have been notably tilted and faulted. (After Emerson, U. S. Geological Survey.)

ing probably took place as a result of the crustal disturbances toward the end of the period. In the west the Triassic conditions seem to have continued without much change into the next (or Jurassic) period.

During the Jurassic period the relations of land and water in North America were very simple. In the earlier Jurassic all was dry land except portions of the western fringe of the continent from southern California to Alaska, where marine strata 2,000 to 10,000 feet thick accumulated. Late in the period the conditions were the same, except for a long, narrow arm of the sea or mediterranean which extended from the Arctic Ocean southward across the site of the Rocky Mountains to Arizona. There is no evidence for the existence of anything like real mountains anywhere on the continent during the period.

Profound crustal disturbances marked the close of the Jurassic period in the western part of the continent. Strata which had accumulated to great thickness during millions of years of time, mainly over the sites of the Sierra Nevada and Cascade Mountains, finally yielded to a tremendous force of lateral compression, especially in the Sierra region, and were folded, crumpled, and upraised. Thus the Sierra-Cascade district was originally built up into a high mountain range. Since then, the Sierra Nevada has been much cut down by erosion and has also been rejuvenated by faulting and tilting of the great earth block. The Cascade Range from northern California into British Columbia was apparently not so profoundly raised, and its present height is mainly due to subsequent volcanic activity. The rocks of the Klamath Mountains of northwestern California were also folded at that time. There was tremendous submarine volcanic activity from California to Alaska.

During the mountain-making disturbances on the western side of the continent great quantities of molten granite were forced up into the lower portions of the folding strata. Because of profound subsequent erosion this granite is now widely exposed as, for example, in the great walls of the Yosemite Valley.

During the earlier half of the last period (the Cretaceous) of the Mesozoic era, sea water spread from Mississippi northwestward to the site of Denver and southward over Texas and much of Mexico. At the same time much of the western margin of the continent from Alaska to California was submerged. All the rest of the continent was land. During this time sediments accumulated on lowlands just east of the site of the present Rocky Mountains, and also east of the Appalachians, as proved by the numerous fossils of land plants found in these deposits.

As Cretaceous time went on the marine waters gradually spread until the whole Atlantic and Gulf coastal plain regions from Long Island, New York, to Mexico became submerged under marine water, and a wide arm of the sea, or great mediterranean, spread from Texas north to the mouth of the Mackenzie River. The Gulf of Mexico was thus directly connected with the Arctic Ocean. This great in-

FIG. 43.—Map showing general relations of land and water in North America during later Cretaceous time, several million years ago. Lined areas represent water. (From the author's "Introduction to Historical Geology." Courtesy of D. Van Nostrand Company.)

terior sea was nowhere connected with the Pacific Ocean, though portions of the Pacific border of the continent were submerged. This vast interior sea was not only the largest of any which reached well into the continent since the Mississippian period of the Paleozoic era, but it was the last body of marine water which ever extended well into the continent. It should be stated that the later Cretaceous was also a time of unusually widespread submergence of the continents, when most of southern Europe and southeastern Asia, as well as about one-half of both Africa and South America were submerged. Over much of the site of the Rocky Mountains during the late Cretaceous there were low lands receiving continental deposits, and extensive marshes supporting prolific vegetation were common. Much of this vegetable matter became buried, and has since been converted into workable coal.

The maximum thickness of strata accumulated during all of Cretaceous time over the Atlantic coastal plain area was about 1,700 feet; over the Gulf coastal plain region fully 7,500 feet; over the western interior 10,000 to 15,000; and over parts of the Pacific border 25,000 to 30,000 feet, as in California. The last-named figures are truly phenomenal, representing a thickness about equal to the total thickness of all the strata accumulated during the whole Paleozoic era (seven periods) and piled up in the Appalachian Mountain region. This great deposit of strata of mostly early Cretaceous Age is readily accounted for when we realize that these sediments, which accumulated in the marginal sea bottom, were derived from the very rapidly eroding, newly formed lofty Sierra Nevada Range.

Especially in Alabama and Texas the Cretaceous system is remarkable for its richness in chalk deposits. In Alabama a widespread formation of late Cretaceous Age, about 1,000 feet thick, contains much nearly pure white chalk, and in Texas a sim-

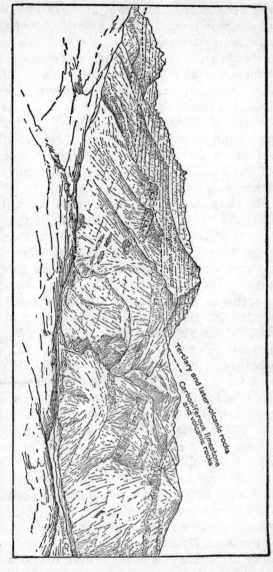

FIG. 44.—Sketch of a mountain range along Skolai Creek, Alaska, showing Tertiary lava beds resting upon deeply eroded tilted limestones and lavas of late Paleozoic (Carboniferous) Age. The present topography has been produced by erosion since the Tertiary lavas flowed out. (After U. S. Geological Survey.)

ilarly constituted formation of early middle Cretaceous Age is from 1,000 to 5,000 feet thick. These
chalk deposits consist almost wholly of carbonate
of lime shells or very tiny single-celled animals
which accumulated under exceptionally clear sea
water which spread over those parts of Alabama
and Texas where the chalk now occurs. Here again
we have a bit of evidence supporting the fact of
very long geologic time. Think of how long it must
have taken for the tiny (even microscopic) shells
to form a widespread layer of chalk nearly a mile
thick!

The close of the Cretaceous period, or what is the
same, the close of the Mesozoic era, was marked
by some of the grandest crustal disturbances in the
known history of the earth. In fact, it is not known
that the western hemisphere was ever affected by
more profound and widespread mountain-making
disturbances than those which took place toward
the close of the Mesozoic era, and continued into
the succeeding Tertiary period. These disturbances
were of three kinds: folding of strata, volcanic
activity, and renewed uplift of old mountains without folding of the rocks. Greatest of all was the
"Rocky Mountain Revolution," during which the
thick strata, which accumulated during the Paleozoic and Mesozoic eras over the site of the Rockies,
yielded to vigorous deformation when they were
more or less folded and dislocated from Alaska to
Central America. This was in truth the birth of
the Rocky Mountains, although their existing altitude and configuration have, to a very considerable
degree, resulted from later uplift and erosion. In
the northern United States and southern Canada the
Rocky Mountain strata, up to over 70,000 feet thick,

were most severely folded and fractured, forming a range which quite certainly was fully 20,000 feet high. In this district a great thrust fault, hundreds of miles long, developed, and rocks as old as the Proterozoic were shoved at least seven miles, and probably as much as twenty miles, westward, over Cretaceous and other rocks much later than the Proterozoic. At the same time the Andes Mountains throughout South America were notably upraised and the rocks folded.

The second type of physical disturbance was volcanic activity which took place on a tremendous scale, and which appears to have started as a direct accompaniment of the Rocky Mountain Revolution. This igneous activity took place not only in the Rocky Mountains but also westward to and in the Sierra-Cascade Range, as well as in the mountains of western British Columbia and Alaska. This activity continued well into the succeeding Cenozoic era, and it is more fully considered in the next chapter.

The third type of crustal disturbance took place on a large scale when the Appalachian Mountains, which had been almost wholly planed away by erosion during Mesozoic time, were reelevated from 1,000 to 3,000 feet by an uplifting force not accompanied by folding. All or nearly all of New York and New England, as well as much of southeastern Canada, were similarly upraised at the same time. This notable uplift of so much of eastern North America is a matter of great importance because the major relief features of that area have been produced by erosion or dissection of the upraised surface since late Mesozoic or early Cenozoic time. In view of the fact that this work of erosion took place almost wholly during the Cenozoic era, it will be discussed in the next chapter.

In conclusion, brief mention may be made of the kind of climate of the Mesozoic era. As shown by the character and distribution of fossil plants and animals, the Mesozoic climate was in general mild and rather uniform over the earth, but with some distinction of climatic zones. Such distinction of climatic zones is unknown for the Paleozoic era, while it was notably less than at present.

CHAPTER XVI

MODERN EARTH HISTORY
(*Cenozoic Era*)

SINCE the Cenozoic era is the last one of geologic time, it will be of particular interest to trace out the main events which have led up to the present day conditions, especially in North America. Both because of the recency of the time and the unusual accessibility of the rocks, which are mostly at or near the surface, our knowledge of the Cenozoic era is exceptionally detailed and accurate. It will, therefore, be more necessary than ever to select only the very significant features of this history for our brief discussion.

During the first half of the Tertiary period portions only of the Atlantic coastal plain were submerged under shallow water, but soon after the middle of the period (Miocene epoch) the sea spread over practically the whole Atlantic coastal plain area from Martha's Vineyard south to and including Florida. During the late Tertiary the marine waters had become greatly restricted, and by the close of the period the sea was entirely excluded from the Atlantic seaboard. The total thickness of these Tertiary strata is less than 1,000 feet, and they all tilt downward gently toward the sea. The strata consist mostly of unconsolidated sands, gravels, clays, marls, etc.

The Gulf coastal plain area from Florida through Texas and south through eastern Mexico was largely overspread by the sea during most of Tertiary time, except the latest. During early Tertiary time an arm of the Gulf reached north to the mouth of the Ohio River. Late in the period but little of the Gulf Plain was submerged, and at its close sea water was wholly excluded. On the Gulf Coast the Tertiary strata from 2,000 to 4,000 feet thick are also mainly sands, gravels, clays, and marls. They are commonly rich in fossils, and they show a gentle tilt downward toward the Gulf.

Throughout Tertiary time local portions of the Pacific border of the continent were submerged, this having been especially true of portions of California, Oregon, and Washington. In spite of the very restricted marine waters, the Tertiary strata of the Pacific Coast, especially in California, are remarkably thick, 10,000 to 20,000 feet being common, while the maximum thickness is fully 30,000 feet. Such great thicknesses are readily explained when we realize that erosion was notably speeded up by pronounced uplifts resulting from crustal disturbances toward the close of the preceding period, and again in the midst of the Tertiary period itself.

To summarize the Tertiary relations of sea and land for North America we may say that only local portions of the continental border ever became submerged, and that, by late Tertiary time, practically the whole continent was a land area. At the close of the period the continent was, as we shall see, even larger than now because the continental shelves of the ocean were then also largely above water.

The whole of the Cenozoic era, including both the
Tertiary and Quaternary periods, has been a time
of profound crustal disturbances throughout much
of the continent, certain of these movements having
continued right up to the present time, with positive

FIG. 45.—Map showing the general relations of land and water in
North America during part of the middle Tertiary period.   (After
Willis, courtesy of the Journal of Geology.)

evidence that some of them are still continuing.
These great movements have included notable foldings of strata, uplifts without folding, faulting, and
igneous activity, the whole effect having been to
greatly increase the general altitude and ruggedness
of the continent.   In fact, North America is not

known ever to have been at once higher, broader, and more rugged than it was very late in the Tertiary, or early in the Quaternary, period. Since that time the only notable change (barring the great Ice Age and its effects) has been a restriction of the area of the continent to its present size by spreading of sea waters over the borders of the continent, that is, over the continental shelves.

We shall now rather systematically consider the more profound earth changes which have affected the continent, producing the existing major relief features, from west to east.

The "Coast Range Revolution" began toward the end of the Tertiary period. Over the site of the Coast Ranges, strata had accumulated, especially during the Cretaceous and the Tertiary periods, to a thickness of thousands of feet. In Quaternary time these strata were subjected to a mountain-making force of compression and more or less folded, faulted (fractured), and uplifted into the Coast Range Mountains. Some portions of the range were intensely folded and faulted and up-raised many thousands of feet, while other portions were only moderately folded and uplifted. It is an interesting fact that the great San Francisco earthquake rift or fault originated at this time. It was a renewed, sudden movement of a few feet along this fault which caused the disastrous earthquake of 1906. Still other considerable earth movements took place in the Pacific Coast region during late Tertiary and Quaternary times. Excellent cases in point were the elevation of the fault-block mountains of southern California to heights of thousands of feet, as in the instances of the San Gabriel and the San Bernardino Ranges. A moderate amount of still later sub-

PLATE 15.—(*a*) A GENERAL VIEW ACROSS THE GRAND CANYON, ARIZONA. Most of the rocks are nearly horizontal strata of Paleozoic age. In the gorge toward the bottom there are Archeozoic rocks. (*Photo by courtesy of the U. S. Reclamation Service.*)

PLATE 15.—(*b*) A MOUNTAIN OF LAKE PALEOZOIC MARINE LIMESTONE. The nearly vertical strata show a thickness of fully 2,000 feet. Panamint Mountain, California. (*Photo by the author.*)

PLATE 16.—(a) GRANITE OF MESOZOIC AGE WEATHERING INTO GREAT ROUNDED MASSES. NEAR TWENTY-NINE PALMS, CALIFORNIA. (*Photo by the author.*)

PLATE 16.—(b) HORIZONTAL BEDS OF WHITE CRETACEOUS CHALK. NEAR SELMA, ALABAMA. (*Photo by L. W. Stephenson, U. S. Geological Survey.*)

sidence has caused the development of San Francisco Bay. The large islands off the coast of southern California have in very recent geologic time (probably Quaternary) been cut off from the mainland by sinking of the land.

The Sierra Nevada Range, which originated by intense folding of rocks late in the Jurassic period, underwent profound erosion until the latter part of the Tertiary period, by which time it had been cut down to a range of hills or low mountains. Then the great fault (fracture) previously described began to develop along the eastern side. As a result of many sudden movements along this fault, which is hundreds of miles long, the vast earth block has been tilted westward with a very steep eastern face and a long, more gradual western slope, the crest of the fault block forming the summit of the range. The amount of nearly vertical displacement along this fault has been commonly from 10,000 to 20,000 feet, and, in spite of considerable erosion of the top of the fault block and accumulation of sediment at its eastern base, the modified fault face now usually stands out boldly from 2,000 to 10,000 feet high. As an evidence that this movement of faulting has not yet ceased we may cite the Inyo earthquake of 1872, when there was a sudden renewal of movement of ten to twenty-five feet close to this fault for many miles. Since the great Sierra block began to tilt, the many mighty canyons, like Yosemite, Hetch-Hetchy, King's River, and Feather River, have been carved out by the action of streams, in some cases aided by former glaciers. King's River canyon has been sunk to a maximum depth of 6,900 feet in solid granite solely by the erosive action of the river!

The Cascade Mountains, too, were reduced to nearly a peneplain condition by late Tertiary time when they began to be rejuvenated by arching or bowing of the surface unaccompanied by great faulting or fracturing, and many canyons, like that of the Columbia River, have since been carved out.

Mention should now be made of the vigorous volcanic activity which took place in the Cascade and Sierra Nevada Ranges. Most of this activity occurred during Tertiary time (particularly in the latter part) and it has continued with diminishing force practically to the present time. In California streams of lava buried many gold-bearing river gravels which have yielded rich mines. Many well-known mountain peaks, such as Shasta, Lassen, Pitt, Hood, and Rainier, from northern California to Washington, are great volcanic cones which date from Tertiary time, and which are now mostly inactive. That this volcanic activity has not yet altogether ceased is shown by renewed eruptions of Mount Lassen (or Lassen Peak, altitude 10,437 feet) in northern California. During its renewed activity, in the years 1914-1916, several hundred outbursts occurred. No molten rock has flowed out, but large quantities of rock fragments, dust and steam have been erupted, in many cases forming great clouds two or three miles high over the top of the mountain (Plate 12). At first writing (October, 1920), Mount Lassen was still showing moderate activity. At Cinder Cone, only ten miles from Mount Lassen, there were two eruptions of cinders and a considerable outpouring of lava within the last 200 years. Still other very recent cinder cones occur in southeastern California and Arizona.

One of the greatest lava fields in the world forms the Columbian Plateau between western Wyoming (including the Yellowstone National Park) and the

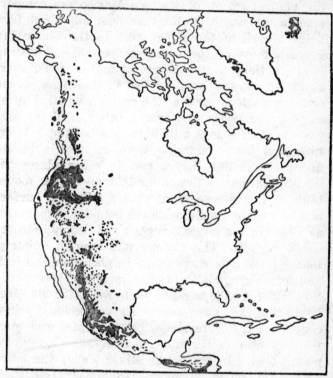

Fig. 46.—Sketch map showing the distribution of volcanic rocks of Cenozoic (mostly Tertiary) Age in western North America. Only Lassen Peak, California, has been very recently active in the United States proper, but a number are more or less active in Mexico and Central America. (Data from Willis, U. S. Geological Survey.)

Cascade Mountains from northeastern California to northern Washington. It covers fully 200,000 square miles and is really considerably larger than shown on the map because the lava in parts of the

plateau region are covered by very recent sedimen‹
tary materials.

The great lava fields of the Deccan, India, and of
the plateau region of western Mexico are comparable in size to the Columbian field and these lava
fields are all of the same age. In the Columbian
Plateau most of the lava was poured out during
later Tertiary time. Sheets of molten rock, averaging fifty to one hundred feet in thickness, spread
out over various parts of the region and piled up by
overlapping layers one over another until the lava
plateau more than a mile high was built up. Many
hills and low mountains were completely buried
under the molten floods, and in other places the
liquid rock masses flowed against the higher mountains. "For thousands of square miles the surface
is a lava plain which meets the boundary mountains
as a lake or sea meets a rugged and deeply indented
coast. . . . The plateau was long in building.
Between the layers are found in places old soil beds
and forest grounds and the sediments of lakes. . . .
So ancient are the latest floods in the Columbia River
Basin that they have weathered to a residual yellow
clay from thirty to sixty feet in depth, and marvelously rich in the mineral substances on which
plants feed. In the Snake River Valley the latest
lavas are much younger (Quaternary). Their
surfaces are so fresh and undecayed that here the
effusive eruptions may have continued to within the
period of human history." (W. H. Norton.) Many
of the lava layers are plainly visible where the
Columbia River has cut its great gorge or canyon.
The Snake River in places has sunk its channel
several thousand feet into the lava plateau without
reaching underlying rock.

Both north and south of the Columbian Plateau there was also much volcanic activity in the Rocky Mountain region during Tertiary time. A single formation in Colorado consists mostly of volcanic "ash" or dust over 2,000 feet thick. There was also much volcanic activity over the Colorado Plateau area of southern Utah, New Mexico, and Arizona. The volcanoes there exhibit all stages from those which are very recent and practically unaffected by erosion to others which have been completely cut away with the exception of the cores or "volcanic necks."

During the second half of the Tertiary period the whole region known as the Great Basin, between the Sierra Nevada Mountains of California and the Wasatch Mountains of Utah, began to be affected by profound faulting or fracturing and tilting of portions of the earth's crust. The two largest faults, one on the western side of the Wasatch Range and the other on the eastern side of the Sierra Range, are each hundreds of miles long. Each of these ranges owes most of its present altitude to the uptilting of great fault blocks, and most of the many nearly north-south Basin Ranges of Nevada and Utah are in reality recently tilted fault blocks.

Turning now to the Colorado Plateau, studies have shown that region to have been more or less periodically raised fully 20,000 feet since the beginning of Tertiary time, but because of profound erosion in the meantime its present altitude is only 6,000 to 9,000 feet. During late Tertiary time the land stood at a much lower level than to-day, so that, practically during the last period (Quaternary) of geologic time, the region has been elevated to its present position. As a direct result of this profound rejuvenation the Colorado River has had its erosive activity tremendously increased, and it has carved out the mightiest of all existing canyons—the Grand Canyon. The work of deepening and widening the canyon is still proceeding at a rapid geologic rate.

As we have learned, the Rocky Mountains and many of its subsidiary ranges were formed by folding and uplift of strata toward the close of the Mesozoic era (Cretaceous period). During much of Tertiary time the newly formed mountains had been considerably reduced by erosion. Then, late in the Tertiary period, much of the Rocky Mountain region, as well as much of the Great Plains area just east of the mountains, became rejuvenated by differential uplift without any notable folding of strata. We can tell that this general uplift amounted to at least several thousand feet because definite formations of relatively late Tertiary strata, originally horizontally deposited under inland bodies of water, gradually rise so that at the base of the Front Range of the Rockies they are fully 3,000 feet higher than they are 200 miles or more farther east. Thus, the original folding and faulting of the Rockies, Tertiary volcanic activity, late Tertiary rejuvenation, and subsequent erosion account for the present altitude and relief featuures of the great Rocky Mountain system.

Portions of the rejuvenated Great Plains region have been notably dissected by erosion since the late Tertiary, this being particularly true of the so-called "Bad Lands," especially in parts of Wyoming and South Dakota, where mostly relatively soft Tertiary strata have been cut to pieces.

Turning our attention now to the eastern half of the continent we find that all, or nearly all, of it was more or less raised toward the close of the Tertiary period. Practically the whole Mississippi Valley east of the Great Plains, as well as much of the country to the north in Canada, was elevated some hundreds of feet and the streams have since the late Tertiary uplift (except where the land was ice-covered during the Ice Age) been at work sinking their channels below the newly upraised surface.

As already pointed out, the lowlands of the Atlantic and Gulf Coastal Plains were mostly submerged under the sea during early middle Tertiary time. By the close of the period they had emerged practically to their present positions, and they have been only moderately affected by erosion.

We have still to explain the existing topography or relief of a large and important part of eastern North America, including the whole of the Appalachian Mountains, Allegheny Plateau, Piedmont Plateau, New York, New England, and the Canadian region to the north. As a starting point in this discussion we should recall the fact that, after the great Appalachian Mountain Revolution toward the close of the Paleozoic era, the predominant geologic process which affected the region under consideration was erosion throughout the succeeding Mesozoic era. By about the close of the Mesozoic (Cretaceous period) the whole region, with some local exceptions, had been worn down to a comparatively smooth plain (peneplain) not far above sea level. Local exceptions were mainly in the New York and New England region as, for example, some of the higher parts of the Adirondack and White Mountains, Mount Monadnock in southern New Hampshire, and Mount Greylock in western Massachusetts. These and other masses rose rather conspicuously above the general level of the great plain of erosion commonly called the "Cretaceous peneplain" because it is believed to have been well developed by the close of that period.

After still more wearing down in early Tertiary time, the vast peneplain was upraised. This uplift was an event of prime importance in the recent geological history of eastern North America because it was literally the initial step in bringing about nearly all of the existing major relief features of the Appalachian-New York-New England-St. Lawrence region. The amount of uplift (unaccompanied by folding) of the peneplain was commonly from a few hundred to a few thousand feet with the greatest amount in general along the main trend of the Appalachians. The fact should be emphasized that nearly all the principal topographic features of the great upraised region have been produced by dissection (erosion) of the uplifted peneplain surface. Thus nearly all the valleys, small and large, including those of the St. Lawrence, Hudson, Mohawk, Connecticut, and Susquehanna, have been carved out by streams since the uplift of the great peneplain (Plate 17).

The streams which flowed upon the old low-lying peneplain surface meandered sluggishly over deep alluvial or flood-plain deposits, and their courses were little if any determined by the character and structure of the underlying rocks, because, with few exceptions, all rocks were worn down to the general plain level. The uplift of the peneplain, however, caused great revival of activity of erosive power by the streams, the larger ones of which soon cut through the loose superficial alluvial deposits and then into the underlying bedrock. Thus the large, original streams had their courses well determined in the overlying deposits, and when the underlying rocks were reached the same courses had to be pursued entirely without reference to the underlying rock character and structure. Such streams are said to be "superimposed" because they have, so to speak, been let down upon and into the underlying rock masses. As Professor Berkey has well said: "The larger rivers, the great master streams, of the superimposed drainage system, in some cases were so efficient in the corrosion of their channels that the discovery of discordant structures (in the underlying rocks) has not been of sufficient influence to displace them, or reverse them, or even to shift them very far from their original direct course to the sea. They cut directly across mountain ridges because they flowed over the plain out of which these ridges have been carved, and because their own erosive and transporting power have exceeded those of any of their tributaries or neighbors."

Fine examples of such superimposed streams which are now entirely out of harmony with the structure of regions through which they flow are the Susquehanna, Delaware, and Hudson. Thus the Susquehanna cuts across a whole succession of Appalachian ridges while, in accordance with the same explanation, the Delaware cuts through the Kittatiny range or ridge at the famous Delaware Water Gap. The ridges are explained as follows: while the great master streams were cutting deep trenches or channels in hard and soft rock alike, numerous side streams (tributaries) came into existence and naturally mostly developed along belts of weak, easily eroded rock parallel to the geologic (folded) structure. Thus the Appalachian valleys have been, and are being, formed, while the ridges represent the more resistant rock formations which have more effectually stood out against erosion. The lower Hudson River flows at a considerable angle across folded formations above the Highlands, after which it passes though a deep gorge which it has cut into the hard granite and other rocks of the Highlands. The simple explanation is that the Hudson had its course determined upon the surface of the upraised Cretaceous peneplain, and that it has been able to keep that course in spite of discordant structure and character of the underlying rocks. In a similar manner we may readily account for the passage of the Connecticut River through a great gap in the Holyoke ridge or range of hard lava in western Massachusetts.

Before leaving this part of our discussion we shall briefly present some evidence showing that the New York-New England-St. Lawrence region at least must have been considerably higher shortly before the Ice Age (Quaternary period). An old channel of the Hudson River has been traced about 100 miles eastward beyond the present mouth of the river and it forms a distinct trench under the shallow sea in the continental shelf. Even in the Hudson Valley, many miles above New York City, the bedrock bottom of the river lies hundreds of feet (near West Point, 800 feet) below sea level. Obviously this submerged channel must have been cut when the land in the general vicinity of New York City was fully 1,000 feet higher than at present. That the land thus stood higher late in the Tertiary and

possibly early in the Quaternary periods is proved
as follows: (1) because most of Tertiary time must
have been needed for the river to erode such a deep
valley after the initial uplift of the peneplain about
the beginning of the period; and (2) because glacial deposits of Quaternary age filled the former
channel to a considerable depth. The valleys of
the coast of Maine, and the submerged lower St.
Lawrence Valley (Gulf of St. Lawrence), in a
similar way lead us to conclude that the region
farther north was also notably higher just before
the Ice Age.

In the eastern hemisphere early in the Tertiary
period a great submergence set in and marine
waters spread over much of western and southern
Europe, northern Africa, and southern Asia. The
sites of the Himalayas, Alps, Pyrenees, Apennines
and other mountains were then mostly submerged.
A very remarkable marine deposit, made up almost
wholly of carbonate of lime shells of a single-celled
animal called Nummulites, formed on the floor of
this vastly expanded early Tertiary mediterranean.
This rock attains a thickness of several thousand
feet. It is doubtful if any other single formation
made up almost entirely of the shells of but one
species is at once so widespread and thick. In the
Alps this remarkable marine deposit may be seen
10,000 feet above sea level, and in Tibet fully 20,000
feet. Much of the rock in the Egyptian pyramids
was quarried from this formation.

Later in the Tertiary in Eurasia and Africa the
marine waters gradually became very restricted, so
that by the close of the period the relations of land
and sea were not strikingly different from the
present, although northwestern Europe, like north-

eastern North America, was notably higher just before the Ice Age than it is to-day.

Eurasia witnessed tremendous crustal disturbances during the middle and later Tertiary time when, due to intense folding and uplift of great zones, the Himalayas, Caucasus, Alps, Pyrenees, Apennines, and other great ranges were formed. The crustal disturbance was most remarkable in the region of the Alps, where the movement resulted in "elevating and folding the Tertiary and older strata into overturned, recumbent, and nearly horizontal folds, and pushing the southern or Lepontine Alps about sixty miles (over a low angle fault fracture) to the northward into the Helvetic region. Erosion has since carved up these overthrust sheets, leaving remnants lying on foundations which belong to a more northern portion of the ancient (early Tertiary) sea. Most noted of these residuals of overthrust masses is the Matterhorn, a mighty mountain without roots, a stranger in a foreign geologic environment." (C. Schuchert.)

The last period of geological time—the Quaternary—was ushered in by the spreading of vast sheets of ice over much of northern North America and northern Europe, and this ranks among the most interesting and remarkable events of known geological time. On first thought the former existence of such vast ice sheets seems unbelievable, but the Ice Age occurred so short a time ago that the records of the event are perfectly clear and conclusive. The fact of this great Ice Age was discovered by Louis Agassiz in 1837, and fully announced before the British Scientific Association in 1840. For some years the idea was opposed, especially by advocates of the so-called iceberg theory. Now however, no important event of earth history is more firmly established, and no student of the subject ever questions the fact of the Quaternary Ice Age.

Some of the proofs of the former presence of the great ice sheet are as follows: (1) polished and striated rock surfaces which are precisely like those produced by existing glaciers, and which could not possibly have been produced by any other agency; (2) glacial bowlders or "erratics" which are often somewhat rounded and scratched, and which have often been transported many miles from their parent rock ledges (Plate 18a); (3) true glacial moraines, especially terminal moraines, like that which extends the full length of Long Island and marks the southernmost limit of the great ice sheet; and (4) the generally widespread distribution over most of the glaciated area of heterogeneous glacial débris, both unstratified and stratified, which is clearly transported material and typically rests upon the bedrock by sharp contact.

The best known existing great ice sheets are those of Greenland and Antarctica, especially the former, which covers about 500,000 square miles. This glacier is so large and deep that only an occasional high rocky mountain projects above its surface, and the ice is known to be slowly moving outward in all directions from the interior to the margins of Greenland. Along the margins, where melting is more rapid, some land is exposed, and often the ice flows out into the ocean where it breaks off to form large icebergs.

The accompanying map shows the area of nearly 4,000,000 square miles of North America covered by ice at the time of maximum glaciation, and also the three great centers of accumulation and dispersal of the ice. The directions of flow from these centers have been determined by the study of the directions of many thousands of glacial scratches on rock ledges. The Labradorean (or Laurentide)

FIG. 47.—Map of North America showing the area buried under ice during the Great Ice Age of the Quaternary period; the three great glacial centers; and the extent of mountain glaciers in the west. (After U. S. Geological Survey.)

glacier spread out 1,600 miles to the south to Long Island and near the mouth of the Ohio River. The vast Keewatin glacier sent a great lobe of ice nearly as far south, that is into northern Missouri. "One of the most marvelous features of the ice dispersion was the great extension of the Keewatin sheet from a low flat center westward and southward over what is now a semiarid plain, rising in the direction in which the ice moved, while the mountain glaciers on the west (Cordilleran region), where now known, pushed eastward but little beyond the foothills." (Chamberlin and Salisbury.)

The Labradorean and Keewatin ice sheets everywhere coalesced except in two places. One of these is an area of about 10,000 square miles mostly in southwestern Wisconsin. In spite of several ice invasions during the Ice Age, this area, hundreds of miles north of the southern limit of the ice sheets, was never ice-covered. There is a total absence of records of glaciation within this area, and so we here have an excellent sample of the kind of topography which prevailed over the northern Mississippi Valley just before the advent of the ice. A much smaller, nonglaciated area occurs in northeastern Missouri near the southern limit of ice extension.

The Cordilleran ice sheet was the smallest of the three, and it was probably not such a continuous mass of ice, the higher mountains projecting above its surface. A surprising fact is that neither this ice sheet nor any other overspread northern Alaska, which is well within the Arctic Circle, during the Ice Age. More than likely the temperature was low enough, but precipitation of snow was not sufficient to permit the building up of a great glacier.

At the same time that nearly 4,000,000 square miles of North America were ice-covered, about 2,000,000 square miles of northern Europe were buried under ice which spread from the one great center over Scandinavia southwest, south, and southeast over most of the British Isles, well into Germany, and well into Russia.

In both North America and Europe the high mountains, well south of the great glacier limits, especially the Sierra, Rockies, Alps, Pyrenees, and Caucasus, supported many large local glaciers in valleys which now contain none at all or only relatively small ones.

Records of glaciation, such as glacial scratches, boulders, lakes, etc., occur high up in the White and Green Mountains, Adirondacks, Catskills, and the Berkshire Hills, thus proving that the ice must have been at least some thousands of feet thick over New England and New York. We have good reason to believe that even the highest summits, except possibly in the Catskills, from 4,000 to over 6,000 feet above sea level, were completely submerged under the ice. On top of a mountain of Archeozoic granite nearly 4,000 feet in altitude, facing the St. Lawrence Valley in northern New York, the writer has found many fragments of sandstone which were picked off by the ice in the low valley, moved southward a good many miles, and uphill several thousand feet to the top of the mountain. The reader may wonder how a great glacier at least a mile thick in northern New York could have thinned out to disappearance within the short distance to the southern border of the State, but observations on existing large glaciers show that it is quite the habit for them to thin out very rapidly near their margins, thus producing steep ice fronts.

The fact that glacial ice flows as though it were a viscous substance is well known from studies of valley glaciers in the Alps and Alaska, and the great ice sheet of Greenland. A common assumption, either that the land at one of the great centers of ice accumulation during the Ice Age must have been many thousands of feet higher, or that the ice must there have been immensely thick, in order to permit ice flowage so far out from the center, is not necessary. Viscous tar slowly poured upon a level surface will gradually flow out in all directions, and at no time need the tar at the center of accumulation be very much thicker than elsewhere. The movement of glacial ice from the great centers of dispersal during the Ice Age was much the same in principle, only in the case of the glaciers the accumulations of snow and ice were by no means confined to the immediate centers.

The fronts of the vast ice sheets, like those of ordinary valley glaciers, must have undergone many advances and retreats of greater or less consequence. In the northern Mississippi Valley, and also in Europe, there is positive proof for four or five important advances and retreats of the ice which gave rise to the true interglacial stages. The strongest evidence is the presence of successive layers of glacial (morainic) débris piled one upon another, a given layer often having been oxidized, eroded, and even covered with plant life before the next or overlying layer was deposited. Such is the condition of things throughout much of Iowa, where wells sunk into the glacial deposits commonly pass through layers of partly decomposed vegetable matter at depths of from 100 to 300 feet. Near Toronto, Canada, the finding of warm climate plants between two glacial deposits proves that the climate there during an interglacial stage was much like that of the southern States to-day. During the great interglacial stages the vast glaciers were notably restricted in size, and in some or possibly all, cases they may have wholly disappeared from the continent.

In former years there was a tendency to ascribe mighty erosive power to the vast slow-moving ice sheets, but to-day scarcely any geologist would hold that the ice really produced large valleys solely by ice erosion, or that mountains were notably cut down. Throughout the glaciated region, especially toward the north, the deep preglacial residual soils and rotten rocks were nearly all scoured off by the passage of the ice. That the ice, where properly shod with rock fragments, actually eroded to at least little depths into hard and fresh rocks is well known, but the evidence is clear and conclusive that the preglacial hills and mountains, and most of the valleys (including all the large ones), were rarely more than a little modified in shape and size.

One of the principal effects of the Ice Age is the widespread distribution of glacial deposits, and other deposits which were formed under water in direct association with the ice. Such materials have been described in the chapter on "Glaciers and Their Work."

As a direct result of the Ice Age, many thousands of lakes came into existence throughout the glaciated region where few, if any, previously existed. Many of these lasted only while the ice was present because their waters were held up by walls of ice acting as dams. Thousands of others still persist, most of these having their water levels maintained by dams of glacial débris left by the ice across valleys. Good examples of lakes of both types, including a summary of the remarkable history of the Great Lakes, are considered in the chapter on "A Study of Lakes."

Many drainage changes, gorges, and waterfalls have also directly resulted from the great Ice Age.

In fact it is not too much to say that practically all true gorges and waterfalls of the glaciated region have originated as a direct result of the Ice Age. The most remarkable combination of waterfall and gorge thus produced is that of the world-famous Niagara, described in the chapter on "Stream Work." Not only are Niagara Falls and gorge of postglacial origin but there was no Niagara River as such before the Ice Age. In New York the well-known Ausable Chasm, Trenton Falls Gorge, and Watkins Glen are all excellent examples of gorges cut since the Ice Age by streams which, because their old valleys were filled with glacial débris, have been forced to take new courses. A gorge of very special interest is that at Little Falls in central New York. This gorge, two miles long, with its precipitous walls hundreds of feet high, is the most important gateway for traffic between the Atlantic border and the Great Lakes region. The bottom of this defile contains six tracks of the New York Central and West Shore Railroads, the Barge Canal, an important highway, and the Mohawk River. Before the Ice Age there was a stream divide instead of a gorge, several hundred feet above the present river level. During a late stage of the Ice Age, when the Great Lakes drained through the Mohawk Valley, a tremendous volume of water passed over the divide and cut it down to form nearly all of the gorge except the inner or bottom trench which has since been eroded by the Mohawk River.

Only a few of the numerous stream changes directly due to the Ice Age will be briefly referred to. Certain of the principles involved are exceptionally well illustrated in the general vicinity of Saratoga Springs and Lake George, New York.

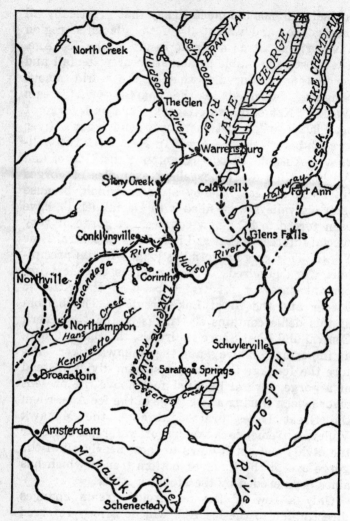

FIG. 48.—Sketch map of the region between Lake George and Schenectady, New York, showing how certain of the main drainage courses have been revolutionized by the great retreating ice sheet and the deposits it left. Preglacial courses shown by dotted lines only where essentially different from the present streams. (By the author, as published by New York State Museum.)

During the retreat of the great glacier a lobe of ice occupied the Lake George Valley and forced the Hudson River west over a divide at Stony Creek. Then, because of heavy glacial deposits near Corinth, the Hudson could not continue south through what had been the preglacial valley of Luzerne River, but it was forced eastward over a divide in a low mountain ridge to Glens Falls. The remarkable shift of the Sacandaga River from its preglacial channel was caused by the building up of a great morainic ridge across the valley in the vicinity of Broadalbin.

The drainage of the basin of the upper Ohio River has also been revolutionized as a result of the glaciation. All the drainage of western Pennsylvania passed northward into Lake Erie just before the Ice Age instead of southwestward through the Ohio River as at present.

Rivers as large as the Mississippi and the Missouri were also more or less locally deflected from their preglacial courses. Thus the Missouri, which in preglacial time followed the James River Valley of eastern South Dakota, was forced, by a great lobe of retreating ice, to find its present course many miles farther west.

How long ago did the Ice Age end? In seeking an answer to this question we should bear in mind not only the fact that the Ice Age ended at different times, according to latitude, the more southern districts having been first freed from ice, but also the fact that approximately 4,000,000 square miles of the polar regions are now ice-covered, so that in a real sense those portions of the earth are still in an Ice Age. Some of the best estimates of the length of postglacial time for a given place are based upon the rate of recession of Niagara Falls, the average of the estimates being about 20,000 years. The evidence for this conclusion is briefly set forth in Chapter III. A careful study of the rate of recession of St. Anthony Falls, Minnesota, has led to the conclusion that the last retreat of the ice occurred there from 10,000 to 16,000 years ago. Certain clays deposited under tidewater since the last withdrawal of ice in Sweden show a remarkable succession of alternating layers thought to represent seasonal changes. By counting the layers it has been estimated that Stockholm was freed from ice only 9,000 years ago.

Although the actual duration of the Ice Age is by no means accurately known, we can be quite sure that the time represented is far longer than that of postglacial time. That it must have lasted fully 500,000 years seems certain when due consideration is given to amount of time necessary to bring about the repeated changes of climate between the glacial and interglacial stages; the amount of plant accumulation during the interglacial stages; the amount of weathering and erosion of the various layers of glacial deposits. Some estimates run as high as 1,500,000 years for the duration of the Ice Age, and an average is about 1,000,000 years, which probably indicates, at least roughly, the order of magnitude of the time involved.

When it is considered not only that the fact of the great Ice Age was not even thought of until 1837, but also that many factors enter into the general problem of the climate of geologic time, it is not surprising that the cause (or causes) of the glacial climate is still not definitely known. A few of the various hypotheses which have been advocated to account for the glacial climate will now be very briefly referred to. One is that the increased cold (not more than 10 to 15 degrees for the yearly average) was brought about by the notably increased altitudes of late Tertiary and early Quaternary times in northern North America and Europe. In this connection it is interesting to note that the four times of real glaciation during geologic time (mid-Proterozoic, early Paleozoic, late Paleozoic, and early Cenozoic) did occur directly after great crustal disturbances and notable uplifts of land. According to this hypothesis the interglacial stages would have to be explained by a rather unreasonable assumption of repeated rising and sinking of the glaciated lands.

Another hypothesis, long held in favor, is based upon certain astronomical considerations. Thus we now have winter in the northern hemisphere when the earth is nearest the sun, but in about 10,500 years, due to wobbling of the earth on its axis, our winter will occur when the earth is farthest from the sun, thus making the winters longer and colder, and the summers shorter and hotter. After a much longer period of time the earth will be millions of miles farther from the sun in winter than in summer and this would still further accentuate the length and coldness of the winters. The interglacial stages represent the 10,500 year periods when the earth in winter (northern hemisphere) is nearest the sun. A difficulty in the way of accepting this hypothesis is that it is inconceivable that each glacial and interglacial stage lasted only 10,500 years. Another objection to the hypothesis as an explanation of Ice Ages is that it is directly opposed by the fact of widespread glaciation at low latitudes either side of the equator during the late Paleozoic Ice Age.

Another hypothesis is based upon variations in quantity of carbonic acid gas and water vapor in the air. Increase or decrease of these constituents causes increase or decrease of temperature because they have high capacities for absorbing heat. "The great elevation of the land at the close of the Tertiary seems to afford conditions favorable both for the consumption of carbon dioxide in large quantities (by weathering of rocks) and for the reduction of the water content of the air. Depletion of these heat-absorbing elements was equivalent to the thinning of the thermal blanket which they constitute. If it was thinned, the temperature was reduced. . . By variations in the consumption of carbon dioxide, especially in its absorption and escape from the ocean, the hypothesis attempts to explain the periodicity of glaciation (i. e., glacial and interglacial stages)." (Chamberlin and Salisbury.)

Still another suggested explanation is based upon variability of amount of heat radiated by the sun. Slight variations are now known to take place, and possibly in the past during certain periods of time these variations may have been sufficiently great to cause a glacial climate with interglacial stages.

Here, as in the case of so many other great natural phenomena, a single, simple explanation does not seem sufficient to account for all the features of the several well-known glacial epochs of geologic time. Two or more hypotheses, or parts of hypotheses, must more than likely be combined to explain a particular Ice Age.

CHAPTER XVII

EVOLUTION OF PLANTS

HAVE we any knowledge regarding the beginning of life on our planet? Our answer to this question must be decidedly in the negative. We can, however, be very positive in regard to two important matters concerning life in early geological time, namely, that plants must have existed before animals, and that the very oldest known (Archeozoic) rocks of the earth contain vestiges of organisms. We may be sure that plants preceded animals because animal life ultimately depends upon plants for its food supply or, in other words, all animals could never have been carnivorous. Now, if we can prove that organisms existed during Archeozoic time, it is evident that plants at least must have lived in that oldest known era of earth history. That living things did then exist is proved by the common occurrence of graphite, a crystallized form of carbon, in the oldest known of the Archeozoic rocks. The facts that flakes of graphite are abundantly scattered through many layers of strata of Archeozoic Age, and that adjacent layers of strata contain such varying amounts of graphite, render it practically certain that such graphite represents the carbon of organisms. Graphite existing under such conditions could not be of igneous origin. Carbonaceous or bituminous strata, so called because they contain more or less decomposed organic matter, would, when crystallized under conditions of metamorphism, yield graphite-bearing rocks exactly like those of Archeozoic Age, and there is every reason to believe that this was their origin. But, since only graphite (carbon) of the Archeozoic organisms remains, the rest having disappeared through chemical change or decomposition, it is impossible to say whether much or all of it represents original plants or animals. As to plants, some years ago fossil remains of very primitive, single-celled (blue green) algae were found in Archeozoic rocks, but the presence of any form of animal life has not been proved.

In the next, or Proterozoic era, some plants and animals of definite types are known to have existed and, from here on in the present chapter, it is our purpose to consider the salient points in the geological history of plants, taking up the main types in the regular order of their appearance from the remote Proterozoic days to the present. The very oldest known definitely determinable Proterozoic fossils are the more or less rounded masses of crudely concentric layers of carbonate of lime from one to fifteen inches in diameter found in middle Proterozoic limestone of western Ontario, Canada. Similar forms are abundant in late Proterozoic strata of Montana. They occur in large numbers as layers or reefs, in many cases repeating themselves through hundreds or even thousands of feet of strata. Careful studies have shown that these forms are the limey secretions of some of the very simplest types of plants, that is thallophytes (e. g., seaweeds), which lived in water.

Before proceeding to describe the plants of Paleozoic and later time, the reader should be impressed

with the important fact that plants of higher and
higher types came into existence throughout geological time in almost exactly the botanical order of
their classification, that is to say, from the very simplest types (thallophytes) of Proterozoic time there
were gradually evolved, through the long geological
ages, higher and higher plant forms reaching a
climax in the complex and highly organized plants
of the present time.   This is the most significant
general fact in regard to the geological history of
plants.   For the convenience of the reader the
largest subdivisions in the classification of plants
are here given.

OUTLINE CLASSIFICATION OF PLANTS

I. Cryptogams
    (seedless and
    flowerless)

    1. Thallophytes (e. g., seaweeds, mushrooms)
    2. Bryophytes (e. g., mosses)
    3. Pteridophytes (e. g., "club mosses," "horsetails,"
        ferns)

II. Pteridosperms
     (seed-bearing,
     flowerless)

    (e. g., seed ferns—wholly extinct)

III. Phanerogams
      (seed-bearing,
      flowering)

    1. Gymnosperms (e. g., cycads, conifers)
    2. Angiosperms (e. g., grasses, lilies, oaks, roses)

Throughout the first two periods—Cambrian and
Ordovician—of the Paleozoic era, plant life appears
to have made little or no progress toward higher
forms.   The very simple thallophytes (e. g., seaweeds) continued to secrete concentric layers of
carbonate of lime in almost exactly the same way
as during the middle and late Proterozoic era.   Remarkable reefs of such forms occur in the late Cambrian limestone near Saratoga Springs, New York,
where one locality has been set aside as a state park.
During the Ordovician there were seaweeds of the
more familiar branching types without carbonate of
lime supports, and these have left very perfect impressions in some of the Ordovician strata.

During the Silurian period seaweeds continued, as, in fact, they did throughout succeeding geologic time to the present. The Silurian strata seem to contain some vestiges of the first-known land plants, though the records are meager and some of the specimens are of a doubtful character. Most interesting of all is a fern or fernlike plant found in France. When we consider the profusion of land plants (all of relatively simple types) of the next or Devonian period, it seems certain that their progenitors must have existed in the Silurian, and their remains may very likely be discovered.

Beginning with the Devonian period of the Paleozoic era the records show that important advances had taken place in the evolution of the plant kingdom. Among the very simple thallophyte plants some seaweeds of unusually large size occur in fossil form, but the important fact is that all the principal subdivisions of the typical higher non-flowering plants (pteridophytes) as well as pteridosperms, and even some primitive representatives of the lower order flowering plants (gymnosperms) were well represented in the Devonian. Our knowledge of land plants earlier than the Devonian amounts to almost nothing and they certainly could not have been at all prominent, but the fossil records make it very clear that many Devonian land areas were clad with rich and diversified plant life. There were even forests, probably the first on earth, but they were far different, both in general and in particular, from those of to-day because the trees were all of exceptionally low organization types. During the next two periods—Mississippian and Pennsylvanian—there was no really important progress in the evolution of plants, and since these remarkable types of land plants have left such wonderfully preserved records in strata of the Pennsylvanian or great Coal Age, we shall proceed to descriptions of the main types of that time, especially those which contributed to the formation of beds of coal.

As shown by the abundant records, the land plant life of Pennsylvanian time must have been not only prolific but exceedingly varied. Thousands of species have been unearthed from the coal-bearing formations alone, and these must represent only a fraction of all species of plants which lived during the period. Most prominent of all were the giant Lycopods constituting the lowest main subdivision of the pteridophytes (see above classification). These great, nonflowering plants were at once the biggest, most common and conspicuous trees of the extensive swamp forests, and they were the greatest contributors to the formation of coal (Plate 19a). Many species have been described. They commonly attained heights of 50 to 100 feet and diameters of 2 to 6 feet. In one important type the fairly numerous branches bristled with stiff, needle-shaped leaves. When the leaves dropped off the older or trunk portions, scars were left spirally arranged around the trunks of the trees. In another important type the leaf scars were vertically arranged on the lower portions of the tree trunks. The upper portions of the trunks (rarely branched) were thickly set with long, slender leaves, which in some species were two or three feet long. An interesting fact is that the inner parts of the trunks of the great lycopods were filled with soft, pithy material. This explains why the fossil trees are nearly always flattened out, as a result of burial within the earth. The nonbranching type of lycopod has been totally extinct for millions of years, while the branching type is to-day represented only by small, mostly delicate, trailing plants familiarly known as "club mosses" and "ground pines." The most conspicuous trees of the great Pennsylvanian lowlands and swamps have, indeed, left meager modern representatives, and here we have an excellent illustration of a once prominent group of plants which has dwindled away almost to extinction.

Another common type of Pennsylvanian vegetation was the so-called "horsetail" plant or giant rush. The much smaller scouring rush, represented by several species to-day, is the direct descendant of this type which, during later Paleozoic time, grew to be 50 to 90 feet high and 1 to 2 feet in diameter. The long, slender trunks filled with pith were segmented with variously shaped leaves arranged in whorls around the joints. A fine, vertical-fluted structure without leaf scars characterized the surfaces of the trunk.

Recent study has shown that many of the Pennsylvanian plants, long classed as true ferns, were really "seed ferns," as described below. Many of the true ferns grew to be real trees up to fifty or sixty feet high, but all Paleozoic types were primitive in structure as compared with modern ferns.

Very remarkable among the later Paleozoic plants were the pteridosperms, represented by the so-called "seed ferns." These now wholly extinct plants seem to have formed the connecting link between the seedless, flowerless plants (cryptogams) and the seed-bearing, flowering plants (phanerogams), because they bore seeds but not flowers. Many of them were small and herbaceous, but others were tall trees, in general appearance resembling the tree ferns. "Seed-ferns," which play such an important part in the evolution of plants, are not known to have existed after early Mesozoic time (Plate 19b).

During the latter half of the Paleozoic era some very primitive types of flowering plants (gymnosperms) existed. Most abundant of these were the so-called cordaites, which were the tallest trees of the time, some having reached heights of over 100 feet. The upper portions only bore numerous branches supplied with many simple, parallel-veined, strap-shaped leaves up to six feet long· and six inches wide. Excepting the pithy cores the trunks of these trees were of real wood covered with thick bark. Trees of this kind became extinct in the early Mesozoic era.

Very late in the Paleozoic (Permian period) two other types of the simple flowering plants (gymnosperms) made their appearance. These were the cycads and conifers, which were the most conspicuous trees during the first two periods of the Mesozoic era. The cycads reached their culmination in the Jurassic period, but they still exist in modified form in some parts of the world. The short, stout trunk was crowned with long, stiff, palmlike leaves. In fact, the cycads are distantly related to the palms, which belong to a higher group of plants. Some specimens of cycads, especially from the Mesozoic strata of South Dakota, are so wonderfully fossilized that even the detailed structures of trunks, leaves, flowers, and seeds are so perfectly preserved that almost as much is known about these plants of millions of years ago as though they were living forms.

The conifers, with which are classed present-day pines, spruces, and many other evergreen trees, gradually took on a more modern aspect, so that late in the Mesozoic era they were much like those now living. Among the most interesting trees were the sequoias, to which the living "big trees" and redwoods of California belong. These began in relatively late Mesozoic time, reached their climax in numbers, variety of species, and widespread distribution in the early Cenozoic era; and are now almost extinct, being represented by only two species in local portions of California. Cordaites, trees which were so large and abundant in later Paleozoic time, were reduced to extinction in the early Mesozoic era.

During Mesozoic time the thallophytes, represented by seaweeds, were common. Among the pteridophytes the ferns and "horsetail" plants were fairly common, but the very large forms gradually gave way to much smaller ones during Mesozoic time. The giant lycopods of later Paleozoic time dwindled almost to extinction even in early Mesozoic time, so that from that time to the present they have been very small and relatively insignificant.

Hundreds of millions of years of earth history had passed before the true flowering plants—the angiosperms—appeared upon the earth. The Cretaceous period marked their advent. So far as known, these plants originated along the eastern side of North America, and very soon after their establishment they spread over the earth with amazing rapidity and dominated the vegetation as they do to-day, more than half of the existing species of plants being angiosperms. Among the common types which have been unearthed from Cretaceous strata

PLATE 17.—GENERAL VIEW IN THE APPALACHIAN MOUNTAINS ALONG NEW RIVER, VIRGINIA. This is a typical portion of the great area which, during Mesozoic time, was reduced by erosion to the condition of a low-lying plain ("peneplain"). Since early Cenozoic time the peneplain has been upraised and New River has carved out its V-shaped valley to its present depth, while tributary streams have carved out a series of valleys along belts of weak rocks nearly at right angles to the main valley. The remarkably even sky line marks approximately the old peneplain surface. (*Photo by Hillers, U. S. Geological Survey.*)

PLATE 18.—(a) A Big Glacial Bowlder of Plutonic Igneous Rock
Carried Miles from Its Parent Ledge by the Ice Sheet Which
Passed Over the Adirondack Mountains During the Ice Age. (*Photo
by the author.*)

PLATE 18.—(b) A Long, Winding Ridge of Sand and Gravel (Called
an "Esker") Deposited by a Stream in a Channel in the Ice Near
the Margin of the Great Glacier During Its Retreat from the
Adirondack Mountains. (*Photo by the author.*)

are palms, grasses, maples, oaks, elms, figs, magnolias, willows, beeches, chestnuts, and poplars.

The introduction of the higher flowering plants (angiosperms) "was, perhaps, the most important and far-reaching event in the whole history of vegetation, not only because they almost immediately became dominant, but also because of their influence upon the animal life of the succeeding periods. Hardly had flowers appeared, before a great horde of insects, which fed upon their honey or pollen, seem to have sprung into existence. The nutritious grasses and the various nuts, seeds, and fruits afforded a better food for noncarnivores than ever before in the history of the world. It was to be expected, therefore, that some new type of animal life would be developed to take advantage of this superior food supply. As we shall see in the discussion of the Tertiary (next chapter), the mammals, which kept a subordinate position throughout the Mesozoic, rapidly took on bulk and variety and acquired possession of the earth as soon as they became adapted to this new food, quickly supplanting the great reptiles of the Mesozoic." (Cleland.)

During the present or Cenozoic era vegetation gradually took on a more and more modern aspect until the existing species were developed. The grasses especially developed and spread rapidly, but the cereals did not evolve until late in the era. Certain single-celled plants, called diatoms, may be especially mentioned, for they must have literally swarmed in some of the Tertiary seas which spread over parts of the present lands. "The microscopic plants which form siliceous shells, called diatoms, make extensive deposits in some places. One stratum near Richmond, Virginia, is thirty feet

thick and is many miles in extent; another, near
Monterey, California, is fifty feet thick, and the
material is as white and fine as chalk, which it re-
sembles in appearance; another, near Bilin, in
Bohemia, is fourteen feet thick. . . . Ehrenberg
has calculated that a cubic inch of the fine, earthy
rock contains about forty-one thousand millions of
organisms. Such accumulations of diatoms are
made both in fresh waters and salt, and in those of
the ocean at all depths." (J. D. Dana.)

CHAPTER XVIII

GEOLOGICAL HISTORY OF ANIMALS (EXCLUDING VERTEBRATES)

A STUDY of the animals of the past is not only of great interest in itself, but also it furnishes a mainstay of the great doctrine of organic evolution. At the very outset of our discussion the reader should have already in mind at least the main subdivisions of the animal kingdom in order to reasonably well understand where the important animal types of the different geological ages fit in, and how those types bear upon the doctrine of evolution. The accompanying, very brief, general classification includes the usually recognized subkingdoms with special reference to representatives of those which are of most geological and evolutionary significance. Reading downward in this classification, the degree of complexity of organization steadily increases from single-celled animals to man himself.

I.	Protozoans,	e. g.	foraminifers (with lime carbonate shells)
II.	Cœlenterates,	e. g.	Sponges / So-called "jellyfishes," graptolites / Corals
III.	Echinoderms,	e. g.	So-called "sea lilies" / So-called "starfishes" / So-called "sea urchins"
IV.	Worms,		
V.	Molluscoids,	e. g.	So-called "sea mosses" / Brachiopods

259

VI. Mollusks,	e. g.	Clams, oysters	
		Snails	
		Cephalopods, e. g.	Pearly nautilus, ammonites So-called "cuttle fishes"

VII. Arthropods,	e. g.	Trilobites Crabs, lobsters So-called "sea scorpions" Insects

VIII. Vertebrates,	e. g.	Ostracoderms Fishes Amphibians Reptiles Birds Mammals (including man)

Before entering into a brief but rather systematic discussion of some of the most important types of animals which lived during geological time, it may be well for the reader to have in mind some of the most important conclusions which have been reached as a result of the study of the fossil animal records. These conclusions may be summarized as follows:

1. Animal life existed many millions of years ago.

2. Not only the animals of to-day, but also those of any given geological period, directly descended from those of preceding geological periods.

3. Animal life has undergone continuous change since its introduction upon the earth, so that each group of strata, representing a particular geological age, contains a characteristic assemblage of fossil animals.

4. Many of the changes in the history of animals have been progressive or evolutionary, so that strata of early geological time contain distinctly more primitive or lower order forms than the strata of late geological time. But, while the line of evolution has been maintained without a break, culminating in man, there have been many offshoots of a retrogressive nature.

5. Even as far along in geological time as the early Paleozoic era, the highest subkingdom—vertebrates—had no representative whatever. In other words, all the important subdivisions of animal life from a little below fishes to man have been evolved since about the close of the Ordovician period.

6. Any species of animal which ever became extinct has never been known to reappear, and literally tens of thousands of species are known to have become extinct.

7. No species like those now living are found in the more ancient strata, such being confined to the strata of relatively recent geological dates.

8. While more and more highly organized animals have continuously been evolved, many of the earlier and simpler types have persisted, a remarkable case in point being the single-celled animals called foraminifers which may be traced, without very notable change, through the tens of millions of years of geological time from the late Proterozoic era to the present day.

9. Many species have been able to maintain themselves practically without change through long stretches of geological time, while others have had only very brief existence.

When did animal life begin on the earth, and what were the first forms like? We can only partially answer the first question by saying that animals have existed for hundreds of millions of years, certainly as early at least as Proterozoic time. Up to the present time we are utterly in the dark as to what the earliest animal forms looked like, but we have positive knowledge that the oldest forms found as fossils in the rocks represent creatures which were far more primitive and lower in organization than many animals of to-day, and that since those oldest known forms lived, the animal kingdom has undergone various profound alterations. In view of the above statements, and also the fact that the oldest known plant forms were extremely simple or single-celled, it is more than likely that the first animal life of the earth was single-celled. In harmony with this view is the fact that fossil single-celled animals are found in the very oldest (Proterozoic) rocks which contain any definitely determinable fossil animals.

Do the most ancient known rocks show that animal life existed during Archeozoic time? In the preceding chapter we pointed out the fact that the carbon (in the form of graphite), so commonly present in those most ancient known strata, proves the existence of life of some kind during Archeozoic time. But because the only definitely determinable fossil forms found in the Archeozoic rocks are rather indistinct, very primitive remains of single-celled plants (algae), we cannot be sure whether the carbon represents plant or animal life or both. Because of the intense alteration (metamorphism) of those very old strata, any animal forms have long since been obliterated as such. We may, however, in the light of the vast evolution which took place through succeeding geological time, be very sure that any animals which may have existed during Archeozoic time were in general much simpler forms than those of even early Paleozoic time.

The early and middle Proterozoic strata throw no more light upon the early history of animal life than do the Archeozoic strata. The upper or later Proterozoic rocks, however, contain the oldest recog-

nizable animal fossils. Very recently fossil remains
of single-celled, shell-bearing protozoans have been
found in northern France, while the upper Proterozoic strata of the Rocky Mountains in Montana,
and the Grand Canyon of Arizona have yielded
worm tracks, a molluscoid (brachiopod) and fragments of lower forms of arthropods. This record,
although very meager, clearly proves that animal
life was so well advanced by late Proterozoic time,
that next to the highest subkingdom was actually
represented (see above classification), and that
there must have been a long line of simpler and
simpler ancestors, probably extending far back into
the Archeozoic era. When we stop to consider that
Archeozoic and Proterozoic time was fully as long
as all succeeding geological time, it is not so surprising that fairly highly developed animals (except vertebrates) had been evolved before the close
of the Proterozoic era.

In regard to abundance of fossil animals the oldest
(Cambrian) Paleozoic strata stand out in marked
contrast to the Proterozoic. Many hundreds of
species of animal fossils have been described from
Cambrian strata, and a great many others yet
remain to be discovered. Cambrian fossils are remarkably numerous, varied in species, and complex
in organization (Plate 13). All subkingdoms of
animals except the vertebrates were represented,
though usually only by the simpler types in each
subkingdom. It is quite generally agreed that no
less than 50 per cent of animal evolution had
taken place before the beginning of the Cambrian
period. The reader should, however, clearly bear
in mind that tremendous advances in evolution have
taken place since early Cambrian time when not

only all forms from lower scale arthropods to the highest mammals (including man) have evolved, but also when many thousands of species of lower subkingdom animals developed.

Why are the very early Paleozoic strata so rich in fossils, while the immediately preceding Proterozoic rocks show so few? The seemingly sudden appearance of so many highly developed animals in earliest Paleozoic (Cambrian) time is one of the most important considerations in the history of animal life, and it is by no means definitely understood. The following statements bear directly upon the problem: The early animal forms were probably soft or gelatinous without shells and lived mostly in the open sea where food (seaweeds, etc.) was abundant. Such animals were very unfavorable for preservation in fossil form. Then, late in Proterozoic time or very early in the Paleozoic, a severe struggle for existence set in, probably due to crowding along shores, and hard parts began to develop both for support and defensive purposes. Such hard parts or shells were commonly favorable for fossilization. This view is strongly supported by the fact that very thin shells only are known from late Proterozoic rocks, and mostly very thin shells from the earliest Cambrian, the heavier shells having been evolved later. A fact of importance to bear in mind in this connection is that just at the critical time (late Proterozoic) in shell development, the lands of the earth were undergoing widespread and deep erosion as pointed out early in the chapter on "Ancient Earth History." The earliest Cambrian strata, therefore, nearly everywhere rest upon the deeply eroded surface of the Proterozoic rocks so that the transition strata—the very ones which would contain most fossils of the early shell development stage—are nearly everywhere missing. Finally, mention should be made of the fact, that all Archeozoic strata are profoundly altered (metamorphosed), and so are nearly all Proterozoic strata, except the later. Fossils once present in those rocks would of course have been obliterated by the process of metamorphism, but the fact remains that very considerable thicknesses of practically unaltered Proterozoic strata show few if any animal fossils.

We shall now proceed to a rather systematic consideration of the most interesting and significant types of creatures which have inhabited the earth since the beginning of Paleozoic time at least twenty-five million years ago. It is our purpose to bring out the salient features in the history of each subkingdom of animals, beginning with the lowest or simplest, and taking up in turn the higher and higher subkingdoms. By this method the reader may easily follow the main thread of organic evolution or progressive change which runs through most of the known history of animal life of our planet, and which is so important in the science of geology.

Protozoans, which include all the tiny single-celled animals, are known in fossil form even in late Proterozoic rocks and, as proved by the fossil records, they have been more or less abundant ever since, even now swarming in large portions of the surface sea waters. One of the most remarkable facts in the history of animal life is, that such exceedingly simple creatures persisted almost without change through the tens of millions of years when such profound and even revolutionary changes took place in the animal kingdom in general. The only fossil protozoans are those which developed delicate shells either of carbonate of lime (the foraminifers)' or silica. Special mention should be made of the Cretaceous period when foraminifers must have been exceedingly profuse in clear sea waters which spread over the Gulf Coastal Plain of the United

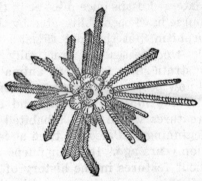

FIG. 49.—A compound colony of fossil graptolites characteristic of late Ordovician time, fully 450,000,000 years ago. Each little prong once held a tiny individual living graptolite which was a very simple type of animal belonging to the subkingdom called "cœlenterates." (Modified after Ruedemann.)

States, parts of southern England, much of France, and other areas, as proved by their fossil shells which are common in formations of chalk hundreds of feet in thickness and many miles in extent.

The cœlenterates, which comprise the simplest of the many-celled animals, are saclike forms with mouth openings, but with few other differentiations of parts. All are marine animals. Of these the sponges are porous, and the other types (including corals) have tentacles around their mouths. Sponges have been more or less common from early Paleozoic time to the present, and they have undergone relatively little change. "Jellyfishes," which are in truth not fishes at all, are wholly soft or gelatinous cœlenterates which have left some very remarkable impressions and casts in strata of very early Paleozoic age, those very ancient forms evidently having been almost exactly like those of to-day. Graptolites were slender, plumelike, delicate forms consisting of colonies of tiny individuals, in many cases in branching or radiating combinations. They existed only during the first half of the Paleozoic era. Both because they floated in the open sea, thus permitting widespread distribution, and because they underwent many distinct species changes during short geologic intervals, they are among the most useful fossils for separating the various subdivisions of strata of the earlier Paleozoic.

Corals comprise another important branch of the cœlenterates. During the Cambrian period there

FIG. 50.—Corals, representing the very simple subkingdom of animals called "cœlenterates": a, fossil shell of an individual "cup coral" found only in Paleozoic strata; b, a compound or "chain coral" skeleton found only in relatively old Paleozoic strata; and c, part of a modern coral colony showing living corals.

were coral-like sponges and possibly simple corals, but from the early Ordovician to the present true corals have been common, especially in the clearer, warmer seas. Their carbonate of lime skeletons have accumulated to help build up great limestone formations representing almost every geologic age from early Paleozoic time to the present. Paleozoic corals were in general notably different from those of later time. There were three main types including the compound "honeycomb" and "chain" types, and the solitary or compound "cup" type. They all had four, or multiples of four, radiating partitions; were rarely branched; and were generally large, some individual cup corals ranging in length from half an inch to a foot or more. Modern corals (beginning with the Mesozoic) have six or eight partitions; are nearly all profusely branched; and are mostly tiny individuals.

Echinoderms are all marine animals, including the so-called "starfishes," which are not really fishes. They have body cavity, with digestive canal, low order nervous system, and a water circulatory system. Most of them have radially segmented shells or skeletons. The oldest fossil forms are found in Cambrian strata, these being very simple or primitive types, with a bladderlike head set on the end of a segmented stem, both head and stem having been supported by carbonate of lime. Such forms lived only to middle Paleozoic time. Ordovician strata contain representatives of all the main types of echinoderms in well-fossilized forms.

A stemmed echinoderm of special interest, first known from the Ordovician, has persisted to the present day. It is the so-called "sea lily" or "stone lily," consisting of a complex, headlike portion attached to the sea bottom by a long segmented stem, the whole being supported by lime carbonate. They were very numerous during the Silurian, but they seem to have culminated in variety of species and numbers of individuals during the Mississippian period when they were exceedingly profuse. Hundreds of species of "stone lilies" are known from

Mississippian strata alone, and in certain localities, as at Crawfordsville, Ind., and Burlington, Ia., the "stone lily" remains are so numerous that when liv-

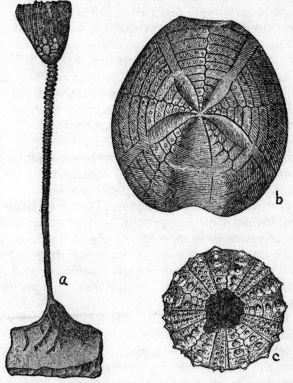

FIG. 51.—Fossil echinoderms or so-called "starfishes": a, simple type known as the "stone lily" with head, stem, and roots intact from Silurian strata; b and c, irregular and regular higher type echinoderms called "sea urchins" from Cretaceous strata.

ing they must have literally forested parts of the sea bottom. From Mississippian time to middle Mesozoic time they occupied a relatively subordinate position when they again developed in great profusion.

The Mesozoic forms were distinctly more like those of to-day, and it scarcely seems credible that any creature could have contained such a multiplicity of hard parts, more than 600,000 segments having been counted in a single fossil from Jurassic strata. The "sea lilies" of to-day are relatively unimportant.

The familiar five-pointed "starfishes," so common along our seacoasts, are first known from the Ordovician, and they persisted through the many millions of years to the present time with remarkably little change. The so-called "sea urchins" live in rounded, segmented lime-carbonate shells bristling with movable spines. "Sea urchins" are first known from the Ordovician, but they did not become abundant and diversified until Mesozoic time, when many of them took on a very modern aspect.

Worms are known to have existed ever since late Proterozoic time, as proved by the occurrence of tracks, borings and more rarely delicate impressions on rock surfaces. Because of their softness they have rarely been well fossilized and are, therefore, of no great evolutionary or geological importance.

The subkingdom molluscoids has been richly represented by both the so-called "sea mosses" and brachiopods. The "sea mosses" form colonies of tiny mosslike tufts, resembling corals outwardly, though they are much more highly organized. They have been common from Ordovician time to the present, their carbonate of lime skeletons often having contributed to the building of limestone formations. Brachiopods always have two external shells or valves, in most cases working on a hinge, and also a pair of long, spiral-fringed arms associated with the soft part of the animal inside the shells.

They differ from the other type of bivalve (e. g., clam, oyster) in that they are symmetrical with reference to a plane passed through the middle of the shells at right angles to the hinge line. They have rarely grown to be more than a few inches long. A few scant brachiopod remains are known from the late Proterozoic, but throughout known geologic time they reached their greatest development in the Paleozoic era, more especially in the Devonian period. Combining number of species and number of individuals, the brachiopods probably hold the record of all important groups of fossil

FIG. 52.—Fossil brachiopods belonging to the subkingdom of animals known as "molluscoids": a, b, c, forms characteristic of the Ordovician, Devonian, and Triassic periods, respectively.

animals, more than 7,000 species being known. Many layers of rock are filled with their shells (Plate 21). Since the close of the Paleozoic they have fallen off notably, and are now represented by relatively few small forms. From the standpoint of evolution it is interesting to note that in very early Paleozoic time the brachiopods were mostly small, of relatively simple organization, and their thin shells were not joined by hinges. Later they became larger and more complex and their thicker shells worked on hinges. Nearly all the Paleozoic forms had long, straight hinge lines, which made it difficult for their enemies to open them. Along with the change to narrower, curved hinge lines came the decline of the tribe. They have been of great value to the geologist in subdividing the geological column of strata into its many formations.

The mollusks, which are more highly organized than the molluscoids, have more or less distinctly developed heads and locomotive organs. Many thousands of species are now extinct, the classes of most geological importance being represented by clams, snails, and the pearly nautilus. Most of them have shells and gills for breathing. The members of the simplest group, well represented by the clam tribe, possess two similar shells working on hinges, so that in this regard they are much like brachiopods, but, unlike the latter, they are not symmetrical with reference to a plane at right angles to the hinge line. Cambrian strata contain the oldest known of the fossil forms where they are small, relatively thin-shelled, and rare. In marked contrast to the brachiopods these bivalves have rather steadily increased in numbers of species and individuals to the present time, now being represented by thousands of forms. During the Mesozoic era they greatly outnumbered the brachiopod bivalves and took on a more distinctly modern aspect, when the oyster tribe and closely related types were prominently developed. Culmination in size and thickness of shell seem to have been reached in early Cenozoic time, strata of that age in certain places, for example in Georgia and southern California, being filled with oyster shells 10 to 20 inches long and 4 to 6 inches thick! In addition to their gigantic size and thickness, many of the shells were fluted or ribbed, and so they represented an extreme type of defensive armor among the lower animals.

Snails have existed from the earliest Paleozoic era to the present time, and the outstanding fact of interest concerning them is that they furnish one of the finest illustrations of an important class of animals which has undergone practically no conspicuous change or evolution during all those millions of years of time.

We shall now turn our attention to the highest order of mollusks—the cephalopods. These creatures, whose heads are armed with powerful tentacles and supplied with complex eyes, propel themselves by forcible ejection of water. One general type—the chambered cephalopod—has a shell divided into compartments (e. g., modern pearly nautilus) which are successively built up and abandoned by the animal as it grows larger. These chamber-shelled cephalopods constitute one of the most remarkable and instructive illustrations of evolutionary change within any important subgroup of invertebrate animals, ranging from early Paleozoic to the present. Both because of the abundance of fossil forms in rocks of all these periods of geological times, and because certain of the evolutionary changes are so clearly expressed in the well preserved shell portions, they are specially adapted for study. In the late Cambrian only straight and slightly curved forms with smooth, nearly straight chamber partitions existed. Notable advance took place during the next (Ordovician) period when there were straight, curved, open-coiled, and even close-coiled forms. All had simple partitions, and the straighter forms predominated. "The size attained by the Ordovician cephalopods was probably never surpassed by representatives of the class. Some of the (straight) shells were twelve to fifteen feet in length, and a foot in diameter. From this great size they ranged down to or below the size

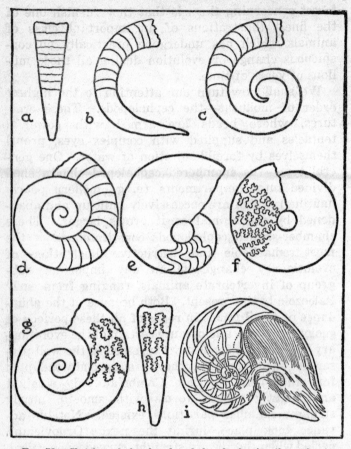

FIG. 53.—Sketches of chambered cephalopods showing the main steps in the evolution of the shell forms and compartment partitions: a, b, the only kinds in Cambrian time; c, d, forms added in the Ordovician; e, added in the Devonian; f, added in the late Paleozoic; g, h, characteristic of the Mesozoic era; and i, a living form (pearly nautilus) cut through. (Drawn by the author.)

of a pipe stem." (Chamberlin and Salisbury.) They were more than likely the undisputed masters of the Ordovician seas. Silurian time marked no important change in their structures, but the coiled forms predominated for the first time. During the second half of the Paleozoic era all preceding types with simple partitions persisted, but in some forms the simple partitions gradually became angled and finally rather complexly curved. During the Mesozoic era the partition lines of the close-coiled forms evolved until a most remarkable degree of complexity was attained, comparable, indeed, to the sutures of the human skull plates. These remarkable forms called ammonites, of which more than 2,000 species are known, began with the Mesozoic, reached their climax, and passed out of existence toward the close of the same era. Certain strata of Jurassic age are literally filled with ammonites, some shells being several feet in diameter. Various eccentric changes took place in the ammonites shortly before their extinction. Some shells became uncoiled and even straight, thus outwardly at least showing reversion to the original early Paleozoic ancestors, but with retention of the complex partitions. Others assumed spiral shapes and still others became curved or coiled at each end. While these extraordinary evolutionary changes were going on among the chambers of cephalopods during Mesozoic time, some of the ancient close-coiled forms with very simple partitions managed to persist. In fact this simple type, almost exactly like its early Paleozoic ancestor, has been the only one out of this whole remarkable class of animals to persist to the present time, being now barely represented by the well-known pearly nautilus of the Indian Ocean.

During the Mesozoic era the highest type of cephalopod, represented by modern squids and so-called "cuttlefishes," branched off and developed in

great profusion. These had slender internal shells,
but no external chambered shells. An inky black
liquid secreted in a bag was forced out to cloud the
water when the animal was escaping its enemy, thus
antedating by millions of years the principle of

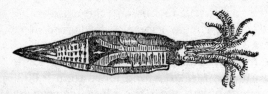

FIG. 54.—A fossil nonchambered cephalopod of Jurassic age. It
was closely related to the modern squid, and its ink bag is well shown
just to the left of the middle. (Modified after Mantell.)

smoke screen so effectively used by ships during
the World War. Some Jurassic species got to be
over two feet long, and a few specimens of that age
have been found in such perfect state of preservation that drawings of the fossils have actually been
made with the ink (after moistening) taken from
their own ink bags.

Before concluding this chapter we shall take up
the salient points in the geological history of arthropods which constitute the highest subkingdom of
all animals except the vertebrates. They are now
very abundant and varied, familiar examples being
crabs and insects. A few scant remains of simpler
forms are known from the Proterozoic, but since
very early Paleozoic time they have been very
common and have undergone great evolutionary
changes. A few striking examples only will be
dwelt upon. Among the most common and interesting of all Paleozoic animals were the trilobites,
distantly related to modern lobsters and crabs.

Some of these grew to be two feet long, but usually they were only one or two inches long. First known from the earliest Paleozoic, they reached their culmination relatively early in the era and then dwindled away to utter extinction before its close. "They were characteristic of the Paleozoic era, beginning in great variety in the Lower Cambrian and dominating the seas of the Cambrian (300 species) and Ordovician (950 species). In the Silurian, though they were still common, the trilobites were nevertheless on the decline (485 species), and this ebbing of their vital force is seemingly shown in many picturesque forms replete with protuberances, spines, and exaggeration of parts. As a rule, in evolution, one finds that when an organic stock is losing its vital force there

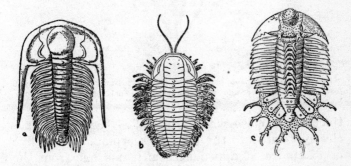

FIG. 55.—Restorations of trilobites based upon actual fossils characteristic of earlier Paleozoic time: a, Cambrian; b, Ordovician; c, Devonian; b shows the appendages.

arises in it an exaggeration of parts, as if heroic efforts were being made to maintain the race. Spinosity in animals is often the prophecy of tribal death. In the Devonian, the variety and number of the trilobites were greatly reduced (105 species),

at a time when the ancient types of fishes, which
undoubtedly fed on these crustaceans (trilobites),
began to be common in the seas. In the
later Paleozoic seas, the trilobites were relics,
or animals surviving from a time better suited
to their needs, and one by one they vanished,
until a little before the close of the Paleozoic era
none were left." (Schuchert.)

An extraordinary type of arthropod which
ranged throughout Paleozoic time and became ex-

FIG. 56.—A giant sea scorpion of Devonian time. Length nearly 9
feet. (After Clarke and Reudemann, New York State Museum.)

tinct at its close was the so-called "sea scorpion,"
closely related to the modern scorpion. Their five
or six pairs of appendages all came out from the
head portion, one pair in some cases having been
developed as powerful pincers. Their culmination
in size was reached during the Devonian when some
forms grew to the astonishing length of over eight
feet! Such gigantic creatures must have been
tyrants of the seas until they were subdued by the
oncoming powerful fishes. True scorpions are
known from rocks as old as the Silurian. Lobsters

and crabs made their appearance during the Mesozoic era.

Since insects constitute the highest subdivision
of arthropods, they include the very highest forms
of animal life except the vertebrates. The oldest
known fossil insects are from Pennsylvania strata,
more than 1,000 species having been described from
rocks of that age. They were all simple or primitive types like cockroaches and dragon flies, and
were remarkable for size. Giant cockroaches got
to be four inches long. One form of dragon fly,
with a spread of wing of over two feet, was probably the largest insect which ever lived (Plate 19).
Development of insect life was especially favored
during the great Coal Age because of the prolific
vegetation, but more than likely insects originated
somewhat earlier. Early in the Mesozoic era a
great progressive change began to come over insect
life and higher forms gradually evolved until by the
close of the era many of the highest types like flies,
ants, and bees were common. As might be expected,
the highest insects did not develop until after the
appearance of the true flowering plants in later
Mesozoic time, butterflies apparently not having
evolved until early in Cenozoic time. Many of the
thousands of known species of fossil insects are
from strata of Tertiary age during which time they
may have been even more numerous than to-day,
although there are about 400,000 species now living.
An almost incredible case is a Tertiary stratum only
a few feet thick in Switzerland from which nearly
1,000 species of insects have been unearthed. Another famous locality is Florissant, Colorado, where
during early Tertiary time there was a small lake
into which showers of fine volcanic dust fell and

entombed vast numbers of insects, more than **2,000** species having been unearthed. Still another extraordinary occurrence is along the shores of the southern Baltic Sea where more than 2,000 species of insects have been found in a fossil resin called amber. The insects were caught in the still soft sticky resin while it was exuding from the trees, and thus we have the insects, fully two or three million years old, literally embalmed and marvelously preserved, often in beautifully transparent amber.

CHAPTER XIX

GEOLOGICAL HISTORY OF VERTEBRATE ANIMALS (INCLUDING MAN)

VERTEBRATES comprise the highest subkingdom of all animals with man himself at the very top. They are characterized by the possession of a vertebral column, which, in all but the very simple or primitive forms, is an ossified backbone. Their main subdivisions are given in the classification table near the beginning of the preceding chapter. The oldest known vertebrates, found in fossil form in middle Ordovician strata, were represented by curious and bizarre creatures called ostracoderms, or more popularly "armor fishes." They were not true fishes because they were really somewhat lower in the scale of organization than fishes. Some were distinctly fishlike in appearance, and others notably resembled certain of the arthropods, so that some students consider them to have formed the connecting link between the highest invertebrates (arthropods) and low order fishes of the vertebrates. The vertebral column always consisted of cartilage or gristle and, in most forms, it extended through tail fin. None had true side fins like fishes, but many were provided with a pair of jointed flappers or paddles. The jawlike portions of the heads moved over each other sidewise as, for example, in beetles and not up and down in true vertebrate fashion. Two eyes were always very close together.

One of the most striking features was the protection
of the head and fore part of the body by an armor
of bony plates, while the rest of the body had scales.
They seldom grew to be more than six or seven

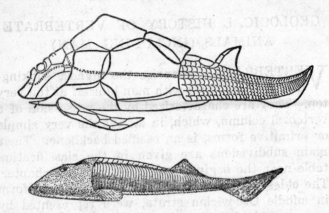

FIG. 57.—Two restored forms of very primitive and ancient (Devonian) types of vertebrates called "ostracoderms." They were lower
in organization than true fishes. (After Dean-Woodward and British
Museum, respectively.)

inches long. Beginning in the Ordovician, they remained rare during the Silurian, and then in the
Devonian period they reached their climax of development only to become extinct at its close. Many
species were abundantly represented in many parts
of the world. By some the ostracoderms are
thought to have been a primitive (sharklike) fish
development in the wrong direction, and hence they
became extinct.

Fishes, represented only by very primitive sharks,
are known to have existed as early as the Silurian
period, but the remains are scant. During the Devonian period, however, they showed a marvelous
development into many species and countless myr-

iads of individuals. The Devonian is, therefore, commonly called the "Age of Fishes." These very ancient (Devonian) primitive (fish) types of vertebrate animal life are of profound significance in organic evolution because they were the direct progenitors of the great groups of still higher vertebrates which since later Paleozoic time gradually increased in diversity and complexity of structure through amphibians, reptiles, birds, and mammals finally to man himself.

In marked contrast to the most typical and highly organized fishes so abundant to-day, all Devonian fishes were of simple types with cartilaginous skeletons and vertebrated tails. Many of them were also generalized types, that is, associated with

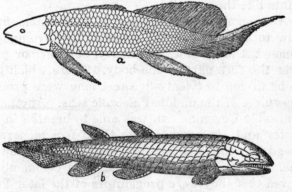

FIG. 58.—Restorations of characteristic Devonian fishes, based upon actual fossils: a, a "lung fish" with leglike fins (after Huasakof) ; b, a "ganoid." (After Nicholson.)

their clearly defined fish characters were others connecting them with certain higher vertebrates, as, for example, amphibians and reptiles. Thus all their tail fins were vertebrated as in reptiles; their labyrinthine, internal tooth structure was to be an amphibian feature when those creatures evolved; many had protective armor or bony scales like most early amphibians and many modern reptiles; and many had paired fins which were something like jointed legs. Most abundant and highly organized of the Devonian fishes were "ganoids," characterized by a covering of small plates or bony scales set together but not overlapping like in typical modern fishes. Their intricate tooth structure and limblike fins strongly suggest the amphibians of later Paleozoic time. The skeleton of cartilage gradually became somewhat ossified during succeeding geologic periods. From their great profusion and diversity in the Devonian period the ganoids have steadily fallen away until they now have very few descendants like the gar pike.

Another important group of remarkable fishes, now totally extinct, but common in Devonian and somewhat later time, had heavy, bony armor plates over the fore part of the body. Those which grew to be fifteen to twenty-five feet long were probably the rulers of the middle Paleozoic seas. Another remarkable Devonian fish was able to breathe in both water and air because, like their few modern descendants, they had both gills and lungs. Because of their leglike fins and lung sac, it is commonly believed that they were progenitors of the later Paleozoic amphibians. The simplest of all fishes, the sharks, began in the Silurian, underwent no important change through the millions of years since, and are now of course well represented. During early Cenozoic time the sharks seem to have reached culmination in size—sixty to eighty feet long, with teeth five or six inches long.

Among modern fishes the most abundant by far, and the most highly organized, are the true bony fishes, called the "teleosts," which made their first appearance in the middle of the Mesozoic era. Those earliest forms clearly show their descent from the ganoids. Apparently they have not yet passed their prime.

We shall now consider the next higher group of vertebrates, the amphibians, which breathe by gills when young and later develop lungs. Many live both on land and in water like the frogs. Unlike fishes they have legs with toes and not fins. Beginning probably in the Devonian as a branch of the fishes, amphibians showed a marvelous development during later Paleozoic and very early Mesozoic times when they reached their climax, after which they fell off remarkably, being now relatively unimportant like the frogs and salamanders. They are of special significance because they were the first of all the back-boned animals (vertebrates) to inhabit the land which they dominated only until the great rise of reptiles of Mesozoic time. The reptiles in fact evolved from the amphibians in the late Paleozoic when many transition forms occurred. (Plate 19.) During those ancient days the numerous and very diversified amphibians were like giant salamanders, commonly five to eight feet long, with one Triassic form fifteen to twenty feet long, and with heavily armored skulls two to four feet long.

Turning now to the reptiles we find that they are much more distinctly land animals than the preceding types of vertebrates. Reptilian life of the earth began in late Paleozoic time as an evolutionary branch of the amphibians. The earliest forms were in many ways much like the amphibians, but gradually they diversified and progressed so that before the close of the Mesozoic era, which has long been called the "Age of Reptiles," they were the rulers of the world. "They covered the land with gigantic herbivorous and carnivorous forms; they swarmed in the sea, and, as literal dragons, they dominated the air." (Scott.) Mesozoic reptiles are of special interest and significance not only in themselves, but also because from one of their branches the birds were evolved, and from another the mammals. "In advancing from the amphibian to the reptile the evolution of the vertebrates was far from finished. The cold-blooded, clumsy and sluggish, small-brained and unintelligent reptile is as far inferior to the higher mammals, whose day was still to come, as it is superior to the amphibian and the fish." (Norton.)

Since the reptiles of the Mesozoic era constitute one of the few most remarkable and diversified classes of animals which ever inhabited the earth, we shall attempt to give the reader a fair idea of the most typical groups which have been totally extinct since the close of the Mesozoic era some millions of years ago. Of the swimming reptiles which lived in the seas many types are known and only a few will be described. Among these one important type was the ichthyosaur, a fishlike form which not uncommonly grew to be twenty to forty feet long (Plate 18). The large head, sometimes four or five feet long, contained as many as 200 big sharp teeth and enormous eyes up to a foot in diameter. The body was heavy set, and the neck very short. There were four short, stout swimming paddles, and the tail was vertebrated. Some specimens of ichthyosaurs have been so perfectly preserved in Mesozoic strata

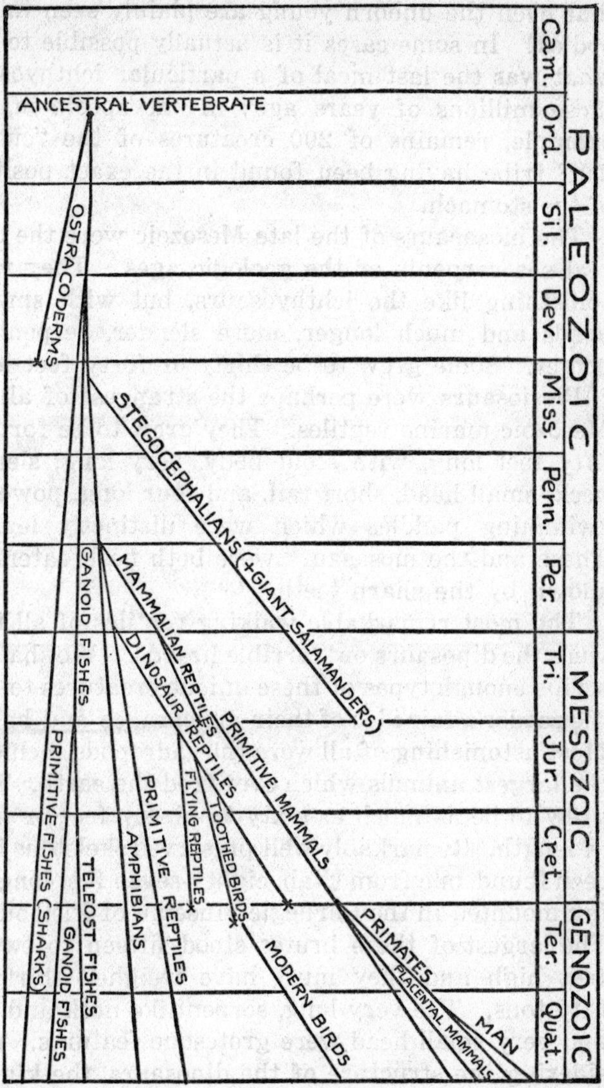

FIG. 59.—Chart showing the main branches in the history of vertebrate (back-boned) animal life reaching its culmination in man. (By the author, in part after Cleland.)

that even the unborn young are plainly seen in the
bodies! In some cases it is actually possible to tell
what was the last meal of a particular ichthyosaur
those millions of years ago; in one specimen, for
example, remains of 200 creatures of the "cuttle-
fish" tribe having been found in the exact position
of the stomach.

The mosasaurs of the late Mesozoic were the only
real sea serpents of the geologic ages. They were
something like the ichthyosaurs, but with smaller
heads and much longer, more slender, serpentlike
bodies. Some grew to be thirty or forty feet long.

Plesiosaurs were perhaps the strangest of all the
Mesozoic marine reptiles. They grew to be forty to
fifty feet long, with stout body, very long, slender
neck, small head, short tail, and four long, powerful
swimming paddles which were distinctly leglike.
These and the mosasaurs were both flesh eaters, as
shown by the sharp teeth.

The most remarkable walking reptiles of all time
were the dinosaurs or "terrible lizards." We shall describe enough types of these unique creatures to give
the reader a fair idea of their appearance and habits.
Most astonishing of all were the sauropods including
the largest animals which ever trod the earth. They
grew to be as much as sixty to ninety feet or more
in length. Remarkably well preserved skeletons have
been found, one from Utah, eighty-seven feet long, being mounted in the Carnegie Museum of Pittsburgh.
The largest of these brutes stood fifteen to twenty
feet high and they must have weighed thirty to
fifty tons. The very long, serpentlike neck and tail,
and very small head were grotesque features. Considering the structure of the dinosaurs, the kind of
strata in which they are embedded, and the asso-

PLATE 19.—(*a*) RESTORATION OF A LATE PALEOZOIC (COAL AGE) LAND-
SCAPE. Showing the main kinds of plants which have entered into the
making of most of our coal. Giant "club mosses" both with and without
branches, in the left background; giant "horsetail" (or "scouring rush")
plants on the right; and seed ferns in the left foreground. A primitive
reptile in the water; two large amphibians or giant salamanders, called
"stegocephalians," on the land; and a great "dragon fly," two feet wide,
in the air. (*From a drawing by Prof. Williston. Courtesy of D. Van
Nostrand Co.*)

PLATE 19.—(*b*) PHOTOGRAPH OF A FOSSIL FERN OR SEED FERN FROND
ON A PIECE OF SHALE MILLIONS OF YEARS OLD. The specimen is of the
Pennsylvanian Age and was taken from the coal fields of Pennsylvania.
(*After White, U. S. Geological Survey.*)

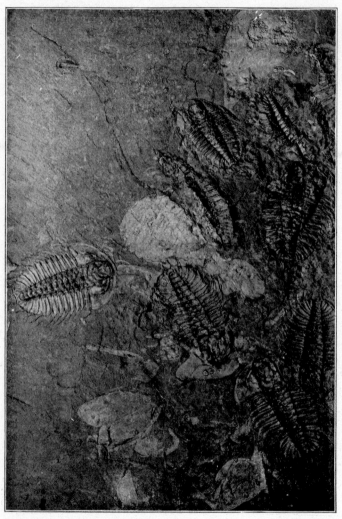

PLATE 20.—A SLAB OF VERY EARLY PALEOZOIC (CAMBRIAN) ROCK, COVERED WITH SOME OF THE OLDEST DEFINITELY DETERMINABLE ANIMAL REMAINS. These creatures lived in a sea which overspread the site of the Rocky Mountains of southern Canada fully 500,000,000 years ago. Most of the fossils are trilobites (including some very small ones) and other related crustacean forms (lighter portions). (After C. D. Walcott, Smithsonian Institution, Washington, D. C.)

ciated fossil remains, it seems clear that they mostly
lived in and near fresh water and on near-by lowlands. The character of their teeth shows that they
fed entirely on soft plants which they must have
habitually bolted because their teeth were not well
adapted to grinding food. It is difficult to believe
that a single huge beast could have consumed less
than a few hundred pounds of vegetable matter per
day, and, on account of the very small size of the
head, he must have spent most of his time eating.

FIG. 60.—Skeleton of a great four-legged (sauropod) dinosaur. A
mounted skeleton in the American Museum of Natural History, New
York, is sixty-seven feet long. This creature lived millions of years ago
during the Jurassic period. (After Marsh.)

Also the comparatively very small size of the brain,
and its simplicity of structure, render it certain that
they were extremely stupid creatures. "To make
up for this they had an enormous enlargement of
the spinal cord in the sacral region (i. e., over the
hind legs). This sacral brain—if we may so call it
—was ten to twenty times bigger than the cranial
brain. It was necessary in order to work the
powerful hind legs and tail." (Le Conte.)

Another dinosaur, in some respects like the sauropod, was the stegosaur which grew to be twenty to
thirty feet long, and heavier than the elephant. Unlike the sauropod, it had a short neck and was
armored with a double row of great plates over its

back, and sharp spines (one to three feet long) toward the end of the tail. The excessive stupidity of the creature is proved by the fact that its very simple brain weighed less than three ounces! Stegosaurs

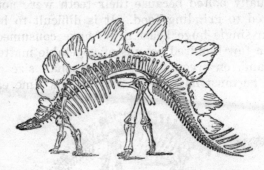

FIG. 61.—Skeleton of the curious kind of dinosaur (stegosaur) of Mesozoic Age with great bony plates over the back. Length about thirty feet. (After Marsh.)

were plant eaters as indicated by the tooth structure, and, though they looked ferocious, they were probably not fighters, certainly at least nothing like the carnivorous types of dinosaurs we shall soon describe.

The ferocious dinosaurs of Mesozoic time were carnivorous, or flesh eaters, as shown by their numerous sharp teeth in relatively large heads. The largest known type is the tyrannosaur, an almost perfect skeleton of which, 40 feet long and 16 feet high, is mounted in the American Museum of Natural History in New York (Plate 23). So far as known, this was the largest carnivorous animal which ever walked on the earth. It is evident from the structure that it walked on its hind legs, the front ones having been much shorter and used something like arms. There were also various other

smaller forms of two-legged flesh-eating dinosaurs,
many of the wonderfully preserved tracks in the
Triassic sandstones of the Connecticut River Valley
having been made by such creatures when they
walked around over soft, sandy mud flats at least
eight or ten million years ago. The sandy mud
with its tracks became somewhat hardened and
then deeply buried under much more sediment
which, through the ages, has been eroded off, thus
exposing to view certain of the layers covered with
tracks. Some bones of dinosaurs have also been
found in the Connecticut Valley.

Another remarkable type of two-legged dinosaur
was much like the flesh eaters just described, but
they were plant eaters. The largest of these grew

Fig. 62.—Skeleton (restored) of a great two-legged dinosaur of the
Mesozoic era. This type of plant eater grew to be fully twenty-five feet
long. (After Marsh.)

to be 30 feet long and 15 to 20 feet high, comparable, therefore, to the tyrannosaur in size. A
wonderful collection of almost perfect skeletons
may be seen in the museum in Brussels, Belgium.

In mining coal 1,000 feet below the surface in Belgium, twenty-two complete skeletons and several partial skeletons were found in an ancient river deposit of Cretaceous Age. A marvelously preserved specimen of one of these two-legged plant eaters found in Wyoming, has been called a "dinosaur mummy" because the skin and much of the flesh of the creature had shriveled down upon its bones. The minutest details of the texture of its skin are almost perfectly preserved.

Another type of dinosaur, so different from the others, should be briefly described. This was tricera-

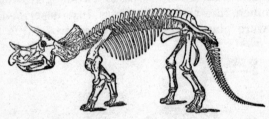

FIG. 63.—Skeleton of a dinosaur (triceratops) with a large remarkable head. This creature grew to be twenty-five feet long during Cretaceous time. (After Marsh.)

tops, or the "three-horned face" beast, so named because of the three powerful horns which projected forward from the top of the very large, flattened skull. It grew to be twenty to twenty-five feet long. Skulls six to eight feet long have been unearthed. Just where the brain might have developed, the skull dished downward, and so one authority considers triceratops to have had the largest head and smallest brain of all the great reptiles.

It is well known that dinosaurs of many types lived during the great "Age of Reptiles," though by no means all types ranged through the whole era. No dinosaurs are definitely known to have crossed the line into the Cenozoic era. One of the most astonishing facts in the history of animal life is the extinction of the mighty dinosaurs, but no very satisfactory explanation has yet been offered. Probably their great size was a contributing factor, for it is well known "that while very large animals spend nearly all their time in eating, small animals spend a small proportion of theirs, and most of it in other activities. Now, as long as food is abundant, the larger animals of a race have the better chances, but if a scarcity of food ensues, the larger animals may all be suddenly swept out of existence." (Matthew.) Whatever may have been the real reason for dinosaur extinction we can at least be sure "that with the extensive changes in the elevation of land areas (Rocky Mountain Revolution) which mark the close of the Mesozoic, came the withdrawing of the great inland Cretaceous seas along the low-lying shores of which the dinosaurs had their home, and with the consequent restriction of old haunts, came the blotting out of a heroic race. Their career was not a brief one, for the duration of their recorded evolution was twice that of the subsequent mammalian (Cenozoic) age. They do not represent a futile attempt on the part of nature to people the world with creatures of insignificant moment, but are comparable in majestic rise, slow culmination, and dramatic fall to the greatest nations of antiquity." (Schuchert.)

Among the most extraordinary animals not only of the Mesozoic, but also of all time, were the flying reptiles or literal dragons of the air. Some were very small, while others were the largest creatures which ever flew, with a spread of wing of twenty to twenty-five feet—twice that of any modern bird. Unlike birds they had no feathers, but the two wings consisted of large membranes (batlike) supported by one enormously elongated finger of each front limb. The other fingers were armed with sharp claws. The early Mesozoic flying reptiles had sharp teeth, while the later ones were mostly entirely toothless, but all were carnivorous. Their short bodies were supplied with tails of varying lengths, one long-tailed

Fig. 64.—A small carnivorous flying reptile of Mesozoic time. Spread of wings about two feet. (Restored by Marsh.)

species having a rudder at the end. Their heads were fairly large, but of light build. The creature called "pteranodon" was not only the largest of the flying reptiles, but also probably the most highly specialized creature which ever lived, everything possible apparently having been sacrificed to facilitate flight (Plate 24a). The hollow bones were so wonderfully light and strong that it has been estimated that the living animal, with twenty-five foot spread of wing, and head four feet long, could not have weighed more than twenty-five pounds! The rear portions of the body and hind limbs were very weak.

It should not be thought that the above-described groups of reptiles were the only ones which existed during Mesozoic time. There were also certain groups still living, like turtles, lizards, and crocodiles, but they were doubtless mostly completely under the dominance of certain of the now long-extinct types above described. The oldest-known fossil snakes are from very late Mesozoic rocks, where they are small and comparatively rare. More than likely they evolved from lizards by deterioration of the legs. Poisonous snakes were not evolved until early in the next (Cenozoic) era.

We shall now turn our attention to next to the highest class of vertebrate animals—the birds. They and the mammals are the only warm-blooded animals. What is their ancestry? From what original stock did they branch off? The oldest-known bird lived during the Jurassic period, and it was so decidedly reptilian in character as to render it practically certain that birds are specialized descendants of certain Mesozoic reptiles, though not, as might be supposed, of the flying reptiles. The few known specimens of the Jurassic birds were found in the famous lithographic limestone quarries of Bavaria. At least two of the specimens are in a marvelous state of preservation, with practically the whole skeleton intact and almost perfect impressions of the feathers on the rock. That the creature was really a bird is proved not only by its feathers, but also its beak, brain, limb bones, and feet. Among the reptilian characters are its long, vertebrated tail, teeth set in sockets, and long claws on the wings. This reptilian bird was about the size of a small crow (Plate 23).

By late Cretaceous time the birds made notable evolutionary progress and they became diversified, more than thirty species being known from Cre-

taceous rocks. These were distinctly more modern
in structure and appearance than the Jurassic bird.
The only important reptilian characteristic still
retained was the possession of teeth. The tail had
become much shortened and the brain was still

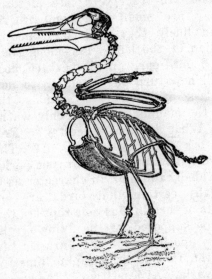

FIG. 65.—An early type of bird with teeth. This bird grew to a height
of about nine inches in Cretaceous time, millions of years ago. (Restored
by Marsh.)

relatively smaller than in modern birds. One type,
about nine inches high, was a powerful flier, as shown
by the strong keel and wing bones. Another important Cretaceous type was almost wholly a water
dweller, with powerfully developed legs used in
swimming. Its teeth were set in grooves instead of
in sockets, thus indicating degeneration of tooth
structure. This type was notable for its size—five
to six feet in length.

During the early part of the Cenozoic era birds became still more advanced and numerous, with many modern groups represented. Some of the more primitive types were, however, still left over during the Tertiary, as, for example, a toothed bird, in which the teeth were merely dentations of the bill, thus being the most degenerate of all types of tooth structure.

Mammals comprise the highest class of all animals. They are, of course, all warm blooded and characterized by suckling their young. So far as known, mammal life began in the early Mesozoic era as a branch of primitive reptiles, but they made little progress throughout the era when they occupied a very subordinate position in the animal world. They were few in number, small, and primitive in structure. There is no evidence for the Mesozoic existence of any of the higher forms of mammals, that is, those which give birth to well-formed young which are prenatally attached to the mother by the so-called placentum. "During the eons of the Mesozoic, from late Triassic time until its close, the mammals (including the remote progenitors of humanity) were in existence, but held in such effective check (by reptiles) that their evolutionary progress was practically insignificant. This curb is strikingly illustrated by the wonderful series of tiny jaws and teeth of these diminutive creatures found in the Comanchian (early Cretaceous) of Wyoming, in actual association with the single tooth of a carnivorous dinosaur, many times the bulk of the largest mammalian jaw. The removal of this check resulted (in the Tertiary period) in the speedy evolution of the archaic mammals." (Schuchert.)

The phenomenal development of mammals during the Tertiary period forms one of the most wonderful chapters in the whole evolution of organisms. Even very early in the Tertiary, many important higher (placental) types of mammals had evolved, and the simpler, more primitive Mesozoic forms became very subordinate. By the close of the Tertiary the higher types of mammals had become marvelously differentiated into most of the present-day groups or types. A very significant feature of the evolution was the steady increase in relative size of brain. The vast numbers of fossil skeletons and bones of mammals found in Tertiary strata is scarcely believable. In our brief discussion we can do no more than describe a few representative examples of the Cenozoic evolution of mammals.

The great diversity of modern placental animals may be suggested by a few examples, as the tiger, dog, horse, camel, elephant, squirrel, hedgehog, whale, monkey, and man. Forms like these, traced back through their ancestors to the very early part of the Tertiary period, gradually become less and less distinct until they cannot be at all distinguished as separate groups, but rather there are ancestral generalized forms which show combinations of features of the later groups. Those early Tertiary generalized placental mammals had four feet of primitive character, with five toes on each foot; the whole foot, which from toe to heel touched the ground, was not adapted to swift running; the teeth were simple (primitive) in type and of full original number (forty-four); the toes were supplied with nails which were about intermediate between real claws and hoofs in structure; and the brain was relatively much smaller and simpler in structure than in most modern mammals.

The history of the horse family furnishes an excellent illustration of certain evolutionary changes among mammals. Skeletons of many species, rang-

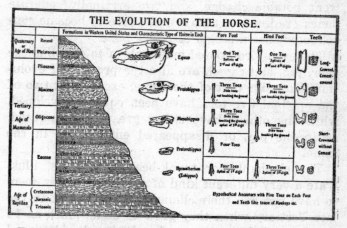

FIG. 66.—Chart showing the main features of interest in the evolution of the horse family through many million years of the present (Cenozoic) era of geologic time. (After Matthew, American Museum of Natural History.)

ing from the early Tertiary to the present, have been found in remarkable state of preservation representing every important change in the history of the horse family. A study of the chart will make clear some of the most striking changes which have taken place. The oldest member of the horse family represented on the chart was about the size of a small fox, with four toes and a degenerated fifth toe (splint) on the front foot, and three toes and splint on the hind foot. Since the chart was made a still more primitive form, even more closely resembling the original five-toed ancestor, has been found. Gradually the middle toe enlarged, while the others disappeared except the two splints or very degenerate toes still left in the modern horse. Increase in size of the animal and brain capacity accompanied these changes. Also the teeth underwent notable change, and two originally separate bones (radius and ulna) of the foreleg became consolidated into a single stronger bone.

The even-toed hoofed mammals of to-day, like the deer, pig, and camel, are also the product of evolution much like that of the horse, except that two of the original five toes have been equally developed, while the others have either greatly degenerated, as in the pig, or disappeared entirely, as in the camel.

The elephants, or trunk-bearing animals, illustrate a very different kind of evolution. They seem to have reached their climax of development in the late Tertiary when they grew to be as much as 14 feet high, and were more abundant and widespread over the earth than at any other time. The modern elephant, like the horse, has been traced back through many intermediate forms to its primitive early Tertiary ancestry. Some of the most important evolutionary changes took place in the head portion. The trunk is a highly developed form of snout, the earliest form of which was much like that of the moden tapir. The tusks are highly specialized and elongated teeth. During the earlier history the chin was very long and supported short tusks, so that there were then four tusks.

Carnivorous mammals, like tigers and wolves, and gnawers, like rats and squirrels, may also be traced back to generalized early Tertiary types.

Another kind of evolution is well illustrated by certain mammals which, even in early Tertiary time, so thoroughly adapted themselves to a water environment as to become whales, porpoises, etc.

The primates include the highest group of all vertebrates, and therefore of all animals. Monkeys, apes, and man belong to the primates. There is no evidence whatever for the appearance of even the simplest and most primitive forms before the open-

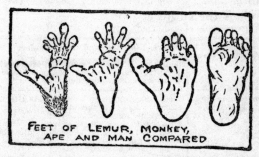

FEET OF LEMUR, MONKEY, APE AND MAN COMPARED

FIG. 67.—Comparison of feet of monkeys and man.

ing of the Cenozoic era, but even very early in Tertiary time, lemurs and primitive types of monkeys existed. Later in the Tertiary true monkeys and apes were common, and by the close of the period some apes were highly enough developed to strongly resemble certain of the oldest and most primitive types of man. We have, however, no positive knowledge of the existence of man in even the latest Tertiary. In the light of much evidence in regard to the antiquity of man, it seems improbable that true human fossils will ever be found in rocks older than the Quaternary, though if we are willing to descend (far enough in the human scale toward apes) it is not unlikely that man-apes may be dis-

covered in very late Tertiary rocks. The difficulty
comes in the classification. Where are we to draw
the line between the higher apes and the lowest
forms of man? But this very difficulty is one of
the strongest arguments in favor of the organic
evolution of man because practically all intermediate forms between true man and certain other high-
grade primates are known from the strata. The
following tabular summary of the geological history
of man is based upon the work of most of the ablest
students of the subject.

3. Homo sapiens (e. g., modern man)	Historic (bronze and iron) age.	Modern
	Neolithic ("recent stone") age (carefully shaped and polished stone implements)	Postglacial but prehistoric
2. Homo primigenius (e. g., Neanderthal man)	Upper Paleolithic ("ancient stone") age (rough bone and stone implements, cave frescoes, bone carvings, etc.)	Late Glacial
	Lower Paleolithic ("ancient stone") age (rude stone implements of so-called "river man")	Middle Glacial
1. Early ancestral forms (e. g., Pithe-canthropus erectus)	Possibly some very crude stone implements	Early Glacial and possibly late Ter-tiary

Of the early ancestral forms, that is, those which
were rather distinctly man-apes, two will be very
briefly referred to. One of these, known as *Pithe-
canthropus erectus,* was a remarkable creature whose
partial skeleton, consisting of the upper part of a
skull, lower jaw, several teeth, and a thigh bone, was
found in early Quaternary deposits in Java in 1891.
It was certainly a man-ape or possibly ape-man of
low order, about 5½ feet high. The skull has a low
crown, very receding forehead, and prominent brow
ridges, but the brain capacity is 850 cubic centimeters, as compared to 500 cubic centimeters in

ordinary higher apes, and nearly 1,500 cubic centimeters in the average modern man. The very recently extinct very low-type aborigines of Tasmania had a skull capacity of 1,199 cubic centimeters.

In 1907 the lower jaw of an anthropoid or manlike ape set with rather human teeth was found associated with very crude stone implements seventy-five feet below the surface in river-deposited sand in Germany. It is of either early or middle Glacial time and quite certainly represents a lower order creature than the oldest Paleolithic man as described below.

Many bones and implements of Paleolithic man (see above table) have been found mainly in river gravels and caves. The relative ages of Paleolithic human bones and implements are best determined by the associated fossil animals. Thus the most ancient truly human fossils are found directly associated with bones of very old types of elephants, rhinoceroses, and hippopotamuses which are definitely known to have lived during middle or early middle Glacial (Quaternary) time corresponding to early Paleolithic time. A very conservative estimate would make the age of such very old human remains at least 150,000 to 250,000 years because the Ice Age was at least 500,000 years long. In a later human stage there are many associations with extinct animals like an older type of mammoth, cave bear, cave hyena, and others of later Glacial time estimated at 50,000 to 150,000 years ago. Last of all was the latest Paleolithic stage corresponding to the close of the Ice Age, the human remains of which are found associated with reindeer and the latest mammoths which roamed in great numbers across Europe. This was probably not more than 30,000 to 50,000 years ago.

Paleolithic man is so called because he fashioned stone weapons and implements. The structure of skull and skeleton shows him to have been a low-type savage, something over five feet high on the average, with a forward stooping carriage. The average

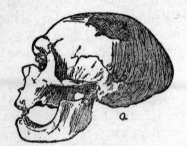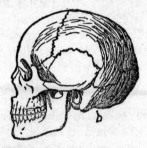

FIG. 68.—Comparison of skulls: a, Paleolithic (Neanderthal) man; b, modern man. (After Woodward, British Museum.)

Paleolithic brain was not greatly inferior in size to that of modern civilized man, but it was not so highly organized and occupied a thick skull with much lower forehead and heavy brow ridges. The bushmen of Australia and the recently extinct Tasmanians are the nearest modern resemblances. Many fine specimens of Paleolithic man have been found, especially in cave deposits. That he was an expert hunter is proved by the great accumulation of bones of now extinct animals found in and about his haunts or camps, bones representing at least 100,000 horses having been found around a single camp site! Only two among the many known Paleolithic man localities will be briefly described. In the Perigord district of southwestern France a number of caves contain human relics ranging in age from early to late Paleolithic. Of special interest among these

relics are fishhooks made of bone, and crude
sketches of animals such as the mammoth and reindeer now extinct in that region. The Aurignac cave,
also in France, was no doubt a family or tribal
burial place. Seventeen Paleolithic human skeletons, associated with bones of extinct animals and
crude art works, were found in the cave. Near the
entrance there were ashes and charcoal mixed with
burned and split bones of extinct animals. Certain
of the caves occupied by late Paleolithic man have
their walls decorated with sketches and even colored
pictures. These are, therefore, the oldest known art
galleries. An excellent example is the cave at Alti-
mira in northern Spain. "As we glance at the pictures one of the first things to impress us is the
excellence of the drawing, the proportions and pos-
tures being unusually good. . . . The next observation may be that, in spite of this perfection of

Fig. 69.—Sketch of a painting by Paleolithic man found in a cave
in west-central France. Various animals, including the extinct mammoth elephant, are represented. (Courtesy of American Museum of
Natural History.)

technique, there is no perspective composition—that
is, no attempt to combine or group the figures. . . .
It is also clear that the work of many different
artists is represented, covering a considerable period
of time. The walls show traces of many other
paintings that were erased to make way for new
work." (Wissler.)

The Neolithic, or "recent stone" age was a gradual development from the late Paleolithic, and man was then more highly developed and more similar in structure to modern man. His stone implements were more perfectly made, and often more or less polished and ground at the edges. "The remains of Neolithic man are found, much as are those of the North American Indians, upon or near the surface, in burial mounds, in shell heaps (the refuse heaps of their settlements), in peat bogs, caves, recent flood-plain deposits, and in beds of lakes near shore where they sometimes built their dwellings upon piles. . . . Neolithic man in Europe had learned to make pottery, to spin and weave linen, to hew timber, and build boats, and to grow wheat and barley. The dog, horse, ox, sheep, goat, and hog had been domesticated." (Norton.)

"Man is linked to the past through the system of life, of which he is the last, the completing creation. But, unlike other species of that closing system of the past, he, through his spiritual nature, is more intimately connected with the opening future." (J. D. Dana.)

CHAPTER XX

MINERALOGY

WE are more or less familiar with the division of all materials of nature into the animal, vegetable, and mineral kingdoms. With slight exceptions minerals are the materials which make up the known part of the earth. In a very real sense, then, mineralogy is the most fundamental of the various branches of the great science of geology because the events of earth history, as interpreted by the geologist, are recorded in the mineral matter (including most rocks) of the earth. When we examine the rocky material or mineral matter of the earth in any region we find that it consists of various kinds of substances each of which may be recognized by certain characteristics. Each definite substance (barring those of organic origin) is called a mineral. Or, more specifically, a mineral is a natural, inorganic, homogeneous substance of definite chemical composition. According to this definition a mineral must be found ready made in nature, must not be a product of life, must be of the same nature throughout, and its composition must be so definite that it can be expressed by a chemical formula. All artificial substances, such as laboratory and furnace products, are excluded from the category of minerals. Coal is not a mineral because it is both organic and of indefinite composition. A few examples of very common substances which perfectly satisfy the definition of a mineral are quartz, feldspar, mica, calcite, and magnetite. Only two substances—water and mercury—are ordinarily liquid minerals. There are nearly a thousand distinct mineral species, and to them and their varieties several thousand names have been applied.

It is a surprising fact that of the eighty or more chemical elements, that is substances which cannot be subdivided into simpler ones, only eight make up more than 98 per cent of the weight of the crust of the earth, though, with one very slight exception, none of the eight exist as such in mineral form. The eight elements are oxygen (nearly 50 per cent), silicon (over 25 per cent), aluminum (over 7 per cent), iron (over 5 per cent), calcium (or "lime"), magnesium (or "magnesia"), sodium (or "soda"), and potassium (or "potash").

Certain rock formations are made up essentially of but one mineral in the form of numerous grains as, for example, limestone, which consists of calcite (carbonate of lime). Most of the ordinary rocks are, however, made up of two or more minerals mechanically bound together. Thus, in a specimen of granite on the author's desk several distinct mineral substances are distinguishable by the naked eye. These mineral grains are from one to five millimeters across. Most common among them are hard, clear, glassy grains called quartz; nearly white, hard grains, with smooth faces, called feldspar; small, silvery white plates, easily separable into very thin flakes, called mica; and small, hard, black grains, called magnetite. It is the business of the mineralogist to learn the characters of each mineral, how they may be distinguished from each other, how they may be classified, how they are found in nature, and what economic value they may have. It is an important part of the business of the geologist to learn what individual minerals combine to form the many kinds of rocks, how such rocks originate, what changes they have undergone, and what geological history they record. It is thus clear that the great science of geology is much broader in its scope than mineralogy.

One of the most remarkable facts about minerals is that most of them by far have a crystalline structure, that is they are built up of tiny particles known as molecules. Such crystalline minerals are often more or less regular solid forms bounded by plane faces and sharp angles, such forms being known as "crystals." How do crystals develop such regularity of form? Any solid is considered to be made up of many very tiny (submicroscopic) molecules held together by an attractive force called cohesion. In liquids the molecules may more or less freely roll over each other, thus altering the shape of the mass without disrupting it. In gases the molecules are considered to be relatively long distances apart and moving rapidly. During the process of change of a substance from the condition of a liquid or gas to that of a solid, due to lowering of temperature or evaporation, the cohesive force pulls the particles (molecules) together into a rigid mass. Under favorable conditions such a solid has a regular polyhedral form. "This results from the fact that the particles or molecules of the substance which, while it was liquid or gaseous, rolled about on one another, have been in some way arranged, grouped and built up. To illustrate this, suppose a quantity of small shot to be poured into a glass: the shot will represent the molecules of a substance in the liquid state, as for example a solution of alum. If, now, we suppose these same shot to be coated with varnish or glue so that they will adhere to each other, and imagine them grouped as shown in Figure 70a, they will represent the arrangement of the molecules of the alum after it has become solid or crystallized. This arranging, grouping, and piling up of molecules is called crystallization, and the solid formed in this way is called a crystal. Figures 70b and 70c show the shot arranged to reproduce

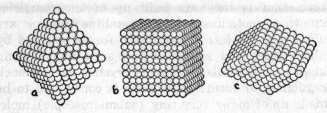

FIG. 70.—Piles of shot arranged to give some idea of the manner in which molecules are bound together in various crystal forms. (After Whitlock, New York Museum.)

two common forms of crystals (e. g., fluorite and calcite)." (Whitlock.)

A combination of certain facts regarding crystals furnish all but absolute proof of some sort of regularity of arrangement of particles within them. Among such facts are the following: (1) the wonderful regularity of arrangement of faces upon crystals is practically impossible to account for except as the outward manifestation of regularity of structure or systematic network arrangement of the interior; (2) most crystals split or cleave more or less perfectly in one or more directions presumably in accordance with certain layered structure of the constituent particles; (3) all of the many known forms of crystals can be accurately grouped in regard to their effects upon the passage of light (especially polarized light) through them, each kind or type of network structure presumably producing a different effect upon light; and (4) X-ray photographs have proved that particles, or at least groups of particles, are very systematically arranged within crystals.

It will be instructive for us to make a comparison between the growth of crystals and organisms. Both really grow, but each species of organism is rather definitely limited in size while there is no known limit to the size which may be attained by a crystal so long as material is supplied to it under proper conditions. As a matter of fact crystals vary in size from microscopic to several feet in length, those less than an inch in length being most abundant by far. Organisms mostly grow from within, while crystals grow from material externally added. It is an astonishing fact that in crystals as well as organisms growth takes most rapidly on a wound or broken place. Thus if a crystal is removed from the solution in which it is growing and put back after a corner has been broken off, the fractured surface will build up more rapidly than the rest. Finally, crystals are not necessarily limited in age like organisms. Under certain natural conditions, as, for example, weathering, crystals may decay or be broken up; but where they are protected as constituent parts of rock formations well below the earth's surface they may remain unchanged for indefinite millions of years. Thus in a ledge of the most ancient known or Archeozoic rock only recently laid bare by erosion one may see crystals which are precisely as they were when they crystallized many millions of years ago.

One of the most remarkable properties of a crystal is its symmetry, by which is meant the greater or less degree of regularity in the arrangement of its faces, edges, and vertices. A given substance may, according to circumstances, crystallize in a variety of forms or combinations of forms, but, with very few exceptions, all crystals of a given substance exhibit the same kind or grade of symmetry. There are three kinds of crystal symmetry, namely, in respect to a plane, a line or axis, and a point or center. A plane of symmetry divides a crystal into halves in such a way that for every point on one side of the plane there is a corresponding point directly opposite on the other side. Crystals may be cut into halves along various surfaces which are not symmetry planes. An axis of symmetry is a line about which a complete rotation (or in a few cases rotation combined with reflection) brings the crystal into the same relative position two, three, four or six times, these being called two, three, four, and sixfold axes of symmetry—no others being possible. A crystal has a center of symmetry when any line passing through it encounters corresponding points at equal distances from it on opposite sides. There are just 32 classes or combinations of the symmetry elements among crystals and just 232 definite crystal forms. Not only is it demonstrable that no more can exist, but actual experience with crystals of hundreds of species of minerals has never revealed any more. Obviously, then, symmetry furnishes us with a very scientific basis of classification of crystals, all of the 232 crystal forms constituting the 32 symmetry classes being in turn referable to seven fundamental crystal systems. To bring out the relations of the faces of a crystal and further aid in classification, prominent, straight lines or directions passing through the center of a crystal are chosen as crystallographic axes. Such axes may or may not coincide with symmetry axes. Basing our definitions upon both symmetry axes and crystallographic axes, the seven systems are as follows:

1.   Isometric.   There must be at least four three-fold axes of symmetry, while the highest grade

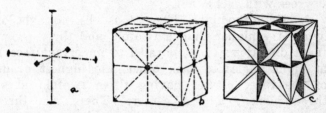

FIG. 71.—Figures showing, a, crystal axes of Isometric system; b, points of emergence of the nine axes of symmetry in a cube of the Isometric system; c, nine planes of symmetry in a cubic crystal. (After Whitlock, New York State Museum.)

symmetry class of the five in the system includes three fourfold, four threefold, and six twofold axes of symmetry; nine planes of symmetry; and a center of symmetry. There are three interchangeable crystallographic axes at right angles to each other.

2.   Tetragonal.   There must be one and only one fourfold symmetry axis, while the highest of its seven symmetry classes contains also four twofold axes of symmetry; five planes; and a center. Characterized by three crystallographic axes at right angles to each other, only two of them interchangeable.

3.   Trigonal.   Characterized by one and only one threefold symmetry axis, the highest of the five

classes having also three twofold axes; four planes; and a center. Crystallographic axes as for hexagonal.

4. **Hexagonal.** One and only one sixfold axis of symmetry must be present, but the highest of the seven classes also has six twofold axes; seven planes; and a center. Characterized by four crystallographic axes, one vertical and three interchangeable horizontal axes making angles of 60 degrees with each other.

5. **Orthorhombic.** There must be no axis of symmetry higher than a twofold and three prominent directions (i. e., parallel to important faces) at right angles to each other, the highest grade of the three classes having three twofold axes; three planes; and a center. There are three noninterchangeable crystallographic axes at right angles.

6. **Monoclinic.** There is no axis of symmetry higher than a twofold and only two prominent directions at right angles to each other, the highest of the three classes having one twofold axis; one plane; and a center. There are three noninterchangeable crystallographic axes, only two of which are at right angles.

7. **Triclinic.** There is no axis of symmetry of any kind, and there are no prominent directions at right angles. One of the two classes has a center of symmetry only, and the other no symmetry at all. Characterized by three noninterchangeable crystallographic axes, none at right angles.

A fact which should be strongly emphasized is that crystals only, of all the objects of nature, can be definitely referred to the above seven systems comprising the 32 classes of symmetry, and 232 crystal forms. Since there are about 1,500 mineral species and only 232 fundamental forms, it necessarily follows that two or more species may crystallize in the same form within a class, so that it is not always possible to tell the species of mineral merely by its crystal form. It is, however, a remarkable fact that, where two or more substances crystallize

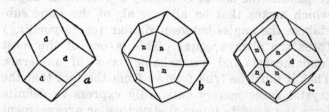

Fig. 72.—Figures illustrating three crystal forms with exactly the same symmetry elements; a and b are separate forms, and c is a combination of the two. The mineral "garnet" nearly always crystallizes in one of these forms.

in the same class (i. e., show the same grade of symmetry) each substance almost invariably exhibits "crystal habit" which is a pronounced tendency to crystallize in certain relatively few forms or combinations of forms out of the many possibilities. It is clear, then, that grade of symmetry combined with "habit" are of great practical value in determining crystallized minerals, because, on the basis of symmetry, a crystal is referred to a certain definite symmetry class in which only a limited number of substances crystallize, and then, by its characteristic "habit," the particular substance can be told.

From the above discussion it should not be presumed that crystals always develop with perfect geometric symmetry. As a matter of fact such is seldom the case because, due to variations of conditions or interference of surrounding crystals in liquids (ordinary or molten), a crystal usually grows more rapidly (by building out faces) in certain directions than in others. Under such conditions actual crystals are said to become distorted because they are not geometrically perfect.

Whether geometrically perfect or not, all crystals respond to the law of constancy of interfacial angles which means that on all crystals of the same substances the angles between similar (corresponding) faces are always equal. This is one of the most fundamental and remarkable laws of minerals. That it must be true follows from the fact that the crystal faces merely outwardly express in definite form the definite internal structure or arrangement of particles which have built up the crystal. In other words, the real structural symmetry of a crystal never varies no matter how much its geometric symmetry may vary. The practical application of the law of constancy of interfacial angles lies in the fact that in many cases a mineral may actually be identified merely by measuring the interfacial angles of its crystal form.

The relative lengths of the crystallographic axes is a very important feature of all crystals except those of the Isometric system in which the axes are always of equal length so that the ratio is 1:1:1. In all the other systems, however, at least one axis differs in length from the others and, since the amount of difference is absolutely characteristic of each substance, the axial ratio of a crystal, when carefully determined by measurement of the angles between the different faces, affords a never-failing method of determining the mineral for

all systems except the isometric. By way of illustration, the tetragonal crystal of the mineral zircon, with only one axis different in length, shows the very definite axial ratio 1:1:0.64, while the orthorhombic crystal of sulphur, with all three axes of different lengths, has an axial ratio 0.813:1:1.903. These ratios of course always hold true no matter what the size or particular outward form of the crystal.

As might be expected from the above discussion of the remarkable structure of crystals, experience has proved that the relative lengths of all intercepts (or distances from the center) of all faces upon any crystal can be expressed by whole numbers, definite fractions, or infinity. It necessarily follows that the ratios between the intercepts of the faces of any face on a crystal to those of any other face on the same crystal may always be expressed by rational numbers, and this is known as the law of definite mathematical ratio. It is a remarkable fact that very small whole numbers or fractions, or infinity or zero, will always express the intercepts of any crystal face.

Thus far our discussion has centered about crystals as individuals, but, in most cases by far, they form groups or aggregates. Most commonly crystal grouping is very irregular, but by no means rare is parallel grouping where whole crystals, or more usually parts of crystals, have all corresponding parts exactly parallel. But most remarkable of all are the twin crystals in which two or more crystals intergrown or in contact have all corresponding parts in exactly reverse order. The conditioning circumstances under which twin crystals develop are unknown.

318 GEOLOGY

In the light of the facts and principles above explained, the reader will more than likely agree with the author that crystals rank very high among nature's most wonderful objects. But there are still other characteristic features of crystals naturally resulting from their marvelous structure. Some of these will now be briefly referred to.

Many crystals and crystalline substances exhibit the important property known as cleavage which is

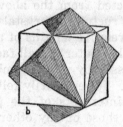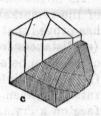

Fig. 73.——Figures illustrating twin crystals: a, gypsum (Monoclinic system); b, fluorite (Isometric system); c, cassiterite (Tetragonal system). (After New York State Museum Bulletin.)

the marked tendency to break easily in certain directions yielding more or less smooth plane surfaces. As would be expected, a cleavage surface is always parallel to an actual, or at least a possible, crystal face, and it takes place along the surfaces of weaker molecular cohesion. The degree of cleavage varies from almost perfect, as in mica, to very poor or none at all, as in quartz. The number of cleavage directions exhibited by common minerals is illustrated as follows: mica, one; feldspar, two; calcite, three; and fluorite, four.

It is a striking fact that when a crystal or cleavage piece is placed in a solvent, the action proceeds with different velocities in crystallographically different directions and little pits or cavities, called etching figures, are developed on some or all of the faces. Since the symmetry of these etching figures and their arrangement upon the faces are directly related to, and natural effects of the crystal symmetry, the figures often furnish an important method of placing a doubtful crystal or even merely a cleavage fragment in its proper symmetry class.

Another marvelous property of crystals and crystalline substances is their effect upon light. Since the study of the passage of light through crystals has really become a large separate branch of mineralogical study, we can no more than state a few fundamental facts and principles in the short space at our disposal. Light is caused by vibrations of the so-called "ether," and always travels in straight lines. The vibration directions are at right angles to the direction of transmission of the light. When a ray of light enters a crystal or crystalline mineral representing any crystal system except the isometric it is doubly refracted (i. e., broken into two rays), each of the two rays is polarized (i. e., made to vibrate in a single plane only), and one ray vibrates almost at right angles to the other. Double refraction is strikingly shown by placing a piece of clear calcite (Iceland spar) over a dot on paper when two dots instead of one are visible. The amount of double refraction varies with the substance, and in some degree according to the direction of passage of light through a crystal. Isometric crystals only are singly refracting and hence a ray of light is not affected in passing through them. Crystals of all the other six systems doubly refract and polarize light and in three systems—Tetragonal, Hexagonal, and Trigonal—one direction (coincident with the main axis of symmetry) produces single refraction

only, while in the remaining three systems—Orthorhombic, Monoclinic, and Triclinic—there are always
two directions of single refraction whose positions
vary with the substance. Many crystals outside the
isometric system also exhibit a remarkable tendency
to absorb light differently in different crystallographic directions, thus producing two or three color
tints, which vary according to the substance. After
gaining a practical knowledge of the above and
many other optical properties of crystals, it is possible by the aid of a specially constructed (polar-
izing) microscope, to recognize (with few exceptions)
each one of the many mineral species. This method
is of great value in determining the various minerals which are aggregated in the form of a rock,
in which case a very thin slice of the rock is studied
with the microscope.

An important criterion for the recognition of
minerals is hardness, by which is meant the resistance of a smooth surface to abrasion or scratching.
The generally adopted scale of hardness follows:

1.—Soft, greasy feel, and easily scratched by the
finger nail (e. g., talc).
2.—Just scratched by the finger nail (e. g., gypsum).
3.—Just scratched by a copper coin (e. g., calcite).
4.—Easily cut by a knife, but does not cut glass
(e. g., fluorite).
5.—Just scratches soft glass, and is cut by a knife
(e. g., apatite).
6.—Harder than steel, and scratches glass easily
(e. g., orthoclase).
7, 8, 9, and 10.—Harder than any ordinary substance and represented in order by quartz,
topaz, corundum, and diamond.

Minerals also show a great variety of colors.
Many of them like quartz and calcite are colorless or

PLATE 21.—(a) PHOTOGRAPHS OF SMALL SLABS OF ORDOVICIAN STRATA FULL OF FOSSILS. These slabs are actual bits of sea bottom at least 450,000,000 years old. The left picture shows "stone-lily" stems, so-called "sea mosses," brachiopods. Right picture shows various species of brachiopods. (*Photo by the author.*)

PLATE 21.—(b) AN OUTCROP OF MIDDLE ORDOVICIAN STRATIFIED LIME-STONE IN NORTHERN NEW YORK. This ledge is full of fossils similar to those above. The material was deposited on the floor of the Ordovician sea which overspread much of the continent. (*Photo by the author.*)

PLATE 22.—RESTORATION SHOWING THE GENERAL APPEARANCE OF SOME OF THE LARGEST ANIMALS WHICH EVER TROD THE EARTH. A mounted skeleton in the American Museum of Natural History is sixty-seven feet long, and the skeleton of a similar creature in the Carnegie Museum, Pittsburgh, is eighty-seven feet long. They lived millions of years ago during the middle and late Mesozoic era. (After C. R. Knight. Courtesy of the American Museum of Natural History, New York.)

white, others like galena (steel-gray) and pyrite
(brass-yellow) show inherently characteristic colors, while still others like amethyst (purple) and
sapphire (blue) are colored by impurities.

There is also a great range in relative weights or
density of minerals, commonly called the specific
gravity, which range from less than one for ice to
21.5 for platinum, and even somewhat higher. The
average specific gravity of all minerals of the earth
is about 2.6.

In the light of the above discussion of the general
properties of minerals, we shall now proceed to name
and briefly describe some of the minerals which are
either very common, or of special interest, or of
special economic importance. Only those features
are listed by which the mineral species may be
recognized at sight, or by the aid of very simple
nonchemical tests.

AMPHIBOLE. A number of species closely related
in composition, crystal form, and properties are
here included. They are silicates of lime and magnesia usually with aluminum and iron. Most common by far are those which crystallize in the Monoclinic system with prismatic faces and two good
prismatic cleavages meeting at about 24 degrees.
Color, commonly brown to black, but sometimes
green or white. Hardness varies from 5 to 6, and
specific gravity from 3 to 3.4. *Hornblende*, the most
common species, is a dark colored silicate of lime,
magnesia, aluminum, and iron. It is one of the few
most common of all mineral species, especially in
igneous and metamorphic rocks. *Tremolite* is a
white to light gray silicate of lime and magnesia
found especially in metamorphic limestones. *Actinolite* is a green silicate of lime, magnesia, and iron

especially common in certain metamorphic rocks. One kind of jade is an amphibole similar to tremo-

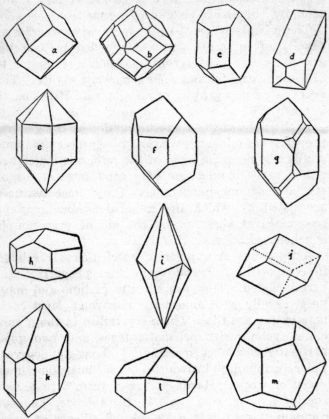

FIG. 74.—Drawings showing forms of crystals of common minerals: a and b, garnet (Isometric); c and d, feldspars (Monoclinic); e, f, and g, quartz (Trigonal); h, i, and j, calcite (Hexagonal); k, augite (Monoclinic); l, hornblende (Monoclinic); m, pyrite (Isometric).

lite and actinolite in composition, while the other kind is a pyroxene (see below). *Jade* is and has been highly prized in the east (especially in China)

MINERALOGY

where it has been carved into many objects of exceptional variety and beauty. Jade is probably the toughest (not hardest) of all minerals because of its wonderful microscopically fibrous structure. In color it is white, gray, and green.

APATITE. Crystallizes in the Hexagonal system with a six-sided prism usually capped at each end by a six-sided pyramid (see Figure 75g). Composition, a phosphate of lime. Color variable, but mostly white, green, or brown. Hardness of 5, or just enough to scratch soft glass. Specific gravity, 3.2. No good cleavage. Tiny crystals are widely disseminated through many common rocks—igneous, metamorphic, and sedimentary. In certain metamorphic limestones excellent crystals a foot or more in length have been found. Apatite, mostly in uncrystallized form, is the source of most of our phosphate fertilizers.

AZURITE. An azure-blue hydrous carbonate of copper which crystallizes commonly in small monoclinic crystals. Hardness, nearly 4, and specific gravity, nearly 4. Commonly occurs in veins deposited by underground water. One of the great ores of copper, especially in Arizona, Chile, and Australia.

BARITE. A sulphate of barium crystallizing in orthorhombic prisms usually of tabular habit. White to light color shades. Hardness, 3.5; specific gravity, 4.5, which is notably higher than the average of light-colored minerals. Three good cleavages parallel to principal crystal faces. A common and widely distributed mineral, especially in many vein deposits associated with certain ores. Used in ground form to give weight to certain kinds of paper and cloth, and a barium compound used for refining sugar is made from it.

BERYL. A silicate of aluminum and the rare chemical element beryllium. Hexagonal crystals

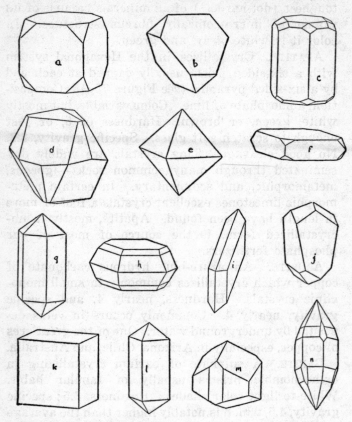

FIG. 75.—Crystal forms of common minerals: a, galena (Isometric); b, sphalerite (Isometric); c, beryl (Hexagonal); d, hematite (Hexagonal); e, magnetite (Isometric); f, barite (Orthorhombic); g, apatite (Hexagonal); h, sulphur (Monoclinic); i, gypsum (Monoclinic); j, chalcopyrite (Tetragonal); k, fluorite (Isometric); l, zircon (Tetragonal); m, tourmaline (Trigonal); n, corundum (Hexagonal).

usually of very simple six-sided prismatic habit (see Figure 75c). Color white, green, blue, or yellow. Specific gravity, 2.8. Cleavage practically absent. It is a very exceptionally hard mineral, being 8 in the scale. Very large crystals have been found, as, for example, in New Hampshire, where single crystals several feet long weigh a ton or more. Beryl is also of special interest because two of its varieties—*emerald* (green) and *aquamarine* (blue)—are well-known gem stones, the emerald being one of the most highly prized gems. The colors are due to slight impurities. Beryl most commonly occurs in dikes of coarse granite called pegmatite, but also in certain metamorphic and sedimentary rocks.

CALCITE. Commonly called "calc spar." A carbonate of lime. Hexagonal crystals in a great variety of forms, but all with crystal faces arranged in sixes around the principal or vertical axis forming rhombohedrons, prisms, or double-pointed pyramids. The principal axis of symmetry is sixfold by a combination of rotation and reflection. Very perfect cleavages in three directions yielding fragments whose faces make angles of 75 and 105 degrees. Color, white when pure, but variously colored when impure. Hardness, 3 (very easily scratched by a knife); specific gravity, 2.7. Calcite is a very common mineral, especially in limestone (including *chalk*) and marble which are usually largely made up of it. Also commonly found in veins, and as spring and cave deposits (stalactites). A porous, stringy variety, called *travertine*, is deposited by certain hot springs, as at Mammoth Hot Springs in Yellowstone Park. A very transparent crystalline variety is called *Iceland spar*. Calcite is a very useful mineral. Limestone and marble are widely used as a building stone, and for decorative purposes, statuary, etc. Limestone is burned for quick-lime, used as a flux in smelting certain ores, in glass making, etc.

CASSITERITE. The one great ore of tin whose composition is oxide of tin. Tetragonal crystallization (Figure 73c). Hardness greater than steel, being over 6 in the scale. Specific gravity 7, which is notably high. Color, brown to nearly black. Cleavage, practically absent. Fairly widespread in small amounts, and in commercial quantities in only a few localities, usually in veins in granite or metamorphic rocks near granite, as at Cornwall, England, also in the form of rounded masses in gravel deposition as in the Malay region.

CHALCOCITE. Crystallizes in the orthorhombic system, usually in tabular form, but crystals not common. A black sulphide of copper with metallic luster. Hardness, nearly 3; specific gravity, nearly 6. No cleavage. Chalcocite occurs in vein deposits as one of the important copper ores, especially at Butte, Montana.

CHALCOPYRITE. Known as "copper pyrites." (Figure 75j.) A deep brass-yellow sulphide of iron and copper. Seldom crystallized in tetragonal forms. Hardness, 3.5; specific gravity, over 4. No cleavage. Metallic luster. Widely distributed in vein deposits associated with other metal-bearing minerals. A very important ore of copper, especially at Rio Tinto, Spain.

CHLORITE. A soft, green mineral, usually in small tabular crystals, in general appearance much like mica (see below), but unlike mica, the almost perfect cleavage leaves are not elastic, though they are flexible. Composition, a silicate of aluminum and magnesia. Always of secondary origin as a result of chemical alteration of certain other minerals, such as biotite-mica, pryoxene or amphibole.

CINNABAR. A vermilion-red sulphide of mercury. An extra soft metallic mineral, only 2.5 in the scale. Specific gravity over 8, which is notably high. Completely vaporizes on being heated. Small trigonal crystals rare. Cinnabar is the one great ore of mercury, occurring in veins, especially in California and Spain.

COPPER. Copper as such (so-called "native copper") is widely distributed in veins, usually in small amounts with other copper minerals, but in the great mines of northern Michigan it occurs in immense quantities as the only important ore. It is readily recognized by its color, softness (less than 3), and notable weight (specific gravity, nearly 9). Isometric crystals uncommon.

CORUNDUM. An oxide of aluminum of hexagonal crystallization, usually in six-sided prisms, capped by very steep pyramidal faces (see Figure 75n). It is next to the hardest of all known minerals (9 in the scale), the diamond only exceeding it. Specific gravity about 4. Three good cleavages making angles of nearly 90 degrees with each other. The color of corundum is usually brown, but it varies greatly. Two of the most highly prized of all precious stones—*ruby* (red) and *sapphire* (blue)— are nearly transparent varieties of corundum, colored by certain impurities. *Oriental topaz* (yellow), *oriental emerald* (green), and *oriental amethyst* (purple) are also clear varieties of corundum. It occurs in various igneous and metamorphic rocks, and in some stream gravels. The finest rubies, associated with some sapphires, occur in gravels in Burma, Siam, and Ceylon. *Emery* is a fine-grained mixture of corundum and other minerals, especially magnetite.

DIAMOND. This mineral is remarkable not only because it is the king of precious stones, but also because it is easily the hardest known substance (10 in the scale). Specific gravity, 3.5. Very brilliant luster. Crystals of usually octahedral habit in the Isometric system. Usually colorless, but often variously tinted. Composition, pure carbon. Burns completely away at high temperature. The greatest mines in the world are in South Africa, where the diamonds occur in masses of rather soft (decomposed) igneous rock, evidently having crystallized during the cooling of the molten masses. In Brazil and India diamonds are found in stream gravels.

FELDSPAR GROUP. The feldspars are by far the most abundant of all minerals in the crust of the earth. (Figures 74c, 74d.) There are several important species or varieties of feldspar with certain features in common as follows: crystal forms, either monoclinic or triclinic (closely resembling monoclinic), in prismatic forms whose faces usually meet at or near 90 or 120 degrees; two good cleavages at or near 90 degrees, hardness at or near 6; specific gravity, a little over 2.5; color, usually white, gray, or pink; and composition, silicate of aluminum with potash, soda, or lime. The two potash feldspars are *orthoclase* and *microcline,* the former being monoclinic, with cleavages at exactly 90 degrees, and the latter triclinic, with cleavages a little less than 90 degrees. A kind of green microcline is known as *Amazon stone.* The soda-lime feldspars go by the general name *plagioclase.* They are triclinic, with cleavages meeting at approximately 86 degrees. Very commonly one of the cleavage faces exhibits characteristic, well defined striations or fine parallel lines caused by multiple twinning during crystal growth. Some of the common plagioclases are *albite,* a white soda feldspar, including most so-called *moonstone; oligoclase,* a usually greenish-white to reddish-gray soda-lime feldspar including *sunstone;* and *labradorite,* a lime-soda feldspar, usually gray to greenish-gray with a beautiful play of colors. The feldspars occur in all three great groups of rocks, but they have most commonly crystallized during the cooling of molten masses of igneous rocks. Where many sedimentary rocks have undergone great change (metamorphism) under conditions of heat, pressure, and moisture, feldspars have very commonly formed. Orthoclase and microcline feldspar are used in the manufacture of porcelain and chinaware. Some special varieties of feldspar are cut or polished for semiprecious stones or decorative purposes.

FLUORITE. A common mineral whose composition is fluoride of lime. (Figure 73b.) Isometric crystals, usually cubes with edges modified, are common. Twinned cubes are also common. Easily scratched by a knife (hardness, 4), and specific gravity a little over 3. Clear and colorless when pure, but variously colored, especially green, blue, yellow, and brown, due to impurities in solution during crystallization. Remarkable because of its four good cleavages meeting at such angles as to permit good cleavage octahedrons to be broken out of crystals. Fluorite is widely distributed, most commonly in vein deposits, often associated with metallic ores. Occurs also as crystals in some limestones and igneous rocks. Some fissure veins of fluorite in limestone in southern Illionis are twenty to forty feet wide. Used mostly as a flux in the manufacture of certain steel, in glass making, and in making enamel ware.

GALENA. Commonly as isometric crystals either as cubes or combinations of cubes and octahedrons. Composition, sulphide of lead. (Figure 75a). Color, lead-gray with metallic luster. Hardness, 2.5; specific gravity high, 7.5. Very brittle. Three excellent cleavages at right angles and parallel to the crystal faces of the cube. Nearly all of the lead of commerce comes from the smelting of galena. It is mined in many parts of the world where it nearly always occurs in typical vein deposits often associated with sphalerite (see below).

GARNET GROUP. The members of this very interesting mineral group very commonly occur in isometric crystallized forms, mostly twelve and twenty-four faced figures or both combined, as shown by Figure 72. All the six species of garnets are silicates, mostly of aluminum usually with either lime, magnesia, or iron. Cleavage, very imperfect or absent. Hardness great, 6.5 to 7.5, and specific gravity 3.1 to 4.3, varying according to species. Color also varies with composition, but most commonly red, brown, and more rarely yellow, black, and green. Garnets are most common as crystals embedded in metamorphic rocks, especially highly altered strata. Also occurs in many igneous rocks and in some sands. Commonly used as a semi-precious stone, and also ground for use as an abrasive, especially in making a kind of sand (or garnet) paper.

GOLD. Gold as such ("native gold") is, in small amounts, really a very widely distributed mineral. It is characterized by its yellow color, softness (less than 3 in the scale), great weight (specific gravity, over 19), and extreme malleability. Most of the commercial gold occurs in river gravels (so-called "placer deposits"), and in veins associated with the very common mineral quartz.

GRAPHITE. Commonly called "black lead," but it is not lead at all. Its composition is pure carbon— the same as that of the diamond. We here have a very remarkable example of a single substance (carbon) which, according to circumstances, crystallizes in two distinctly different systems (diamond in isometric, and graphite in Hexagonal) yielding very thin, flexible flakes; greasy in feel; and easily rubs off on paper. It weighs less than the average mineral (specific gravity, a little over 2). Good crystals of hexagonal tabular form are rare. The most natural home of graphite is in the metamorphic rocks, especially certain of the highly altered strata, where it occurs in the form of more or less abundant flakes, having originated from organic matter. Some also occurs in igneous rocks and in veins. Large quantities are made at Niagara Falls from anthracite by electricity.

GYPSUM. Monoclinic crystals common, usually of simple forms, as shown by Figure 75i. Sometimes twin crystals. Composition, sulphate of lime. Colorless or white when pure. Can be scratched by the finger nail (hardness, 2). Specific gravity, 2.3. Three good cleavages, especially the prismatic, yielding cleavage plates with angles of 66 and 114 degrees. Thin cleavage layers, moderately flexible. There are several varieties: (1) *selenite*, which is clear, crystalline; (2) *satin spar*, fibrous with silky luster; (3) *alabaster*, fine-grained and compact crystalline; and (4) *rock gypsum*, massive granular or earthy. Gypsum is common and widespread especially among stratified rocks often as thick beds which have mostly resulted from evaporation of bodies of water containing it in solution, and often associated with salt beds. Also occurs as scattering crystals in shales and clays, and in some veins. In greatest quantities it is burned to make plaster of Paris. Satin spar and alabaster are often cut and polished for ornaments, etc. (See Figure 73a.)

HALITE. Common salt. Composition, chloride of soda. Isometric crystals, nearly always in cubes with three good cleavages at right angles, and parallel to the faces of the cube. Hardness, 2.5; specific gravity, 2.5. Colorless to white when pure. Characteristic salty taste. Abundant and widespread, often as extensive strata in rocks of nearly all ages, having resulted from evaporation of inland bodies of salt water. Also in vast quantities in solution in salt lakes and the sea. Halite has many uses, as for example, cooking and preservative purposes, indirectly in glass making and soap making, glazing pottery, and in many ore-smelting and chemical processes.

HEMATITE.—One of the common and important iron oxides with less iron than magnetite and no water as has limonite. Crystallizes in hexagonal forms. Color, black, with metallic luster, when crystalline, otherwise usually dull red. Hardness, about 6; specific gravity, about 5. No cleavage. Red streak when rubbed on rough porcelain. Hematite is extremely widespread in rocks of all ages, especially in metamorphic and sedimentary rocks. Some occurs as crystals in igneous rocks, and some in vein deposits. It is the greatest ore of iron in the United States, especially in Minnesota, Michigan, Wisconsin, and Alabama.

KAOLIN. Commonly called "China clay." Composition, a hydrous silicate of aluminum. Crystallizes in scalelike monoclinic forms, but usually forms compact claylike masses. Hardness, a little over 2; specific gravity, 2.6. Color when pure, white. Usually feels smooth and plastic. Very abundant and widespread, especially forming the main body of clay and of much shale. Always of secondary origin, generally resulting from the decomposition of feldspar. It is the main constituent of chinaware, pottery, porcelain, tiles, bricks, etc.

LIMONITE. An important oxide of iron in composition like hematite except for its variable water content. Never crystallized. Hardness, about 5; specific gravity, nearly 4. Color, light to dark brown to nearly black. Leaves a characteristic yellowish-brown streak when rubbed on rough porcelain. Exceedingly common and widely distributed, always as a mineral of secondary origin as a product of weathering of various iron-bearing minerals. Where accumulated in considerable deposits it is an iron ore of some importance.

MAGNETITE. One of the three important oxides of iron containing no water, and richer in iron than hematite. (See Figure 75e.) Commonly crystallizes in isometric octahedral forms alone or combined with twelve-faced forms. Hardness, 6; specific gravity, 5. Color, black with metallic luster. Leaves black streaks on rough porcelain. Characteristically highly magnetic. Widespread as crystals in nearly all kinds of igneous rocks, and as large segregation masses in certain igneous rocks. Also very common in metamorphic rocks, in many cases forming lenses and beds as ore deposits. Occurs in some strata and sands. It is an important ore of iron.

MALACHITE. A light-green hydrous carbonate of copper. In almost every way, except difference in color and slight difference in composition, it is very much like azurite (see above).

MICA GROUP. The micas rank high in abundance among the most common minerals of the earth. All of the several species are silicates of aluminum combined with other chemical elements according to the species. All crystallize in monoclinic six-sided prisms whose angles are nearly 120 degrees. These prisms closely approach true hexagonal forms. All are characterized by one exceedingly good cleavage at right angles to the prismatic faces, yielding very thin elastic cleavage sheets. Hardness, 2 to 2.5; specific gravity, 2.7 to 3. The various species or varieties are not always sharply separated from each other. Most common are: *muscovite,* or so-called *isinglass,* a potash mica which is colorless and transparent in thin sheets when pure; *biotite,* an iron-magnesia mica, black to dark green; and *phlogopite,* a brown magnesia mica.

OLIVINE. Often called *chrysolite.* A silicate of iron and magnesia. Orthorhombic crystals, usually in stout prismatic form. Color, usually yellowish green. Hardness, nearly 7; specific gravity, 3.3. Transparent to translucent. No real cleavage. Its hardness, color, and crystal form generally characterize it. It is a fairly common mineral found mainly as crystalline grains in certain dark-colored igneous rocks. A clear green variety, called *peridot,* is used as a gem stone.

OPAL. An oxide of silicon, like quartz in composition except that it is combined with a varying amount of water. It never crystallizes, probably because of its rather indefinite composition. Hardness 5.5 to 6.5 (softer than quartz) ; specific gravity, about 2. Varieties variously colored. *Common opal,* usually translucent with greasy luster. *Precious opal,* translucent with beautiful play of colors, used as a gem. *Fire opal,* with bright red to orange internal reflections. *Hyalite,* colorless and transparent in small rounded masses. *Wood opal,* wood petrified by opal. *Geyserite,* a white, porous, stringy variety deposited by certain hot springs like the Yellowstone geysers. *Tripolite,* fine-grained, chalklike in appearance, consisting of tiny siliceous shells of very simple plants called diatoms.

PLATINUM. This mineral occurs as an impure native metal, usually alloyed with certain other metals. Native platinum, hardness, 4.5 (exceptionally high for a metal) ; specific gravity as usually alloyed, 14 to 19. Pure platinum, specific gravity, over 21, or one of the very heaviest known substances. Color, light steel-gray, with metallic luster. Very malleable and ductile. A rare metal found commercially mostly in gravel or "placer" deposits mostly in the Ural Mountains, also as grains in certain dark igneous rocks. Used for many scientific instruments, in the electrical industry, as jewelry, etc.

PYRITE. Commonly called "iron pyrites." Sometimes called "fool's gold." (See Figure 74m.) A sulphide of iron which commonly crystallizes in the Isometric system mostly as cubes, twelve-faced pyritohedrons, octahedrons, or combinations of these. Color, light brass-yellow, with metallic luster. Cleavage, practically absent. Hardness, greater than that of steel (over 6 in the scale) ; specific gravity, about 5. Leaves greenish black streak when rubbed on rough porcelain. Differs from chalcopyrite by paler color and much greater hardness. It is a common and very widely disseminated mineral in rocks of all kinds and ages, but especially in metamorphic rocks as veins, and banded or lenslike deposits. Most igneous rocks contain small scattering grains of pyrite. Many deposits of commercial value are known. Great quantities are burned for the manufacture of sulphuric acid ("oil of vitriol") which is one of the most important of all chemicals.

PYROXENE GROUP. Along with quartz and feldspars, the pyroxenes rank among the most common of all minerals. (See Figure 74k.) Composition, very similar to amphibole (see above). Pyroxenes crystallizing in the Monoclinic system are the most important. These crystals are prismatic in habit, with prism faces making angles of nearly 45 or 90 degrees instead of about 124 degrees as in the monoclinic amphiboles which the monoclinic pyroxenes greatly resemble. Two fairly good prismatic cleavages cross at an angle of nearly 90 degrees, instead of at about 124 degrees as in the monoclinic amphiboles. Hardness, 5 to 6; specific gravity, 3.2 to 3.6. Color, variable according to species. The most common variety of pyroxene is *augite*, a dark-green to black silicate of aluminum, iron, lime, and magnesia. Certain pyroxenes also crystallize in the Orthorhombic system. Pyroxene is most abundantly represented as crystals in many kinds of igneous and metamorphic rocks. It is practically useless except as one kind of *jade*.

QUARTZ. Next to the feldspars, quartz is probably the most common of all minerals, especially at and near the earth's surface. (Figures 74a, f, and g.) It is composed of oxide of silicon. Quartz often crystallizes in the trigonal system almost always as six-sided prisms capped by six-sided pyramids, which are really combined three-sided forms, often with alternate corners modified by small faces. These small modifying faces, etching figures, and microscopic tests show that quartz is really trigonal in spite of the common occurrence of simple six-sided outward forms. The pyramidal faces make different angles than those of either apatite or beryl, both of which are somewhat like quartz in crystal form. Hardness, 7 (distinctly high, cannot be scratched by the knife); specific gravity, 2.6 (about average for all minerals). Cleavage, practically absent, and breaks like glass. Colorless when pure, but varieties exhibit many colors. A few only of the many varieties will be briefly described. Among the distinctly crystalline varieties are: *rock crystal*, pure colorless; *amethyst*, purple; *rose quartz*, pink; *milky quartz*, white; and *smoky quartz*, dark—due to tiny inclusions of carbon. Among the fine-grained, compact more or less indistinctly crystalline or noncrystalline varieties, usually translucent with a waxy luster, are: *chalcedony*, bluish gray, waxy looking, usually in small rounded masses; *carnelian*, red; *prase*, green; *agate*, with parallel bands, usually variously colored; *flint* and *jasper*, opaque to translucent, dark to red.

Quartz is exceedingly abundant in all the great groups of rocks. It constitutes the main bulk of sandstones, is common in shales, and occurs in certain other strata. In many igneous rocks, like granite, it is a very prominent constituent. Most of the metamorphic rocks contain its crystalline forms in greater or less amounts. Quartz is the most common of all vein minerals, in many cases associated with valuable ores. Various varieties are widely used for ornamental purposes. Used in making sandpaper, glass, porcelain, mortar, concrete, and in certain ore-smelting processes. Sandstone is widely used as a building stone.

SERPENTINE. A hydrous silicate of magnesia never in distinct crystals as such, but shown to be monoclinic under the microscope. Hardness variable, 2.5 to 5; specific gravity, about 2.6. Mostly of variegated green or yellowish green color with waxy luster, except a fibrous variety (*asbestos*) which is light green to white. The fibrous variety of serpentine is the principal source of asbestos, an amphibole asbestos being less common. Ordinary serpentine (sometimes miscalled "green marble") is widely used as a building and decorative stone. Serpentine is common and widespread, especially in igneous and metamorphic rocks, but never as a really original mineral. It always results from alteration of certain other magnesia-bearing silicate minerals, such as pyroxene, amphibole, olivine, etc.

SILVER. Native silver is not a very rare mineral, and it is mined in certain parts of the world, but most of the metal is obtained from certain silver-bearing minerals, especially sulphides and a chloride. Silver crystallizes rather rarely in the Isometric system. More commonly it occurs as irregular masses, plates, and wirelike forms. Characterized by its color, metallic luster, softness (less than 3 in the scale), and exceptional weight (specific gravity, 10.5). Usually occurs in vein deposits, commonly associated with other metals or metal-bearing minerals, especially copper.

SPHALERITE. A sulphide of zinc commonly in crystalline form belonging in the Isometric system, especially in tetrahedral combination forms (see Figure 75b). Color, usually brown, yellow or nearly black with resinous luster. Hardness, nearly 4; specific gravity, 4. Several good cleavages, yielding fragments whose faces meet at 90 and 120 degrees. Sphalerite is a fairly common and widespread mineral, occurring nearly always in veins in most kinds of rocks. It is very often associated with other ores, particularly the great ore of lead (galena). Sphalerite is by far the greatest ore of zinc.

SULPHUR. Native sulphur. Crystallization, orthorhombic, usually in combination pyramidal forms. (See Figure 75h.) Characterized by yellow color, resinous luster, softness (about 2 in the scale), low specific gravity (about 2), and very poor cleavages. It has most commonly resulted from alteration of certain sulphur-bearing minerals, especially gypsum, the decomposition of which has yielded vast deposits. Some also of volcanic origin. Great quantities are used in making sulphuric acid, matches, gunpowder, fireworks, and for vulcanizing and bleaching rubber goods.

TALC. Often called *steatite*. Monoclinic crystals rare. One perfect cleavage, yielding very thin, flexible leaves. Very soft (hardness, 1). Feels greasy, and looks waxy to pearly. Color, white, gray, to light green. Specific gravity, 2.8. Composition, a hydrous silicate of magnesia, much like that of serpentine. Talc is always of secondary origin, generally derived by chemical alteration of various common minerals rich in silicate of magnesia. *Soapstone* is a common variety resulting from alteration of whole rock masses. Soapstone has many practical uses as for washtubs, table tops, electrical switchboards, hearthstones, stove and furnace linings, blackboards, gas tips, etc. Talc proper is used as a lubricant, to weight paper, in soap, as dustless crayon, talcum powder, etc.

TOPAZ. A silicate of aluminum and fluorine. Orthorhombic crystals common, usually prisms capped at one end by pyramided faces and abruptly terminated at the other. Colorless when pure, but often variously colored due to impurities. Very exceptionally hard (8 in the scale) ; specific gravity, 3.5. One good cleavage across the prism zone; usually found as crystals in, and in cavities in, igneous rocks. Appears always to have formed from highly heated vapors or liquids given off by cooling molten rock masses. Topaz is one of the more highly prized of the gem stones.

TOURMALINE. Composition, very complex, but chiefly a silicate of boron and several metals and semimetals. Commonly as crystals in the trigonal system in both long and short prismatic forms, as shown by Figure 75m, with opposite ends not unlike. Extra hard (7 in the scale) ; specific gravity, about 3. Color, widely various, but brown and black are most common. Practically no cleavage. Tourmaline probably always originated as a high temperature mineral, especially as crystals in granites and related rocks and in certain metamorphic rocks which have been subjected to high temperature and pressure. Certain transparent colored varieties of tourmaline rank high among the semiprecious stones.

TURQUOIS. A hydrous phosphate of aluminum. Massive noncrystalline, blue to green, waxy luster, mostly opaque, hardness of 6, and specific gravity of about 2.7. Turquois is a high temperature mineral found in veins and cavities in certain igneous rocks. It is a rare mineral used as a gem stone.

ZIRCON. A silicate of zirconium usually crystallized in the Tetragonal system as simple four-sided prisms capped by four-sided pyramids. (See Figure 75l.) Very poor cleavages. Color usually brown. Hardness, 7.5 (extra high); specific gravity, nearly 4.7. Brilliant luster. Zircon is very commonly present as scattering crystals of varying size in most igneous rocks. Also common as crystals in various metamorphosed stratified rocks, and less common in some sand and gravel deposits. Certain transparent varieties, especially the brown and pink ones called *hyacinth,* are used as gem stones. Zircon is also the source of oxide of zirconium used in making mantles for certain incandescent lights.

CHAPTER XXI

ECONOMIC GEOLOGY

IN this chapter it is our purpose to briefly consider geology in its direct relations to the arts and industries. When we realize that the value of strictly geologic products taken from the earth each year in the United States alone amounts to billions of dollars, we can better appreciate the practical application of geological science. Such products include coal, petroleum, natural gas, many valuable metal-bearing minerals, and many nonmetalliferous minerals and rocks. In most cases these valuable products of nature have been slowly accumulated or concentrated at many times and under widely varying conditions throughout the millions of years of known geological time. To trace the extent of, and most advantageously remove, such deposits for the use of man is always invariably impossible unless geological knowledge is brought to bear. In many cases the problems involved are intricate, and only the trained geologist is able to at all successfully cope with them. In such cases it is necessary not only to have a thorough knowledge of minerals and rocks as such, but also of their origin and structure. Much of the practical application of geology is carried out by the mining engineer who should have, above all, a thorough knowledge of the great principles of geology.

342

Our plan of discussion is to consider, first, coal, petroleum, and natural gas; then the most important metalliferous deposits of ores; and finally non-metalliferous minerals and rocks of exceptional commercial importance. Underground waters have already been discussed from the practical standpoint in the chapter on "Waters Within the Earth." Certain minerals have already been sufficiently considered from the economic standpoint in the chapter on "Mineralogy."

COAL, PETROLEUM, AND NATURAL GAS

COAL. Most valuable of all geological products is coal. Although it is not, strictly speaking, a mineral, both because of its organic origin and lack of definite chemical composition, coal is generally classed among our mineral resources. Some idea of the national importance of coal in the United States may be gained when we realize that the energy derived from a single year's output is equivalent to that of hundreds of millions of men working full time through the year. The uses of coal are too well known to need mention here.

Coal is, beyond question, of organic (plant) origin as shown by its very composition; perfect gradations between plant deposits like peat and true coal; and the presence of microscopic plant remains and spores in the coal. An excellent summary of just what happens during the transition of ordinary vegetable matter into coal has been given by David White as follows: "All coal was laid down in beds analogous to the peat beds of to-day. All kinds of plants, especially such species as were adapted to the particular region where the deposit was located, in whole or in part went into the deposit.

"Plants are composed chiefly of cellulose and proteins. The former, comprising by far the larger bulk, constitute the framework, whereas the latter are concerned in the vital functions. With these are associated many other substances, among which are chiefly starch, sugars, and fats and oils, constituting reserve foodstuffs; waxes, resin waxes, resins, and higher fats, performing mainly protective functions. . . . These components differ widely in their resistance to various agencies. Those substances involved in the life function and the support of the plant are relatively very stable under the conditions imposed upon them.

"At the death of the plants, governed by conditions imposed in the bog, a partial decomposition, maceration, elimination, and chemical reduction begins, brought about by various agencies, chiefly organic, mainly fungi at first and bacteria later. The most labile are removed first, the more resistant next, and so on, as the conditions require, leaving the most resistant behind in a residue called peat.

"The process of decomposition, elimination, and chemical reduction begun in peat, chiefly by biochemical means, is taken up and continued by dynamochemical means into and through the various successive later stages, and results in the various grades of coal, as lignite, sub-bituminous, and cannel coal, and anthracite."

The principal chemical elements involved in the changes which take place are carbon, oxygen, and hydrogen, as shown by the following analyses of about average samples of each member of the so-called "coal series."

The "coal series"	Carbon	Oxygen	Hydrogen	Nitrogen
Wood (cellulose)..............	50	43	6	1
Peat.........................	59	33	6	2
Lignite......................	69	25	5.5	0.8
Bituminous coal..............	82	13	5	0.8
Anthracite coal..............	95	2.5	2.5	trace
Graphite.....................	100	..	..	..

From this table it is seen that the oxygen relatively diminishes while the carbon relatively increases, though, of course, all three elements actually decrease during the chemical change from cellulose to coal. These three elements disappear mainly in the form of gases, such as water vapor, marsh gas, and carbonic acid gas. The final or graphite stage is almost reached by the graphitic anthracite of Rhode Island, which is so nearly pure carbon as to be really useless as coal.

The conditions under which successive layers of vegetable matter (later turned into coal) become embedded in the earth's crust have been outlined in the chapter on the "Evolution of Plants." The most perfect conditions for prolific plant growth, and accumulation as great beds in the earth's crust, were during the Pennsylvanian period of the late Paleozoic era in many parts of the world, but especially in the United States, China, Great Britain, and Germany. Most of the world's great supply of coal comes from rocks of Pennsylvanian Age, while next in importance are Cretaceous rocks, and some comes from strata of other ages later than the Pennsylvanian, even as late as the Tertiary.

The United States not only has the greatest known coal fields, but it also produces far more coal than any other country. In 1918 the production was 678,000,000 tons, the greatest in our history, or enough, if loaded into cars of forty tons capacity, to fill a train which would reach around the earth at the equator about six times! Equally amazing is the fact that this coal was nearly all consumed by this one nation! In 1936 production was about 488,-830,000 tons. Is there real danger that our supply of coal will soon run out? Hardly so when we consider, first, the fact that probably not more than 1 per cent of the readily available coal has thus far been removed, and, second, the high probability that rate of increase in coal production for the last twenty years will not continue. In fact, during the last two or three years the production has fallen off considerably. But even so, coal, which is our greatest natural resource, and which can never be replaced, should be scientifically conserved. In the case of the very restricted anthracite coal fields what might be called a crisis has already been reached, because a very considerable part of the available supply has been taken out.

Something like 350,000 square miles of the United States are underlain with one or more beds of workable coal (not including lignite)—in some areas five to twenty or more beds one above the other. There are also about 150,000 square miles of country underlain with the more or less imperfect coal called lignite. It has been estimated that there are more than a trillion tons of easily accessible coal, and another trillion tons accessible with some difficulty in the principal coal fields of the United States.

The greatest production of coal by far is from the Appalachian Mountain and Allegheny Plateau districts, from the western half of Pennsylvania to Alabama, where all the coal is bituminous of Penn-

sylvanian Age. Here as well as elsewhere the coal
beds are interstratified with various kinds of sedimentary rocks, most commonly with shales and
sandstones. In the Appalachian field the strata including coal beds are more or less folded toward
the east, while they are nearly horizontal toward the

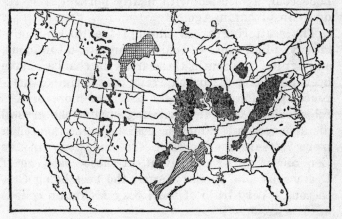

FIG. 76.—Map of the United States, showing the principal coal fields.
Cross-lined areas represent lignitic coals. (After U. S. Geological
Survey.)

west. The famous Pittsburgh coal bed is probably
the most extensive important single coal bed known.
It covers an area of over 12,000 square miles and is
workable, with a thickness of five to fifteen feet,
over an area of 6,000 square miles of parts of western Pennsylvania, Ohio, and West Virginia.

The greatest production of anthracite coal by far
is from central-eastern Pennsylvania, where strata
of Pennsylvania Age, including a number of anthracite beds, are mostly highly folded. Most
remarkable of all in this district is the so-called
"mammoth bed" of anthracite, nearly everywhere

present, with a thickness up to as much as fifty or sixty feet. Less than 500 square miles are there underlain by workable anthracite coal.

Next to the greatest production of coal in the United States is from the two large areas in the middle of the Mississippi Valley. It is all bituminous coal, associated with nearly horizontal strata of Pennsylvanian Age.

The scattering areas through the Rocky Mountains yield all types of coal—anthracite, bituminous, and lignite. In some of these areas the coal beds have been but little disturbed from their original horizontal position, but usually they are more or less folded along with the inclosing strata, the crustal disturbances affecting the coal beds having taken place late in the Mesozoic era and early in the Cenozoic era. Practically all of these coals are of Cretaceous and Tertiary Ages, the best being Cretaceous. Very little of the Rocky Mountain coal is anthracite.

On the Pacific Coast coal production is relatively very small. The coals are there bituminous to lignitic of Tertiary Age, usually folded in with the strata.

In Alaska there are widely distributed, relatively small coal fields, but they have been little developed. Alaskan coals range in age from Pennsylvanian to Tertiary, and in kind from anthracite to lignite.

PETROLEUM. Crude oil or petroleum is an organic substance consisting of a mixture of hydrocarbons, that is, it is made up very largely of the two chemical elements carbon and hydrogen, in rather complex and variable combinations. It is practically certain that petroleum has been derived by a sort of slow process of distillation from

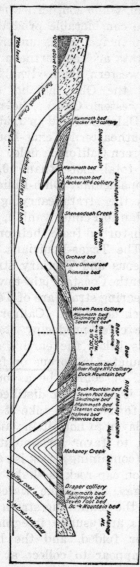

FIG. 77.—Profile and structure section showing folding of strata, with included coal beds, across one of the anthracite coal fields of eastern Pennsylvania. Length of section, a little over 2 miles. (After U. S. Geological Survey.)

organic matter—animal or vegetable or both— in stratified rocks within the earth. Many strata, as for example carbonaceous shales, are more or less charged with dark-colored decomposing organic matter. The chemical composition itself, the kinds of rocks with which it is associated, and certain optical (microscopic) tests all point to the organic origin of petroleum. In southern California at least, certain of the oils have quite certainly been derived from the very tiny oily plants called diatoms which fill many of the strata.

During the last thirty years petroleum has come to be one of the most important and useful natural products. Among the many substances artificially derived from petroleum are kerosene, gasoline, naphtha, benzine, vaseline, and paraffine. The United States leads in the production of petroleum, while southern Russia, Venezuela, and Mexico are considerable producers. In the United States the principal areas underlain with petroleum-bearing strata are the northern Appalachian field (through western Pennsylvania to Central West Virginia); the Ohio-Indiana field (central Indiana to northwestern Ohio); the mid-continental field (eastern Oklahoma and in middle-northern Texas); the southeastern Texas-Louisiana field; and the southwestern California field. The areas underlain with oil total more than 10,000 square miles. In the Appalachian, Ohio-Indiana, and mid-continental fields the strata carrying oil range in age from Ordovician to Pennsylvanian, and they are mostly but little disturbed from their original horizontal position. The Texas-Louisiana oils come mainly from Cretaceous and Tertiary strata which gently downtilt under the Coastal Plain toward the Gulf. California's oil-bearing strata are of Tertiary Age and generally much deformed. California, Oklahoma, and Texas are chief producing states.

Under proper conditions below the earth's surface the derived oil accumulates in porous or fractured rocks. There must, of course, be a source from which the petroleum is derived or distilled; a porous or fractured rock formation to take it up; a cap rock or impervious layer to hold it in; and a proper geologic structure to favor accumulation. The most common porous (containing) rock is sandstone, and the most common cap rock is shale. Oil is rarely found without gas, and saline water is likewise often present. If the containing strata are horizontal, the oil and gas are usually irregularly scattered, but if tilted or folded, and the beds porous throughout, they appear to collect at the

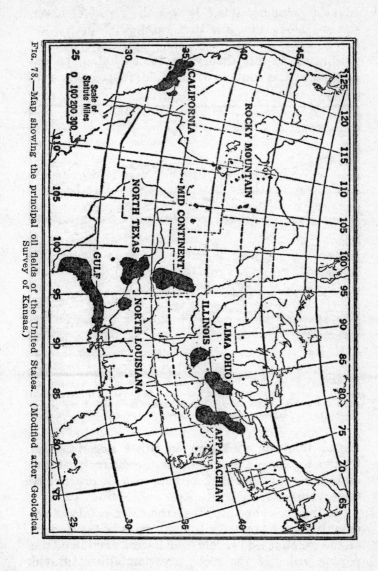

FIG. 78.—Map showing the principal oil fields of the United States. (Modified after Geological Survey of Kansas.)

highest point possible. It was the result of observations along this line that led I. C. White to develop what is known as the "anticlinal theory."
According to this theory, in folded areas the gas
collects at the summit of the fold (anticline), with

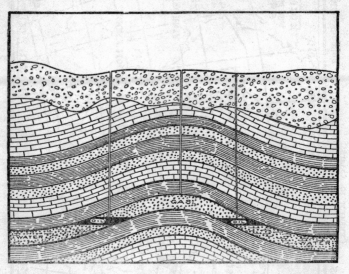

FIG. 79.—A vertical (structure) section showing a very common type
of oil-bearing structure. In this anticline, water, oil, and gas arranged in order of their specific gravities. Removal of the gas would
allow the oil and water to rise higher toward the apex of the porous
layer. (After Indiana Geological Survey.)

the oil immediately below, on either side, followed
by the water. It is, of course, necessary that the
oil-bearing stratum shall be capped by a practically
impervious one.

"If the rocks are dry, then the chief points of accumulation of the oil will be at or near the bottom
of the syncline (downfold), or lowest portion of the
porous bed. If the rocks are partially saturated

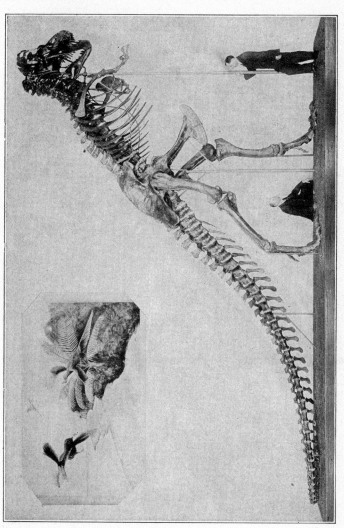

PLATE 23.—SKELETON OF THE GREAT TWO-LEGGED, CARNIVOROUS DINOSAUR REPTILE, CALLED "TYRANNOSAURUS," WHICH LIVED DURING CRETACEOUS TIME. (*Courtesy American Museum of Natural History.*) SMALL PICTURE.—RESTORATION OF THE EARLIEST KNOWN BIRD OF WHICH SEVERAL NEARLY PERFECT SKELETONS HAVE BEEN FOUND. This feathered creature with reptilian characteristics lived at least 5,000,000 years ago. It had a long vertebrated tail, claws on the ends of the wings, and teeth. (*By E. W. Berry.*)

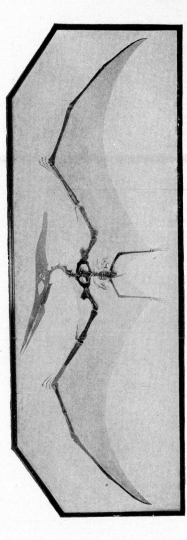

PLATE 24.—(a) SKELETON OF THE LARGEST KNOWN CREATURE THAT EVER FLEW. It was a flying reptile with spread wings of nearly twenty-five feet, and lived during the Cretaceous period several million years ago. (*Courtesy of the American Museum of Natural History.*)

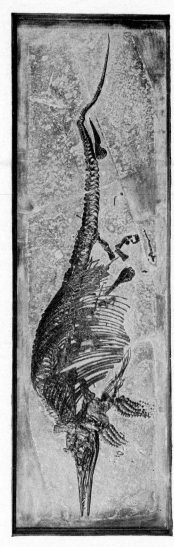

PLATE 24.—(b) SKELETON OF A REMARKABLE SWIMMING REPTILE OF THE MESOZOIC ERA. Length about twelve feet. Parts of skeletons of unborn young are seen. (*Courtesy of the American Museum of Natural History.*)

with water, then the oil accumulates at the upper level of saturation. In a tilted bed, which is locally porous, and not so throughout, the oil, gas, and water may arrange themselves according to their gravity in this porous part." (Ries.)

Although the term "oil pool" is commonly used, there is really no actual pool or underground lake of oil, but rather porous rock saturated with oil. It has been estimated that in an oil field of average productiveness a cubic foot of the porous rock contains from six to twelve pints of oil. The life of a well drilled into an "oil pool" varies from a few months to twenty or thirty years, or sometimes even more, but a heavy producer (especially a "gusher") almost invariably falls off very notably in production in a few months, or at most a few years. The typical Pennsylvanian oil well is said to last about seven years. The fact that the United States is still able to increase oil output is because new fields are found and developed, the most recent being in the interior and northern parts of Texas. It is practically certain, however, that the climax of oil production in the United States will be reached before many years—long before that of bituminous coal.

It is a well-known fact that oil, as well as natural gas, is usually under more or less pressure within the earth. The pressure is so great in some cases that where, in the course of drilling, oil or gas accumulated under proper conditions, as for example those shown by Figure 79, are encountered the pressure may be hundreds of pounds per square inch, or enough to blow to pieces much of the drilling outfit. It is under such conditions that great "gushers" are struck. A wonderful case in point was the famous Lakeview gusher, struck in California in 1910. "Within a few days the well was far beyond control. It continued to flow (for a time shooting high into the air) for eighteen months, finally stopping after it had produced over 8,000,000 barrels of oil, about 6,000,000 of which had been saved. The daily production of the well varied greatly, reaching a maximum of 65,000 barrels." (Pack.) One very common cause of oil pressure is the expansive force of the associated imprisoned gas which steadily increases as the gas is generated. Another is hydrostatic pressure, where under certain structural conditions the pressure of water in a long-tilted layer is exerted against oil accumulated toward the top of an anticline (or upbend) in the strata.

World output of crude petroleum in 1937 was about 2,040,500,000 barrels: United States, 1,277,653,000 barrels; Russia, 199,475,000; Venezuela, 185,701,000; Iran, 78,741,000; Netherland India, 56,275,000; Rumania, 52,176,000; Mexico, 46,907,000; Iraq, 30,604,000; Colombia, 20,293,000; Peru, 17,467,000; Argentina, 16,236,000; Trinidad, 15,503,000.

NATURAL GAS. The most perfect fuel with which nature has provided us is natural gas. Not only is it easily transported even long distances through pipes, but also as a fuel it is easily regulated, leaves no refuse, and is less damaging to boilers than coal. It is a colorless, odorless, free-burning gas, consisting very largely of the simple hydrocarbon called marsh gas or fire damp. Petroleum nearly always has more or less natural gas associated with it, but in some cases considerable quantities of gas may exist alone. Natural gas, like petroleum, is of organic origin—a product of slow natural distillation of vegetable or animal matter, or both, within the earth's crust.

One of the most common modes of occurrence of gas is at the top of an anticline (upfold) in porous rock (like sandstone) between impervious layers (like shale). Figure 79 well illustrates the principle, the gas lying above the oil, and the oil above the water; that is, the three substances are arranged according to specific gravity. Gas may also exist in considerable quantities in irregular bodies of porous or fractured rocks. Natural gas is nearly always under pressure within the earth, hundreds of pounds per square inch being common, while more exceptionally, as in certain West Virginia wells, pressures of over 1,000 pounds have been registered.

The United States is by far the greatest world producer of natural gas, the output for 1936 estimated at 2,175,000,000,000 cubic feet. Texas produces the greatest amount of natural gas, with California, Oklahoma, and Louisiana next in order. Areas underlain with natural gas are, in the main, the same as for petroleum, and they total more than 10,000 square miles. Waste of natural gas has been appalling. Wells driven in quest of oil have often encountered gas, and often abandoned wells have played millions of cubic feet of gas daily into the air for years. The Murraysville well of western Pennsylvania shot 20,000,000 cubic feet of gas per day into the air for six years! Much natural gas is now stored underground in natural gas reservoirs or in suitable partially depleted oil fields.

METAL-BEARING (ORE) DEPOSITS

IRON. Without question the most useful of all metals is iron. As such it is rare in nature, but in chemical combination with other substances it is extremely widespread and very common. Iron makes up about 5 per cent of the weight of the earth's crust, but in the form of ore (i. e., a metal-bearing mineral or rock of sufficient value to be mined) it is notably restricted in occurrence. The three great ores of iron are the minerals hematite, magnetite, and limonite, whose composition and characteristic properties the reader will find stated in the preceding chapter on "Mineralogy."

One of the worst impurities in iron ore is phosphorus, which makes iron "cold short," i. e., brittle when cold. Ore for the manufacture of Bessemer steel must contain very little phosphorus (less than 1/1000 of the metallic iron content of the ore). Sulphur as an impurity in the ore tends to make the iron "hot short." Silica (quartz) is bad because it necessitates the use of more lime for flux in the furnace.

Iron ores occur in rocks of most of the great geologic ages, but in the United States principally in the pre-Paleozoic and Paleozoic. The United States is by far the greatest producer of iron ore in the world, the output for 1917 having been about 75,000,000 tons, the greatest in the history of this or any other country. This one year's output loaded into cars of 40 tons capacity would have made a train about 15,000 miles long! All but about 5,000,-000 tons of this tremendous production was hematite ore. In 1932, the output was only about 10,000,000 gross tons. In 1936, it had risen to 48,788,745.

We shall now very briefly consider several of the greatest iron-mining districts of the United States, giving some idea of the modes of occurrence and origin of the ores. Greatest of all is the Lake

Superior region, not far west and south of the lake in Minnesota, Michigan, and Wisconsin. Considerably more than one-half the iron ore mined in the

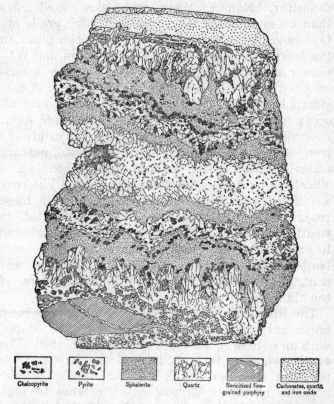

| Chalcopyrite | Pyrite | Sphalerite | Quartz | Sericitized fine-grained porphyry | Carbonates, quartz, and iron oxide |

FIG. 80.—Drawing showing details of part of an ore-bearing vein at Pinos Altos, New Mexico. The chalcopyrite and sphalerite are the ores. Somewhat reduced in size. (After Paige, U. S. Geological Survey.)

United States comes from the single State of Minnesota, and about one-fifth of it from Michigan. Most of the Minnesota ore by far is obtained from the so-called "Mesabi Range," which in 1917 produced 41,000,000 tons of hematite ore. The ore deposits are there of irregular shape, lying at or near the surface (usually covered only by glacial deposits). None of them extend downward more than a few hundred feet. The soft, high-grade ore is removed by steam shovels in great open pits. In the several districts of northern Michigan and Wisconsin the ores (nearly all hematite) are associated with more or less highly folded rocks at considerable depths. The Lake Superior iron ores all occur in rocks of Archeozoic and Proterozoic Ages. According to the best explanation of their origin the iron of the ores was once part of a sedimentary series of rocks in the form of iron carbonate and silicate, interstratified with layers of a flintlike rock associated with slate, quartzite, etc. After these rocks were raised into land and subjected to weathering the old iron compounds were altered to oxides, mainly hematite, and somewhat concentrated. Further concentration of the ore was caused by dissolving out the flintlike layers of the old rocks.

The Birmingham, Ala., region is the second most important iron ore producer in the United States, with an output of 4,259,804 gross tons in 1936. The ore is hematite, forming part of the famous Clinton iron ore deposits of Silurian Age. This deposit, named from Clinton, N. Y., extends through central New York and in more or less interrupted parallel bands through the Appalachian Mountains to near Birmingham where the richest deposits occur. This ore appears to be an original bed (or locally several beds) of fairly rich iron ore deposited on the shallow Silurian sea bottom and then covered by other strata. At the time of the Appalachian Mountain revolution the iron ore was more or less highly folded in with other strata throughout the Appalachians. A remarkable fact regarding the Birmingham district is that in the near vicinity of the ore there are both coal for fuel and limestone flux for smelting the ores.

Another quite important mining region of the United States is the Adirondack Mountain region of northern New York, where less than 1,000,000 tons of ore are mined yearly. Magnetite is the ore, and it occurs in more or less irregular lenses and bands in granite and closely associated rocks of pre-Paleozoic Age. One view regarding the origin of this ore is that it segregated during the process of cooling of the molten granite, and another view (recently advocated by the author) is that it was derived from an older iron-rich igneous formation by either the molten granite or very hot solutions from it and concentrated into the ores. About two million tons of magnetite are mined in the United States yearly, much of this amount from regions in the Adirondacks.

The third important iron ore is limonite, several million tons of which are produced in the United States yearly. Most of it came from the Appalachian Mountains. All of this limonite is of secondary origin; that is, it has been derived from certain early Paleozoic iron-bearing limestones either by weathering or solution, and concentrated into ore deposits.

COPPER. This is one of the most useful of all metals. Several of its very important uses are as a conductor of electricity in the form of wire; in making alloys such as brass and bronze; in copperplate engraving; and in roofing and plumbing. Various minerals containing copper are found in many parts of the world, but only about six of them are really important as ores. These are native copper, chalcopyrite, chalcocite, azurite, malachite, and cuprite, most of which are described in the chapter on "Mineralogy." The number of places where they may be profitably mined as ore is distinctly limited. Fifteen or twenty countries produce more or less copper, but the United States is by far the greatest producer, with an output of over 2,030,000,000 pounds of copper in 1929 which was the largest production on record. Mine production in the United States was estimated at 1,201,422,000 pounds in 1936, the states with largest copper output from mines being Arizona, Montana, Utah, Nevada and Michigan. The leading foreign nations in such production were, in 1936, Chile, Canada, Rhodesia and Belgian Congo. In Europe, Russia and Yugoslavia were the chief copper-mining countries.

In Arizona several great copper-mining districts lie in the southeastern one-fourth of the State. Almost invariably the ores are directly associated with limestone and an igneous rock (granite), both of late Paleozoic Age. The ores are almost always near the border between the two rocks, mostly as great irregular deposits within the limestone, and less commonly as veins within the granite. The original ores were carried in solution and deposited by hot liquids (or vapors) from the cooling granite. At lower levels the ores are mainly sulphides of copper (e. g., chalcopyrite and chalcocite), while at higher levels they are mostly carbonates (malachite and azurite) and oxides (e. g. cuprite). The difference is due to the fact that the ores nearer the surface have been subjected to weathering and altered from their original condition.

The region around Butte, Mont., is one of the greatest copper producers. Nearly all the ores are sulphides of copper (mainly chalcocite) which occur with quartz in a great system of nearly parallel veins in granite of Tertiary Age. "It is supposed that in the copper veins the hot ore-bearing solutions ascended the fractures in the granite, replacing the rock by ore, and resulting in an intense alteration of the walls." (Ries.)

High in rank among the copper-producing States is Michigan, the mines being located on Keweenaw Peninsula, which extends into Lake Superior. For fully fifty years this district has been one of the most famous and important copper producers in the world. A unique feature is that the ore is native copper, associated with some native silver. The rocks containing the ore are steeply tilted lava sheets and conglomerate (cemented gravel) strata of Proterozoic Age. Openings in porous lava and spaces between the conglomerate pebbles have been filled by metallic copper, which was carried off in hot solutions from the cooling lavas. Certain of the mining shafts have been sunk more than 5,000 feet below the surface, these being among the deepest in the world.

Utah ranks third among the copper producers, the greatest mining district being at Bingham Canyon, southwest of Salt Lake City. The rocks are late Paleozoic strata, pierced by a large body of igneous rock. Some of the sulphide ores (mainly chalcopyrite) occur in veins in the igneous rocks and some in large tabular masses in the adjacent limestone. Hot solutions from lower portions of the uncooled igneous rock carried the ore in solution into the limestone and into cracks in the upper cooled igneous rock.

LEAD. Lead must surely be counted among the five or six most useful metals. As in the case of various of the other most important natural resources, the United States is the world's greatest producer of lead, the output of primary lead from the mines being 373,986 tons in 1936. Most of this came from Missouri, Idaho, Utah and Oklahoma. The other countries important in lead production are Mexico, Canada, Germany, India (Burma), Belgium, Italy, Russia and Spain. It comes chiefly from the mineral galena (a sulphide of lead), which is described in the chapter on "Mineralogy." Among the many uses of lead are the following: manufacture of certain high-grade paints from lead compounds; making alloys such as pewter, type metal, solder, babbit metal, in plumbing; in glass making; and in the manufacture of shot.

In the great Joplin region, including parts of Missouri, Oklahoma, and Kansas, the galena, associated with much zinc ore, occurs as veins and great irregular deposits in limestone of early Paleozoic Age. It is generally agreed that underground waters dissolved the ores out of the limestone in which they were disseminated as tiny particles and deposited them in concentrated form at lower levels.

In the famous Cœur d'Alene district of northern Idaho the great output of lead is really obtained from a lead-silver ore; that is, galena rich in silver. This ore is in composition a lead-silver sulphide. It occurs in great fissure veins, mostly following fault fractures in highly folded strata of Proterozoic Age.

Igneous rocks cut through the strata, and it is believed that hot ore-bearing solutions given off from the highly heated igneous rocks rose in the fissures and deposited the ores.

The Park City and Tintic districts of Utah are great producers of lead. The lead ore (galena) is usually rich in silver. It occurs mainly in veins and irregular deposits in limestone of Paleozoic Age closely associated with certain igneous rocks.

One of the most famous mining districts in the world is that around Leadville, Col., where ores of four metals—gold, silver, lead, and zinc—have been extensively mined. The salient points in the rather complex geology are the following: Paleozoic strata, including much limestone, rest upon a foundation of pre-Paleozoic granite. Sheets of igneous rock are interbedded with the strata and many dikes of igneous rocks cut through the whole combination. After the last igneous activity all the rocks were somewhat folded and notably faulted in many places. The ores were dissolved out of the igneous rock and deposited in large masses mostly in the limestone and in fissure veins, especially along and near the fault zones.

ZINC. Another of the few most useful metals is zinc. It never occurs in metallic form in nature, but most of it by far is obtained from the ore mineral sphalerite (sulphide of zinc) described in the chapter on "Mineralogy." A red oxide of zinc ore, called zincite, assumes great economic importance in New Jersey. In 1936, the mine production of recoverable zinc in the United States was approximately 578,149 short tons, and the leading producing states were Oklahoma, New Jersey, Kansas, Montana, Idaho and Utah. The chief zinc-producing foreign countries were Belgium, Canada, Germany, Poland, Australia, the United Kingdom and Russia.

Most important of all in the United States is the Joplin region of Oklahoma, Missouri, and Kansas, in which the ore is closely associated with lead ore. The mode of occurrence and the origin of these ores have been mentioned already in the discussion of lead.

In Montana some of the great east-west fissure veins in granite are rich in silver ores in the upper levels, and in zinc ores (mainly sphalerite) at depths of from some hundreds of feet to nearly 2,000 feet, that is as far down as they have been mined. They, like the great copper veins of the same general district, were carried by hot solutions which rose from the lower still very hot granite and deposited the ores in fissures of the same cooler rock higher up.

Two great ore bodies in the general vicinity of Franklin, N. J., are of unique interest, because they are mostly the red oxide of zinc called zincite. The ore deposits occur in white limestone along or close to its contact with metamorphosed (altered) strata and granite of early Paleozoic Age. It is not definitely known how the ore originated, but it was probably derived in solution from the hot granite and deposits in the limestone by replacement of the latter.

In Colorado the principal zinc mines are around Leadville, where lead ore is nearly always directly associated with the zinc ore. This district is above described in the discussion of lead.

Among many uses of zinc are—for galvanizing; for making certain high-grade paints; in brass and white metal; and for roofing and plumbing.

GOLD. This precious metal has been used and highly prized by man for thousands of years. The discovery of gold in California in 1848 was one of the most important events in the history of the mining world. As early as 1852 that State reached its climax of production with an output of at least $81,000,000 worth of the metal. The Transvaal region of South Africa has for some decades been the world's greatest gold producer. Though long known, the metal has there been worked only since 1886. In 1935, the leading gold-producing countries were South Africa, Russia, Canada, United States, Australia, Japan (including Chosen), and Mexico. World production in 1936 reached the great total of 35,165,000 fine ounces, of which the United States (not including the Philippines) produced about 3,769,-000 fine ounces. Production of gold in the Philippine Islands was about 599,657 fine ounces in 1936.

In tiny amounts gold is really very widespread. It occurs in many stream gravels where so-called "color" may be obtained by washing gravel, and it is even dissolved in sea water. Gold-mining localities are also numerous in many parts of the world, but relatively few of them only have ever paid. The total amount of money spent in actual gold-mining operations; in hopeless but honest operations; and for stock in fake gold mines has no doubt exceeded the actual value of gold produced. In many a case acceptance of a report based upon a very brief examination of the ground by a competent geologist would have saved the cost of hopeless expenditure of money. Someone in nearly every community has a so-called "gold mine."

Most of the commercially valuable gold occurs in nature as native gold, either mixed with gravel and sand (i. e., placer deposits) along existing or ancient stream beds, or in veins mechanically held in the mineral pyrite (described in the preceding chapter) in submicroscopic form, or visibly mixed with quartz in vein deposits. Another kind of ore which assumes considerable importance, as in parts of Colorado, is in the form of telluride of gold always found in veins. In deep vein deposits it is quite the rule to find free or native gold mechanically and visibly mixed with quartz in the upper levels, while deeper down the gold is mechanically, but invisibly, held in combination usually in pyrite, which latter is associated with quartz. This difference is due to the fact that the lower level ores are now just as they were formed, while in the upper levels the ores have been weathered, and the gold set free and often more or less further concentrated by solutions. Vein deposits, including also telluride ores, are found in many kinds of rocks—igneous, sedimentary, and metamorphic—of nearly all ages generally directly associated with igneous rocks. In nearly all cases the best evidence indicates that the vein fillings were formed by hot ore-bearing solutions from the igneous rock, which solutions deposited the ore plus quartz in fissures in either the igneous or adjacent rocks. Among the many localities where fissure veins of the kind just described are of great economic importance are the "Mother Lode" belt of the Sierra Nevada Mountains of California; Cripple Creek (telluride ore), Georgetown and the San Juan region of Colorado; Goldfield, Tonopah, and Comstock Lode of Nevada; and near Juneau, Alaska.

Placer deposits, that is, free gold mixed with gravel and sand, also yield much gold. They are most prominently developed in California and Alaska. These gold-bearing "gravels represent the more resistant products of weathering, such as quartz and native gold, which have been washed down from the hills on whose slopes the gold-bearing quartz veins outcrop, and were too heavy to be carried any distance, unless the grade was steep. They have consequently settled down in the stream channels, the gold, on account of its higher specific gravity, collecting usually in the lower part of the gravel (placer) deposit." (Ries.) Such gold occurs as grains, flakes, or nuggets. When a chunk of gold-bearing vein quartz, with crevices filled by thin plates of the metal, is carried downstream pieces are gradually broken away, and the tough, very malleable gold bends or welds together into a single mass called a "nugget." Nuggets varying in weight up to over 2,000 ounces have been found. Many placer deposits are along existing drainage channels, while others occur in abandoned and even buried former channels.

Most of the gold of South Africa comes from Witwatersrand district where the native metal occurs in a unique manner in beds or layers of conglomerate associated with other strata, all the rocks being considerably folded and somewhat faulted. Some of the mines are more than a mile deep (vertically), the deepest in the world. The gold either accumulated in placer form with gravel which later consolidated into conglomerate, or it was introduced into spaces between the pebbles subsequently by ore-bearing solutions.

SILVER. For many years Mexico and the United States have been the world's greatest silver producers, sometimes one and sometimes the other leading. The leading silver-producing countries in 1935 were Mexico, United States, Peru, Canada, Australasia, Japan and Germany. The estimated world production for 1936 was 249,171,000 fine ounces, of which Mexico produced 78,000,000 and the United States 60,721,000. The leading silver states in 1936 were Idaho, Montana, Utah and Arizona.

In Montana most of the silver is in the native form, more especially in the upper portions of the great veins rich in copper and zinc ores near Butte. These ores and their origin are described above under the captions "Copper" and "Zinc."

The two greatest silver districts of Nevada are Tonopah and Comstock Lode where silver and gold minerals are associated as ores in Tertiary igneous rocks, the ores having been deposited in veins by hot ore-bearing solutions from the igneous rocks.

In Idaho the Cœur d'Alene district produces most of the silver, the ore there being a silver-bearing lead ore (galena). The nature and origin of these deposits are described above under the caption "Lead."

In Utah the silver is also obtained from silver-bearing galena especially in the Tintic, Cottonwood Canyon, and Bingham Canyon districts where the ores occur mainly as irregular deposits and in fissure veins in Paleozoic strata (chiefly limestone) directly associated with igneous rocks, hot ore-bearing solutions from the igneous rocks having furnished the ores.

Tin. Production of tin in the United States has never been important, a little tin having been mined in South Carolina, Black Hills of South Dakota, and Southern California. Alaska, however, produced 102.6 long tons in 1936 (valued at $106,700), and has produced in all about 1,076. World production was about 180,000 long tons in 1936, 66,739 from the Malay States, 31,546 from Netherland India, 24,074 from Bolivia, 12,267 from Siam, and 11,260 from China.

The only important ore of tin is the mineral cassiterite (oxide of tin) described above in the chapter on "Mineralogy." In the Malay region the ore all occurs in placer deposits and is, therefore, of secondary origin, the source of the ore not being known. In Bolivia the tin ore occurs in veins in and close to granite, the ore having been carried by very hot vapors or liquids which were derived from the still highly heated granite.

Tin is used chiefly in the making of tin plate, bronze, pewter, gun metal, and bell metal.

ALUMINUM. The mineral called bauxite (a hydrous oxide of aluminum) is the great ore from which aluminum is obtained by an electrical process. Bauxite is noncrystalline, relatively light in weight, white to yellowish in color, and in rounded grains or earthy or claylike masses. France, United States, Hungary, Italy and British Guiana are the chief producers of bauxite, most of which is treated for metallic aluminum. In 1936 the United States produced more than 224,929,000 pounds of aluminum. In the United States the principal deposits are in Arkansas, Alabama and Georgia. Bauxite is probably always a secondary mineral formed by decomposition of igneous rocks rich in certain aluminum silicate minerals. In some cases, as in the Georgia-Alabama region, the bauxite appears to have been formed and concentrated in deposits by hot solutions from uncooled igneous rocks.

Aluminum is most used in the manufacture of wire for electric current transmission. It is also mixed with certain other metals like copper, zinc, magnesium, and tungsten to form special types of alloys, some of which possess remarkable tensile strength up to nearly 50,000 pounds per square inch. Aluminum is used in powdered form to generate very high temperatures in certain welding processes. It is also made into many kinds of utensils and instruments.

MERCURY. This metal commonly known as "quicksilver," is of special interest because it is the only one which exists in liquid form at ordinary temperatures. The metal occurs in only small quantities in nature, most of it by far being obtained from the red mineral cinnabar described in the chapter on "Mineralogy." Civil war in Spain prevented normal production of quicksilver in 1936. Russia's output is not entirely known. Otherwise, the United States, Mexico, Italy and Bolivia were chief producing countries. The states of largest output were California, Texas, Oregon and Arkansas.

In California most of the ore occurs in veins and irregular deposits in metamorphosed strata of Mesozoic and Cenozoic ages usually closely associated with igneous rocks. There, as well as in other parts of the world, hot vapors from igneous rocks carried the volatile ore upward and deposited it in fissures.

Among the many uses of mercury are in making fulminate for explosives; making certain drugs and chemicals, pigments, electrical and physical apparatus; silvering mirrors; and in the amalgamation process of extracting gold and silver.

OTHER ECONOMIC PRODUCTS

BUILDING STONES. Some of the principal features which should be considered in building stones are power to resist weathering, power to withstand heat, color, hardness, and density, and crushing strength. Building stones representing rocks of nearly all important geologic ages are widely distributed throughout the world.

Granite, including certain other closely related rocks, is one of the oldest and most useful building stones. The New England States are the greatest producers, while the Piedmont Plateau district (east of the Appalachians) from Philadelphia to Alabama also contains important granite quarries. In the Adirondack Mountains, in Wisconsin and Minnesota, through the Rocky Mountains, and the Sierra Nevada Mountains there are extensive areas of granite which are relatively little quarried. The granite occurs only in regions of highly disturbed rocks, usually in mountains or hills, where great volumes of the molten rock were forced into the earth's crust, cooled, and later laid bare by erosion.

Marble, according to geological definition, is a metamorphosed limestone, that is a limestone which has been crystallized under conditions of heat, pressure, and moisture within the earth. More loosely in trade any limestone which takes a polish may be called marble. The greatest marble-producing districts of the United States are western New England (especially Vermont) and the Piedmont Plateau and Appalachian Mountains in rocks of Paleozoic age. In northern New York and the mountains of the west there are relatively few marble quarries.

Ordinary *limestones* are widely distributed in many States where they range in age from early Paleozoic to Tertiary. Most of the quarries supply stone for near-by markets. The so-called Bedford limestone of Indiana has, for many years, been perhaps the most widely used limestone for building purposes in the United States.

Sandstones, which are stratified rocks consisting mainly of rounded quartz grains cemented together, are widely used in building operations. Like limestones, they are very widespread in formations of all ages except the very old. There are many sandstone quarries supplying more or less local markets throughout the country. Two of the best known and most widely used sandstones are the so-called brownstone of Triassic Age extending interruptedly from the Connecticut Valley of Massachusetts to North Carolina, and the Berea, Ohio, sandstone of light gray color and uniform texture.

Slate is mostly a metamorphosed shale, that is a shale which has been subjected to great pressure within the earth so that the stratification has been obliterated and a well defined cleavage has been developed at right angles to the direction of application of the pressure. Good slate is fine-grained, dense, and splits readily into wide thin plates. It occurs only where mountain making pressure and metamorphism have been brought to bear upon the strata. Most of our great slate quarries are located in early Paleozoic rocks from New England through the Piedmont Plateau. Some quarries are also located in Arkansas, Minnesota, and westward to California.

CLAY. "Clay, which is one of the most widely distributed materials and one of the most valuable, commercially, may be defined as a fine-grained mixture of the mineral kaolinite with fragments of other minerals, such as silicates, oxides, and hydrates, and also often organic compounds, the mass possessing plasticity when wet and becoming rock-hard when burned to at least a temperature of redness." (Ries.)

Most clays originate by the weathering of rocks, particularly igneous and metamorphic rocks rich in the mineral feldspar. As a result of the decomposition of the feldspar, much clay is formed, the main substance of which is kaolin. Both feldspar and kaolin are described in the preceding chapter. When the resulting clay rests upon the rock from which it has been derived it is called residual clay. Much of the clay is, however, carried away, mainly by streams, and deposited in lakes or the sea, or on river flood plains. Some clay deposits are of wind-blown origin, and still others are formed by the grinding action of glaciers. Clays are very widespread, and they are directly associated with rocks of all geologic ages.

Among the many important uses of clay are the following: manufacture of common brick, fire brick, pottery, chinaware, porcelain ware, tiles, terra cotta, and Portland cement.

LIME AND CEMENT. Limestone, which is one of the most common and widespread of all stratified rocks, forms the basis for the manufacture of the important substances lime (or "quicklime") and Portland cement. Lime results when pure limestone (carbonate of lime) is "burned" or heated to a temperature high enough to drive off the carbonic acid gas. The greatest use of lime is for mixing with water and sand to make mortar. A few of its other numerous uses are in plastering; whitewashing; purifying certain steel; in making gas, paper, and soap; and as a fertilizer.

Certain limestones containing clay of the right kind and proportion are called natural cement rocks because, after being "burned," they develop the property of "setting," like cement when mixed with water. The "setting" of a cement is due to the fact that certain chemical compounds formed during the heating crystallize when mixed with water, and the hard, tiny interlocking crystals of the newly formed silicate minerals give rigidity to the mass. Of recent years Portland cement has largely superseded the natural rock cements. "Portland cement is the product obtained by burning a finely ground artificial mixture consisting essentially of lime, silica, alumina, and some iron oxide, these substances being present in certain definite proportions." (Ries.) The necessary ingredients are generally obtained by grinding and burning carefully selected mixtures of limestone in some form, and clay or shale. The great and growing uses of cement need not be detailed here.

SALT. Most of the common salt (the mineral "halite") of commercial value occurs in nature in sea or salt lake water; or in beds or strata of rock salt associated with other strata; or as natural brine in openings or pores in certain rocks. Considerable salt is obtained by evaporation of tidewater, as around San Francisco Bay, and of salt lake water, as at Great Salt Lake, Utah. It has been estimated that the Great Salt Lake, whose area is about 2,000 square miles and greatest depth 50 feet, contains several hundred million tons of common salt. This salt has been washed out of the rocks of the surrounding country and gradually accumulated in the lake because it has no outlet.

Most important of all sources of salt is the rock salt which occurs in the form of strata within the earth's crust. Such strata are found in rocks of nearly all ages from the early Paleozoic to the present. They resulted from the evaporation of salt lakes or salty more or less cut-off arms of the sea, after which other strata accumulated on top of them. Thus in the Silurian system of strata underlying all of southwestern New York State there occur almost universally from one to seven beds of salt. The strata including the salt dip gently southward so that at Ithaca, New York, seven salt beds were struck in a well at a depth of about 2,200 feet. Northward the salt comes nearer and nearer the surface. One well penetrated a layer of solid salt 325 feet thick. Some of this salt is being mined much like coal, but most of it is obtained by running water into deep wells to dissolve the salt, the resulting brine being pumped out and evaporated.

Under portions of southern Michigan there are both salt beds and natural brines charging certain porous rock layers. Both the salt beds (of Silurian Age) and the brines (of Mississippian Age) supply great quantities of salt from brines pumped out and evaporated.

In 1936 the United States produced 8,828,936 short tons of salt. Michigan (2,354,282 short tons) and New York were the leading States, followed by Ohio, Louisiana, Kansas, and California. Some of the uses of common salt are given in the description of halite in the preceding chapter.

GYPSUM. The composition and properties of this common and useful mineral are given in the chapter on "Mineralogy." Rock gypsum is the variety of great commercial importance. It is widespread, being quarried in many States, and occurs interstratified with rocks of many ages where it has originated by evaporation or partial evaporation of salt water lakes or more or less cut-off arms of the sea. Salt beds are often associated with gypsum.

Chief producing states are New York, Michigan, Iowa, Texas, Nevada, Oklahoma, California and Colorado. In New York the rock gypsum (usually four to ten feet thick) lies between shale and limestone strata of Silurian age, and it is quarried from the central to the western part of the State. In Michigan the rock gypsum beds, commonly five to twenty feet thick, lie in Mississippian strata in the southern portion of the State. A great bed of exceptionally pure rock gypsum underlies about twenty-five square miles of Webster County, Iowa, in rocks of late Paleozoic Age. The Kansas gypsum deposits extend across the central part of the State in rocks of Permian Age.

Rock gypsum is mainly used in making "plaster of Paris,'" as a retarder in cement, and as a fertilizer (so-called "land plaster").

Calcined gypsum has various uses in building construction and repair and is also employed in the manufacture of plate glass, terra cotta pottery and other products. Gypsum is produced in many countries, and the United States adds to its supply by importation chiefly from the tidewater districts of eastern Canada and the Lower California deposits of Mexico. The output from the quarries of the United States in 1936 was about 2,712,510 tons, an increase over that of any of the years just preceding, but considerably less than that of 1929, when it was more than 5,000,000 tons.

GLOSSARY OF COMMON
GEOLOGICAL TERMS

NAMES of subkingdoms and important classes of fossil plants and animals, and mineral species, are not included; these being briefly and systematically discussed in chapters 17, 18, 19, and 20, respectively. The explanations that follow will, however, prove of genuine value to the average reader or student of geology. Some definitions in this glossary are taken from U. S. Survey Bulletin No. 613.

Anticline.—A kind of folded structure in which strata have been bent upward or arched.

Archeozoic.—The earliest known era of geologic time.

Basalt.—A common lava of dark color and of great fluidity when molten. Basalt is less siliceous than granite and rhyolite, and contains much more iron, calcium, and magnesium.

Base-level.—The lowest level to which a stream can cut (erode) its channel. A whole region may be base-leveled by erosion.

Cambrian.—The first or earliest period of the Paleozoic era of geologic time.

Cenozoic.—The present era of geologic time. It began at least several million years ago.

Chalk.—A soft, fine-grained, white limestone consisting mainly of tiny shells.

Conglomerate.—A sedimentary rock consisting of consolidated or cemented gravel. Often sandy.

Cretaceous.—The last period of the Mesozoic era of geologic time.

Crystal.—A regular polyhedral form, possessing a definite internal molecular structure, which is assumed by a substance in passing from the state of a liquid or gas to that of a

377

solid. Nearly every mineral, under proper conditions, will crystallize.

Crystalline Rock.—A rock composed of closely fitting mineral crystals that have formed in the rock substance, as contrasted with one made up of cemented grains of sand or other materials, or with a volcanic glass.

Crystallography.—The study of crystals.

Devonian.—The middle one of the seven periods of the Paleozoic era of geologic time.

Dike.—A mass of igneous rock that has solidified in a fissure or crack in the earth's crust.

Drift.—Commonly called glacial drift. The rock fragments —soil, gravel, and silt—carried by a glacier. Drift includes the unassorted material known as till (ground moraine) and deposits made by streams flowing from a glacier.

Drowned River Valley.—When a land surface sinks enough to permit tidewater to enter the lower ends of its valleys to form estuaries, a good example being the lower Hudson Valley.

Era.—A name applied to one of the broadest subdivisions of geologic time (e. g. Paleozoic era).

Erosion.—The wearing away and transportation of materials at and near the earth's surface by weathering and solution, and the mechanical action of running water, waves, moving ice, or winds which use rock fragments as tools or abrasives.

Exfoliation.—The splitting off of sheets of rock of various sizes and shapes due to changes of temperature. It is a process of weathering.

Fault.—A fracture in the earth's crust accompanied by movement of the rock on one side of the break past that on the other. If the fracture is inclined and the rock on one side appears to have slid down the slope of the fracture the fault is termed a normal fault. If, on the other hand, the rock on one side appears to have been shoved up the inclined plane of the break, the fault is termed a reverse or thrust fault.

Fault-block.—A part of the earth's crust bounded wholly or in part by faults.

Fault-scarp.—The cliff formed by a fault. Most fault scarps have been modified by erosion since the faulting.

Fissure.—A crack, break, or fracture in the earth's crust or in a mass of rock.

Flood-plain.—The nearly level land that borders a stream and is subject to occasional overflow. Flood-plains are built up by sediment left by such overflows.

Fold.—A bend in rock layers or beds. Anticlines and synclines are the common types of folds.

Formation.—A rock layer, or a series of continuously deposited layers grouped together, regarded by the geologist as a unit for purposes of description and mapping. A formation is usually named from some place where it is exposed in its typical character.

Fossil.—The whole or any part of an animal or plant that has been preserved in the rocks or the impression left on rock by a plant or animal. Preservation is invariably accompanied by some change in substance, and from some fossils the original substance has all been removed.

Geography.—The study of the distribution of the earth's physical features, in their relation to each other to the life of sea and land, and human life and culture.

Geology.—The science which deals with the history of the earth and its inhabitants as revealed in the rocks.

Glacier.—A body of ice which slowly spreads or moves over the land from its place of accumulation.

Gneiss (pronounced nice).—A metamorphic, crystalline rock with mineral grains arranged with long axes more or less parallel, giving the rock a banded appearance. Derived from either igneous or stratified rocks well within the earth under conditions of pressure, and usually also heat and moisture.

Igneous Rocks.—Rocks formed by the cooling and solidification of a hot liquid material, known as magma, that has originated at unknown depths within the earth. Those that have solidified beneath the surface are known as intrusive rocks, or if the cooling has taken place slowly at great depth, as plutonic rocks, e. g. granite. Those that have flowed out over the surface are known as effusive rocks, extrusive rocks, or lavas, e. g., basalt. Volcanic rocks include not only lavas, but bombs, pumice, tuff, volcanic ash, and other fragmental materials or ejecta thrown out from volcanoes.

Joints.—Nearly all rocks, except very loose surface materials, are separated into blocks of varying size and shape by a system of cracks called joints. They may be caused by earth-crust movements, contraction during solidification of molten rocks, or contraction during drying out of sediments.

Jurassic.—The middle one of the three periods of the Mesozoic era of geologic time.

Lava.—An igneous rock which in molten condition has poured out upon or close to the earth's surface, e. g. basalt.

Limestone.—A sedimentary rock consisting essentially of carbonate of lime which generally represents accumulation of shells of organisms, but in some cases precipitates from solution. Often impure.

Loess (pronounced lurse with the r obscure).—A fine homogeneous silt or loam showing usually no division into layers and forming thick and extensive deposits in the Mississippi Valley and in China. It is generally regarded as in part at least a deposit of wind-blown dust.

Marble.—A crystalline limestone, usually a metamorphic rock, the limestone having been altered by heat, pressure, and moisture within the earth.

Meander.—To flow in serpentine curves. A loop in a stream. Most streams in flowing across plains develop meanders.

Mesa.—A flat-topped hill or mountain left isolated during the general erosion or cutting down of a region.

Mesozoic.—Next to the present era of geologic time.

Metamorphic Rock.—Any igneous or sedimentary rock which has undergone metamorphism, that is notable alteration from its original condition. (See Metamorphism.)

Metamorphism.—Any change in rocks effected in the earth by heat, pressure, solutions, or gases. A common cause of the metamorphism of rocks is the intrusion into them of igneous rocks. Rocks that have been so changed are termed metamorphic. Marble, for example, is metamorphosed limestone.

Mineral.—An inorganic substance of definite chemical composition found ready made in nature, e. g. calcite, quartz.

Mississippian.—A period of the Paleozoic era of geologic time—in order of age, the third from the last of the era.

Moraine.—Glacial drift carried on, within, or under a glacier and deposited at the end, along the sides, or under the glacier.

Oil-pool.—An accumulation or body of oil in sedimentary rock that yields petroleum on drilling. The oil occurs in the pores of the rock and is not a pool or pond in the ordinary sense of these words.

GLOSSARY

Ordovician.—Next to the earliest period of the Paleozoic era of geologic time.

Ore.—A metal-bearing mineral or rock of sufficient value to be mined.

Outcrop.—That part of a rock formation which appears at the surface. The appearance of a rock at the surface or its projection above the soil. Often called an exposure.

Paleontology. — The study of the world's (geologically) ancient life, either plant or animal, by means of fossils.

Paleozoic.—An old era of geologic time—third back from the present.

Peneplain.—A region reduced almost to a plain by the long-continued normal erosion of a land surface. It should be distinguished from a plain produced by the attack of waves along a coast or the built-up flood plain of a river.

Pennsylvanian.—Next to the last period of the Paleozoic era of geologic time.

Period.—A name applied to one of the subdivisions of an era of geologic time, e. g. Cambrian period.

Permian.—The last period of the Paleozoic era of geologic time.

Petrology.—The study of rocks, including igneous, sedimentary, and metamorphic rocks.

Physiography. — The study of the relief features of the earth and how they were produced.

Placer Deposit.—A mass of gravel, sand, or similar material resulting from the crumbling and erosion of solid rocks and containing particles or nuggets of gold, platinum, tin, or other valuable minerals, which have been derived from rocks or veins.

Plutonic Rock.—An igneous rock solidified from a molten condition well within the earth. (See Igneous Rocks.)

Proterozoic.—Next to the earliest known era of geologic time.

Quartzite.—A metamorphic rock composed of sand grains cemented by silica into an extremely hard mass.

Quaternary.—The later of the two periods of the Cenozoic era of geologic time.

Rejuvenated.—Any region which has been subjected to erosion for a greater or less length of time and then reelevated so that the streams are renewed in activity.

Rock.—Any extensive constituent of the crust of the earth, usually consisting of a mechanical mixture of two or more minerals, e. g. granite, shale. Less commonly a rock consists of a single mineral (e. g. pure marble), or of organic matter (e. g. coal).

Sandstone.—A sedimentary rock consisting of consolidated or cemented sand. Often shaly or limy.

Schist.—A rock that by subjection to heat and pressure and usually moisture within the earth has undergone a change in the character of the particles or minerals that compose it and has these minerals arranged in such a way that the rock splits more easily in certain directions than in others. It is a metamorphic rock derived from either sedimentary or igneous rock, more commonly the former.

Sedimentary Rocks.—Rocks formed by the accumulation of sediment in water (aqueous deposits) or from air (eolian deposits). The sediment may consist of rock fragments or particles of various sizes (conglomerate, sandstone, shale); of the remains or products of animals or plants (certain limestones and coal); of the product of chemical action or of evaporation (salt, gypsum, etc.); or of mixtures of these materials. Some sedimentary deposits (tuffs) are composed of fragments blown from volcanoes and deposited on land or in water. A characteristic feature of sedimentary deposits is a layered structure known as bedding or stratification. Each layer is a bed or stratum. Sedimentary beds as deposited lie flat or nearly flat, but subsequently they have often been deformed by folding and faulting.

Shale.—A sedimentary rock consisting of hardened thin layers of fine mud.

Silurian.—A period of the Paleozoic era of geologic time— in order of age, the third from the beginning of the era.

Slate.—A rock that by subjection to pressure within the earth has acquired the property of splitting smoothly into thin plates. The cleavage is smoother and more regular than the splitting of schist along its grain. It is a metamorphic rock nearly always derived from shale.

Soil.—The mantle of loose material resting upon bedrock, either in its place of origin or transported by water, wind, or ice.

Strata (or stratified rocks).—Sedimentary rocks which, by the sorting power of water (less often by wind), are arranged in more or less definite layers or beds separated by stratification surfaces.

Stratification.—The separation of sedimentary rocks into more or less parallel layers or beds.

Stratigraphy.—The branch of geologic science that deals with the order and relations of the strata of the earth's crust.

Structure.—In geology, the forms assumed by sedimentary beds and igneous rocks that have been moved from their original position by forces within the earth, or the forms taken by intrusive masses of igneous rock in connection with effects produced mechanically on neighboring rocks by the intrusion. Folds (anticlines and synclines) and faults are the principal mechanical effects considered under structure. Schistosity and cleavage are also structural features.

Syncline.—A kind of folded structure in which strata have been bent downward. It is an inverted arch—the opposite of an anticline.

Talus (pronounced tāy'lus).—The mass of loose rock fragments that accumulates at the base of a cliff or steep slope.

Terrace.—A steplike bench on a hillside. Most terraces along rivers are remnants of valley bottoms formed when the stream flowed at higher levels. Other terraces have been formed by waves. Some terraces have been cut in solid rock, others have been built up of sand and gravel, and still others have been partly cut and partly built up.

Tertiary.—The earlier of the two periods of the Cenozoic era of geologic time.

Triassic.—The earliest period of the Mesozoic Era of geologic time.

Unconformity.—A break in the regular succession of sedimentary rocks, indicated by the fact that one bed rests on the eroded surface of one or more beds which may have a distinctly different dip from the bed above. An unconformity may indicate that the beds below it have at some time been raised above the sea and have been eroded. In some places beds thousands of feet thick have been washed away before the land again became submerged and the first bed above the surface of unconformity was deposited. If beds of rock may be regarded as leaves in the volume of geologic history, an unconformity marks a gap in the record.

Vein.—A mass of mineral material that has been deposited in or along a fissure in the rocks. A vein differs from a dike in that the vein material was introduced gradually by deposition from solution, whereas a dike was intruded in a molten condition. Quartz and calcite are very common vein minerals.

Volcanic Rocks. — Igneous rocks erupted at or near the earth's surface, including lavas, tuffs, volcanic ashes, and like material.

Weathering. — The group of processes, such as the chemical action of air and rain water, and of plants and bacteria, and the mechanical action of changes of temperature, whereby rocks on exposure to the weather change in character, decay, and finally crumble into soil.